Palgrave Studies in World Environmental History

Editors:

Dr Vinita Damodaran, University of Sussex, UK
Dr Rohan D'Souza, Shiv Nadar University, India
Dr Sujit Sivasundaram, University of Cambridge, UK
Dr James Beattie, University of Waikato, Hamilton, New Zealand

Editorial Board Members:
Prof. Mark Elvin, ANU, Environmental historian of China
Prof. Heather Goodall, Sydney Institute of Technology, Environmental historian of Australia
Dr Edward Melillo, Amherst College, Environmental historian, USA
Dr Alan Mikhail, Yale, Environmental history of the Middle East
Prof. José Augusto Pádua, Federal University of Rio, Environmental historian of Latin America
Dr Kate Showers, University of Sussex, Environmental historian of Africa
Prof. Graeme Wynn, University of British Columbia, Environmental historian, Canada
Dr Robert Peckham, Hong Kong University, Environmental history/health history, world history, Hong Kong

The widespread perception of a global environmental crisis has stimulated the burgeoning interest in environmental studies. This has encouraged a wide range of scholars, including historians, to place the environment at the heart of their analytical and conceptual explorations. As a result, the understanding of the history of human interactions with all parts of the cultivated and non-cultivated surface of the earth and with living organisms and other physical phenomena is increasingly seen as an essential aspect both of historical scholarship and in adjacent fields, such as the history of science, anthropology, geography and sociology. Environmental history can be of considerable assistance in efforts to comprehend the traumatic environmental difficulties facing us today, while making us reconsider the bounds of possibility open to humans over time and space in their interaction with different environments.

This series explores these interactions in studies that together touch on all parts of the globe and all manner of environments including the built environment. Books in the series will come from a wide range of fields of scholarship, from the sciences, social sciences and humanities. The series particularly encourages interdisciplinary projects that emphasize historical engagement with science and other fields of study.

Titles in the Series include:

Simon Pooley
BURNING TABLE MOUNTAIN
An Environmental History of Fire on the Cape Peninsula

Vinita Damodaran, Anna Winterbottom & Alan Lester eds.
THE EAST INDIA COMPANY AND THE NATURAL WORLD

Forthcoming Titles:

Richard Grove & George Adamson
EL NIÑO IN WORLD HISTORY, 3000 BCE – 2000 CE

Palgrave Studies in World Environmental History
Series Standing Order ISBN 978–1–137–41537–0 (Hardback)
978–1–137–41538–7 (Paperback)
(outside North America only)

You can receive future titles in this series as they are published by placing a standing order. Please contact your bookseller or, in case of difficulty, write to us at the address below with your name and address, the title of the series and the ISBN quoted above.

Customer Services Department, Macmillan Distribution Ltd, Houndmills, Basingstoke, Hampshire RG21 6XS, England

---

The East India Company and the Natural World

Edited by

Vinita Damodaran
Senior Lecturer and Director, Centre for World Environmental History, University of Sussex, UK

Anna Winterbottom
Research Fellow, Department of History, University of Sussex, UK

and

Alan Lester
Professor of Historical Geography, University of Sussex, UK

Editorial matter and selection © Vinita Damodaran, Anna Winterbottom & Alan Lester 2015

Remaining chapters © Respective authors 2015
Softcover reprint of the hardcover 1st edition 2015 978-1-137-42726-7

All rights reserved. No reproduction, copy or transmission of this publication may be made without written permission.

No portion of this publication may be reproduced, copied or transmitted save with written permission or in accordance with the provisions of the Copyright, Designs and Patents Act 1988, or under the terms of any licence permitting limited copying issued by the Copyright Licensing Agency, Saffron House, 6-10 Kirby Street, London EC1N 8TS.

Any person who does any unauthorized act in relation to this publication may be liable to criminal prosecution and civil claims for damages.

The authors have asserted their rights to be identified as the authors of this work in accordance with the Copyright, Designs and Patents Act 1988.

First published 2015 by
PALGRAVE MACMILLAN

Palgrave Macmillan in the UK is an imprint of Macmillan Publishers Limited, registered in England, company number 785998, of Houndmills, Basingstoke, Hampshire RG21 6XS.

Palgrave Macmillan in the US is a division of St Martin's Press LLC, 175 Fifth Avenue, New York, NY 10010.

Palgrave Macmillan is the global academic imprint of the above companies and has companies and representatives throughout the world.

Palgrave® and Macmillan® are registered trademarks in the United States, the United Kingdom, Europe and other countries.

ISBN 978-1-349-49109-4   ISBN 978-1-137-42727-4 (eBook)
DOI 10.1057/9781137427274

This book is printed on paper suitable for recycling and made from fully managed and sustained forest sources. Logging, pulping and manufacturing processes are expected to conform to the environmental regulations of the country of origin.

A catalogue record for this book is available from the British Library.

A catalog record for this book is available from the Library of Congress.

Typeset by MPS Limited, Chennai, India.

To Mark Elvin, a pioneering environmental historian who has always been an inspiration

Contents

List of Illustrations	ix
List of Tables	xi
Preface Anna Winterbottom	xii
Notes on Contributors	xvii

Introduction 1
New Imperial and Environmental Histories of the Indian Ocean
Alan Lester

1 Botanical Explorations and the East India Company:
  Revisiting 'Plant Colonialism' 16
  Deepak Kumar

2 Medicine and Botany in the Making of Madras, 1680–1720 35
  Anna Winterbottom

3 Robert Wight and his European Botanical Collaborators 58
  H. J. Noltie

4 The East India Company, Famine and Ecological
  Conditions in Eighteenth-Century Bengal 80
  Vinita Damodaran

5 Colonial Private Diaries and their Potential for
  Reconstructing Historical Climate in Bombay, 1799–1828 102
  George Adamson

6 Mischievous Rivers and Evil Shoals: The English East
  India Company and the Colonial Resource Regime 128
  Rohan D'Souza

7 The *Rafflesia* in the Natural and Imperial Imagination
  of the East India Company in Southeast Asia 147
  Timothy P. Barnard

8 'A proper set of views': The British East India
  Company and the Eighteenth-Century Visualization
  of South-East Asia 167
  Geoff Quilley

9 Unlikely Partners: Malay-Indonesian Medicine and European Plant Science *Jeyamalar Kathirithamby-Wells*	193
10 Plants, Animals and Environmental Transformation: Indian–New Zealand Biological and Landscape Connections, 1830s–1890s *James Beattie*	219
11 St Helena as a Microcosm of the East India Company World *A. T. Grove*	249
Afterword *Vinita Damodaran*	270
Select Bibliography	272
Index	285

List of Illustrations

Cover: William Daniell, *The Watering Place at Anjer Point ... Java,* © National Maritime Museum

2.1 © British Library Board; *Icones Avium Maderaspatanarum* (BL ADD MS 5266) — 39

3.1 Robert Wight and his European botanical collaborators (drawn by Caroline Muir) — 72

5.1 Semi-quantitative monsoon rainfall reconstruction for Bombay from East India Company diaries, government reports and contemporary newspapers. Continuous lines represent instrumental observations from the Colaba Observatory (1847–1859) and Bombay newspapers (1817–1846). See Adamson and Nash (2014) — 112

7.1 *Rafflesia Arnoldii,* in S. Raffles (1835) *Memoir of the Life and Public Services of Sir Thomas Stamford Raffles,* Vol. 1 (London: James Duncan), p. 343 — 154

8.1 Arthur William Devis, *Ara Kooger,* 1783, black chalk on paper, 231 × 183 mm. British Museum, Department of Prints and Drawings, 1876,0708.2371 © Trustees of the British Museum — 174

8.2 William Hodges, engr. John Hall, *Otoo King of O-Taheite,* 1777, engraving, from James Cook, *A voyage towards the South Pole, and round the World: Performed in His Majesty's Ships the Resolution and Adventure, in the Years 1772, 1773, 1774, and 1775* (London, 1777), vol. 1, plate 38. British Museum, Department of Prints and Drawings, Oc2006, Prt.32 © Trustees of the British Museum — 175

8.3 Arthur William Devis, *Prince Lee Boo,* 1783, black and red chalk on paper, 264 × 194mm. British Museum, Department of Prints and Drawings,1943,0409.1 © Trustees of the British Museum — 176

8.4 William Hamilton, engr. James Caldwell, *A Magindano Marriage,* 1779, etching and engraving, from Thomas Forrest, *A Voyage to New Guinea, and the Moluccas, from*

x List of Illustrations

      Balambangan: including an Account of Magindano, Sooloo, and Other Islands; and Illustrated with Thirty Copperplates: Performed in the Tartar Gallery, Belonging to the Honourable East India Company, during the Years 1774, 1775, and 1776, by Thomas Forrest (London, 1779), plate 23. British Museum, Department of Prints and Drawings, 1981, U.498 © Trustees of the British Museum   181

8.5 Thomas Hearne, engr. James Caldwell, *View of Dory Harbour on New Guinea*, 1779, etching and engraving, from Thomas Forrest, *A Voyage to New Guinea, and the Moluccas, from Balambangan: including an Account of Magindano, Sooloo, and Other Islands; and Illustrated with Thirty Copperplates: Performed in the Tartar Gallery, Belonging to the Honourable East India Company, during the Years 1774, 1775, and 1776, by Thomas Forrest* (London, 1779), frontispiece. British Museum, Department of Prints and Drawings, 1978, U.689.+ © Trustees of the British Museum   182

8.6 John Keyse Sherwin, engr. William Sharp, *Captn Thos Forrest*, 1779, etching and engraving, from Thomas Forrest, *A Voyage to New Guinea, and the Moluccas, from Balambangan: including an Account of Magindano, Sooloo, and Other Islands; and Illustrated with Thirty Copperplates: Performed in the Tartar Gallery, Belonging to the Honourable East India Company, during the Years 1774, 1775, and 1776, by Thomas Forrest* (London, 1779), frontispiece. British Museum, Department of Prints and Drawings, 1841, 0313.139 © Trustees of the British Museum   187

10.1 *Colonel and Mrs D. D. Mutter*, from Elizabeth McMullin Muter, *My Recollections of the Sepoy Revolt (1857–58)*. London: John Long Ltd, 1911   220

10.2 Location map of places discussed in the text   225

10.3 Map of the layout of McDonnell's garden. *Source*: Old Land Claims 89: Plan of Horeke Homestead surveyed for Captain McDonnell in c.1857: Archives reference: BA12 23908 A1708 2811/ OLC 89, Archives NZ, Auckland   226

List of Tables

5.1	Chronology of extreme or unusual climatic events	113
5.2	Details of windstorm/cyclone events listed within the diaries consulted	115
5.3	Monthly temperature maxima recorded by James McGrigor and Jasper Nicolls from October 1802 to February 1803.	118
5.4	Monthly temperature maxima within observations recorded by James McGrigor, Jasper Nicolls, Mountstuart Elphinstone and Lucretia West	120
5.5	Monthly temperature maxima from East India Company diaries, compared with the 1973–2013 average	121
11.1	Years of strong, very strong and extremely strong El Niños and La Niñas and years with droughts and heavy rains on St Helena	257

Preface

The English East India Company (EEIC or EIC) was an agent of environmental change that proved catastrophic to many environments and animal habitats that it came into contact with. It was also one of the first organisations to become aware of and systematically record the impact of human activities on the natural world. The records of the East India Company (or more accurately, the several companies that bore this name) span over two and a half centuries from the granting of the first Royal Charter to a group of merchants in 1600 to the assumption of many of the governmental functions of the Company by the British Government after 1857. In geographical terms, the reach of the Company stretched from St Helena in the South Atlantic, a small but important stopping point for returning ships, to the outposts in Southeast and East Asia, from Bencoulen and Amoy in the early days, to Singapore and Hong Kong towards the end of the Company's official existence.

As recent studies of the EIC have emphasised, record keeping was central to the ideological as well as practical functioning of the organisation.[1] The official records of the Company include the Court Minutes drawn up in London and the letters sent to each of the settlements, or 'factories', abroad; the Factory Records kept by each settlement, including minutes of the meetings of the Governor and Council; and correspondence sent to London and to the other factories. These records are now kept mainly in the British Library's Asia, Pacific and Africa Collections,[2] but institutions including the National Archives of India, Elphinstone College of the University of Mumbai, Tamil Nadu State Archives, and the St Helena Archives also hold significant collections. These records provide invaluable information about the environment including: details of the transplantation of food and cash crops like tea and cinchona; bio-prospecting in new settlements; details of crops, livestock, forest and water resources that brought the Company revenue; and details of the climate of the settlements and periods of drought, famine, disease, and extreme weather events such as storms and floods. Additionally, each Company ship was required, from the seventeenth century onwards, to keep a log book. These usually contain barometer readings and depth soundings as well as weather data.[3] From the eighteenth century onwards, the EIC appointed naturalists and ran botanical

Preface xiii

gardens, the records of which provide a wealth of environmental information. A number of these sources are highlighted in the recent invaluable guide to records relevant to science and environment within the India Office Records at the British Library.[4]

As well as the official records, independent traders, travellers, naturalists and artists of all nationalities who passed through the EIC settlements generated a wealth of data in European languages.[5] The passion for collecting that many Company officials cultivated also meant that a great number of manuscripts in Asian, Middle Eastern and, sometimes, African languages, which also provide valuable data about the environment, entered the Company archives.[6] Many of these manuscripts are now being studied and digitised through collaborative partnerships between the British Library and other organisations.[7] Such projects include the study of the Persian manuscripts in collaboration with the Iran Heritage Foundation, and the digital reunification of the Mewar Ramayana manuscript.[8] Several Southeast Asian language collections are also in the process of being made available online.[9]

The work of local artists employed to produce illustrations for naturalists provides a wealth of detail on plant life.[10] Natural objects also circulated between the curious collectors in the Company colonies and the growing number of savant institutions in Europe; these include the exotic animals that once filled the EIC Museum in India house, the herbarium specimens that still remain in the Natural History Museum, and the objects made from every conceivable kind of natural material that crowd the Kew Museum of Economic Botany. A great number of these records, both official and unofficial, also remain in the sites of the EIC's former settlements. An example is the Library of the Acharya Jagadish Chandra Bose Indian Botanic Garden in Kolkata, which possesses invaluable records, including many of the papers of Nathaniel Wallich. While pioneering projects are now under way to reconstruct the treasure trove of environmental data that these archives contain,[11] a wealth of research materials still remain to be exploited by historians, geographers, climate scientists and others.

The current volume forms part of a series of initiatives that have aimed to bring these archives to light and to demonstrate their utility. Much of the initial driving force was provided by the expansive vision of Richard Grove, whose *Green Imperialism*[12] was a pioneering study of the connections between imperialism and the environment. Along with his long-standing collaborators – Vinita Damodaran, Director of the Centre for World Environmental History (CWEH) at Sussex and author of the first environmental history of North-Eastern India; Deepak Kumar, author of the path-breaking *Science and the Raj*; Rohan d'Souza, an expert on water and development policy in the colonial and post-colonial period; and Mark Harrison, one of the foremost experts on disease and environment in British India – Grove was among the first to mark out global environmental history as a new and vibrant field of enquiry. The British Academy funded project entitled 'the East India Company and the Natural World' initiated by Richard Grove included two conferences: an international workshop held at Jawaharlal Nehru University in August 2006 entitled 'Nature and the Raj: Colonial Environments and Indigenous Knowledge', and a second on 'The East India Company and the Natural World' at Sussex in June 2007. A collected volume on *the British Empire and the Natural World* was also produced under the auspices of this project.[13] In 2011, CWEH received generous funding from the Research Themes initiative at Sussex University to hold a further workshop entitled 'Climate, Botany, and Empire'. Many of the papers in this volume were drawn from these three conferences. However, they have been supplemented by commissioned papers in order to ensure that the volume echoes the depth and breadth of the Company archives themselves in terms of approach, chronological period and geographical reach. A number of other participants at these conferences should be thanked for their contributions, including chairing sessions, presenting their work and offering invaluable comments on the papers. They include Penny Brock, Pratik Chakrabarti, Mark Elvin, Jim Endersby, Pauline von Hellerman, Robert Iliffe, Antonia Moon, Mark Nesbitt, Lowell Woodcock, Daniel Rycroft, Kate Showers and Sujit Sivasundaram.

The current volume has benefited from the insights provided by many previous studies of the connections between imperialism and the natural world. As well as the authors already mentioned, Ray McLeod's wide-ranging discussion of nature and empire,[14] Kapil Raj's study of the role of circulation in the making of modern science,[15] and Richard Drayton's exploration of the global history of botanical gardens[16] have proved especially invaluable to many of the authors of chapters in this collection. Studies of the other European trading companies in their engagement with nature that have influenced our essays here include Cook's recent study of the Dutch counterpart of the EIC, the Vereenigde Oost-Indische Compagnie (VOC) and Simon Pooley's forthcoming monograph, the first in the Palgrave Studies in World Environmental History of which this volume is also a part. This volume is unique in its focus on the EIC, as distinct from the later British Empire, and in broadening the angle from South Asia to focus on the entire network of settlements and their interconnections, as theorised by Alan Lester in his introductory essay. Another novel feature of this volume is its truly interdisciplinary scope. The authors have backgrounds in area studies, human and environmental historical geography, art history and practical botany as well as history. Some contributors theorise the interactions between imperialism and environment over the longue durée, while others present a close focus on particular individuals or networks and their interactions with nature. All the papers reflect on the different ways in which the natural world was represented, conceptualised, utilised and ultimately altered as a result or unintended consequence of imperialism; and in turn on how imperialism was shaped by the forces of nature. We hope that the range of topics covered here will open up new routes for enquiry into the history of environment, the EIC,[17] their interaction and the legacies for future generations.

Anna Winterbottom

Notes

1. C. A. Bayly (1996), *Empire and Information: Intelligence Gathering and Social Communication in India, 1780–1870*. Cambridge: Cambridge University Press; Miles Ogborn (2007), *Indian Ink: Script and Print in the Making of the English East India Company*. Chicago: University of Chicago Press; Philip J. Stern (2011), *The Company-State: Corporate Sovereignty and the Early Modern Foundations of the British Empire in India*. New York: Oxford University Press.
2. The records of the East India Company have the general shelfmark IOR (Indian Office Records) and can be ordered manually through the British Library catalogue. Various guides to the collection are available in the APAC reading room including M. I. Moir (1988), *A General Guide to the India Office Records*. London: British Library. For a list of further guides to the collection, see British Library, http://www.bl.uk/reshelp/findhelpregion/asia/india/indiaofficerecords/indiaofficerecordsfurtherreadingontheeastindiacompanyandindiaoffice/iorreading.html (last accessed 22 May 2014).
3. For a useful overview of logbooks and the types of information they contain, see The Royal Maritime Museum (2014), *Understanding ship's logbooks*, URL: http://www.rmg.co.uk/about/partnerships-and-initiatives/cliwoc/understanding-ship's-logbooks (last accessed 24 March 2014).
4. Richard Axelby, Savithri P. Nair, and Andrew S. Cook (2010), *Science and the Changing Environment in India, 1780–1920: A Guide to Sources in the India Office Records*. London: British Library.
5. A useful guide to collections relevant to South Asia other than the official EIC records is M. D. Wainwright and N. Matthews (1965), *A Guide to Western MS and Documents in the British Isles relating to South Asia*. London, New York and Kuala Lumpur: Oxford University Press.
6. An overview of the Asia language records held by the British Library is available at http://www.bl.uk/reshelp/findhelpregion/asia/southasia/sereources.html#Manuscripts (last accessed 20 May 2014).

xvi Preface

7. A complete list of digitised manuscripts is available at British Library, 'Digitised Manuscripts' http://www.bl.uk/manuscripts/Default.aspx (last accessed 22 May 2014).
8. A list of the Persian manuscripts digitalized so far and links to the manuscript images is available at the African and Asia Studies Blog, 'Persian', http://britishlibrary.typepad.co.uk/asian-and-african/persian.html (last accessed 22 May 2014). The reunification of the Mewar Ramayana, composed in India between 1649 and 1653, is described at British Library 'Ramayana' http://www.bl.uk/ramayana (last accessed 22 May 2014).
9. British Library, 'Digital Access to Malay Manuscripts', http://britishlibrary.typepad.co.uk/asian-and-african/malay.html (last accessed 22 May 2014); British Library, 'Digital Access to Thai Manuscripts', http://britishlibrary.typepad.co.uk/asian-and-african/thai.html (last accessed 22 May 2014). Thanks to Dr Antonia Moon for directions to these resources.
10. Henry J. Noltie (2007), *Robert Wight and the Botanical Drawings of Rungiah & Govindoo*. Edinburgh: Royal Botanic Garden and (2002), *The Dapuri Drawings: Alexander Gibson and the Bombay Botanic Gardens*. Edinburgh: Antique Collectors' Club in association with the Royal Botanic Garden Edinburgh.
11. 'Nathaniel Wallich and Indian Natural History' (Kew, 2013) URL: http://www.kew.org/collections/wallich/index.htm (last accessed 11 February 2014) is a collaboration between Royal Botanic Gardens, Kew, the Natural History Museum, London and the British Library, with additional input from the Indian Botanic Gardens, Kolkata, and the National Archives of India. A similar project is the 'Reconstructing Sloane' collaborative research project between the British Museum and the British Library (NHM, 2013), URL: http://www.nhm.ac.uk/research-curation/science-facilities/cahr/sloane/index.html (last accessed 11 February 2014).
12. Richard Grove (1995), *Green Imperialism: Colonial Expansion, Tropical Island Edens, and the Origins of Environmentalism, 1600-1860*. Cambridge: Cambridge University Press.
13. Deepak Kumar, Vinita Damodaran and Rohan d'Souza (2011), *The British Empire and the Natural World: Environmental Encounters in South Asia*. Delhi: Oxford University Press.
14. Ray McLeod (2000), *Nature and Empire: Science and the Colonial Enterprise*. Chicago: University of Chicago Press.
15. Kapil Raj (2007), *Relocating Modern Science: Circulation and the Construction of Knowledge in South Asia and Europe, 1650-1900*. Basingstoke: Palgrave Macmillan.
16. Richard H. Drayton (2000), *Nature's Government: Science, Imperial Britain, and the 'Improvement' of the World*. New Haven: Yale University Press.
17. For an overview of approaches to the East India Company, see also Philip J. Stern (2009), 'History and Historiography of the English East India Company: Past, Present, and Future!', *History Compass*, 7:1146–1180.

Notes on Contributors

George Adamson is a Lecturer in Geography at King's College, London. His research explores historical climate variability and the many dimensions of climate–society interactions in the past, with a particular focus on colonial India. He is currently co-authoring a volume on El Niño in human history.

Timothy P. Barnard is an Associate Professor in the Department of History at the National University of Singapore, where his research focuses on the cultural and environmental history of Southeast Asia. He has written several books, as well as numerous articles and book chapters on Malay society. He is currently working on a book on the social history of the Komodo dragon.

James Beattie teaches and writes on Asian and British imperial environmental history and garden history, and Chinese art collecting. He has written and co-edited seven books on these topics, including co-editing *Eco-Cultural Networks and the British Empire* (2014), with Edward Melillo and Emily O'Gorman. He is also founding co-editor of the Palgrave Studies in World Environmental History and the journal *Oecology: Interdisciplinary Review of Environmental History*.

Vinita Damodaran is Director of the Centre for World Environmental History and Senior lecturer in the Department of History at the University of Sussex. Her expertise is on the indigenous communities and the environmental history of Eastern India. She has published numerous books and articles including co-editing *Nature and the Orient; the Environmental History of South and South East Asia* (1998) and *the British Empire and the Natural World: Environmental Encounters in South Asia* (2011).

A.T. Grove reported on soil erosion in Nigeria 1947–49. He was Cambridge lecturer in Geography until 1982; Director of Centre for African Studies 1980–86; Visiting Professor in Ghana (1963) and at UCLA (1970). He researched the climate history of southern Sahara, Kalahari, and East African lakes; he collaborated with Jean Grove on history of the Little Ice Age and with Oliver Rackham on questions of desertification in southern Europe.

Jeyamalar Kathirithamby-Wells has published extensively on trade and state formation in Southeast Asia during the early modern period as well as on environmental and conservation history. Apart from numerous articles, her publications include *The Southeast Asian Port and Polity* (ed.), with John Villiers (1990) and *Nature and Nation: Forests and Development in Peninsular Malaysia* (2005).

Deepak Kumar is Professor of History at the Zakir Husain Centre for Educational Studies School of Social Sciences, Jawaharlal Nehru University. He has published widely on the history of science in India and received numerous awards and honours. Selected works include *Science and the Raj* (2005), *Disease and Medicine in India* (2001), *Technology and the Raj*, with Roy MacLeod (1995), *The British Empire and the Natural World: Environmental Encounters in South Asia*, with Vinita Damodaran and Rohan D'Souza (2010).

Alan Lester is Professor of Historical Geography at the University of Sussex. He is author of *Imperial Networks: Creating Identities in Nineteenth Century South Africa and Britain* (2001), *Colonization and the Origins of Humanitarian Governance: Protecting Aborigines Across the Nineteenth-Century British Empire*, with Fae Dussart (2014), and co-editor of *Colonial Lives Across the British Empire: Imperial Careering in the Long Nineteenth Century* (2006), with David Lambert.

Henry Noltie works at the Royal Botanic Garden Edinburgh, undertaking taxonomic and curatorial projects, and research on historical aspects of the collections of Indian herbarium specimens and botanical illustrations. He has published monographs on two major collections: *The Dapuri Drawings: Alexander Gibson and the Bombay Botanic Gardens* (2002), and *Robert Wight and the Botanical Drawings of Rungiah and Govindoo* (3 volumes, 2007).

Rohan d'Souza is currently Associate Professor in the Department of History, Shiv Nadar University. He is the author of *Drowned and Dammed: Colonial Capitalism and Flood control in Eastern India (1803–1946)* (2006). Edited books include *The British Empire and the Natural World: Environmental Encounters in South Asia* (2011) and *Environment, Technology and Development: Critical and Subversive Essays* (2012).

Geoff Quilley is Professor of Art History at the University of Sussex. His research focuses on eighteenth-century British art and the maritime imperial nation, on which he has published widely, including *Empire to Nation: Art, History and the Visualization of Maritime Britain, 1768–1829* (2011).

Anna Winterbottom is a British Academy Post-doctoral Fellow in the History Department, University of Sussex and a Research Associate of the Indian Ocean World Centre, McGill University. She has published several book chapters and articles relating to the East India Company and the history of science and medicine.

Introduction: New Imperial and Environmental Histories of the Indian Ocean

Alan Lester

In line with the multi-disciplinary tenor of this volume, my aim in this Introduction is to weave between historiographical traditions that are often kept apart, focusing on the understandings that are generated when they are brought together. Imperial history has a longer and, some would say, more venerable tradition than environmental history, but this volume suggests that more explicit attention to their interpenetration might be worthwhile.[1] Both, in particular, are beginning to share certain spatial conceptions of networks, space and place; conceptions that also characterise recent histories of science and historical geographies. These more relative spatial conceptions lend themselves particularly to histories of knowledge, of cultural contact and trade, of botanical and artistic exchange, of shifting environmental management regimes, and of medicine, in which human and non-human entities combine to form dynamic assemblages. The East India Company itself was one such assemblage, constituted as much by the commodities, specimens and artefacts, and the regimes of knowledge that it shifted around and beyond the Indian Ocean as by the merchants, sailors, lascars, officials, bureaucrats and ships that sustained their movements.

In recent decades the boundaries that used to delimit separate domains of British history, imperial history, area studies and the histories of former colonies have been traversed promiscuously. *Where* to limit certain avenues of historical investigation has become as significant as *when*. 'New imperial historians' have established that, in order to understand British history, one must imaginatively travel in and out of the British Isles, weaving imperial relations overseas into the fabric of the national story. Area studies specialists have been persuaded that we cannot fully understand colonial relations within any one region without tracing entities that move in and out of that region. Historians of the former colonies have begun to think in terms of the trans-national processes which gave rise to their nation states. While, formerly, most historians had generally taken 'social geographies ... entirely for granted ... viewing space and place as a relatively passive backdrop', increasing numbers have now begun seriously to consider the issues that preoccupy geographers.[2] With this 'spatial turn', concepts of place, space and scale now seem just as integral to British and imperial history as do those of chronology and periodisation, and spatial chains of causation just as relevant as temporal ones.

Until the 1980s, imperial histories were premised on a basic spatial division between British core and colonial periphery. This convention served in unacknowledged ways to reproduce an imperialist view of the world, as empire was 'figured as the means of diffusing modernity from the metropolis ... outwards'. However, John MacKenzie's work pioneered a means of bringing empire and Britain, periphery and core, as well as British and imperial historians, closer together. Rather than thinking of core and periphery as two interacting but discrete spatial containers, each maintaining its own essential identity, he saw that one of these containers was actually constituted by the other. MacKenzie's challenge to the boundary between Britain and its empire has since been amplified and extended by the emergence of a large and still growing body of work now conventionally referred to as the 'new imperial history'.[3]

The 'new imperial history' had quite different points of origin from MacKenzie's project. It was marked by a feminist and a postcolonial orientation; it was inspired by work from disciplines other than History, and it had an explicit political agenda. Catherine Hall's work, for instance, examined the dense set of connections between Britain and Jamaica which helped constitute the history of both sets of islands through a continual two-way traffic of people, ideas and policies. This traffic helped inform discussions of the limits of freedom and responsibility for working-class men and women in Britain as well as Jamaican former slaves. The 'new imperial historians' saw their work as having political relevance in the present as it helped shed new light on the past.[4] As they criss-crossed between Britain and colonial sites, largely in the West Indies and India, arguing that the social formations of race, class and gender that defined Victorian power relations were mobile across an imperial terrain, they were breaking down taken-for-granted assumptions about both the maleness and the whiteness of the key actors within imperial and British history.

At the same time, early environmental historians of empire were bringing new, non-human actors into a similarly spatially extensive colonial history. They showed how pathogens, plants and animals moved along imperial circuits as well as people and their ideas. Richard Grove in particular pioneered new conceptions of empire as an interconnected space that was vital in the making of the modern world. His *Green Imperialism* encompassed not just the British Empire, but also those of the Dutch and French. He showed that the notion of the oceanic island 'Eden' was a vehicle for new conceptions of nature that transcended imperial boundaries, and that the traffic in organisms, personnel and ideas that colonialism engendered played a central role in a growing recognition of the limitations of both local and global resources.[5]

Where new imperial histories of Britain, and these environmental histories of a wider spectrum of places converged, was in a new spatial conception of the past. As Doreen Massey notes, 'The identity of places is very much bound up with the *histories* which are told of them, *how* those histories are told, and which history turns out to be dominant.'[6] The thrust of the 'new imperial history' was 'to challenge the nationalist notion' that places such as the British Isles 'have fixed identities or personalities, the product of continuous and inward-looking histories stretching back for generations'.[7] In linking British and imperial history, the 'new imperial historians' were not simply pointing out that popular British culture had an overlooked imperial dimension; they were consciously seeking to undermine versions of British history that created racial outsiders. They recognised that insular island narratives rendered black and Asian former subjects of empire, whose ancestry was fixed in the 'peripheries' of empire, *out of place* within the British Isles. Revealing the ways in which the experiences of excluded others were and are intrinsic components of Britain's history was intended to contribute to a new collective understanding of Britain – one in which post-war migration flows from the 'new' Commonwealth' simply added to a Britain that was 'always already' constituted by flows of people, ideas, practices, objects and images from other lands, and especially from lands over which it exercised imperial dominion.

Environmental histories play a similarly progressive role in re-imaging spatial units. Conceiving, as a number of recent authors have, of the Indian Ocean World as a spatial frame of its own, generates a new way of approaching history that goes beyond the construct of the nation.[8] The economic, social and political foundations of this Indian Ocean World are related to the monsoons, and the period between 1600 and 1900 saw a huge increase in long-distance trade and an intensive exchange of commodities, peoples and ideas as a result of European maritime voyaging. The British, French, Dutch and Portuguese empires combined to effect an unprecedented transformation of the landscapes and environments of the Indian Ocean region as a whole, even as they brought that oceanic expanse into closer alignment with European-centred networks. Following Grove, several authors have shown that the Indian Ocean in general and West and South India in particular were critical in the generation of a new kind of environmental consciousness in the eighteenth and nineteenth centuries. But as Deepak Kumar's chapter shows, the various British, Dutch, Portuguese and French engagements with the Indian Ocean were by no means discrete endeavours: there was considerable interchange in ideas, and practices between European traders and scientists, whilst they all also relied upon pre-existing patterns of maritime interaction, local informants and Mughal understandings of plant science.

Taken together, the 'new imperial historians'' project of repositioning Britain as a nation constituted through empire, and environmental historians' project of tracing large-scale transformations in both human and non-human interactions, in our case, across the Indian Ocean World, suggest the broader need for a more relative conception of spatiality in imperial studies and trans-national histories. The revision of three concepts in particular has been critical in this re-imaging, those of networks, space and place.

Networks

Networked approaches have been one way in which a relative conception of space and place has infiltrated both imperial and environmental history. The network, as a descriptive and an analytical device, allows nodal points to exist at a variety of scales, from individual people through institutional spaces such as the mission station, the laboratory or the botanic garden, to agglomerations such as towns, cities, regions and countries. The phenomena that the historian is interested in can be seen as constituted by flows of capital, movements of people, objects or organisms, and the communication of ideas in textual or visual form, between these nodes, via the physical and imaginative routes connecting them.[9] The networked patterns that these flows delineate take different form according to the projects pursued by their participants, be they projects of state governmentality, such as those in which the East India Company increasingly engaged from the late eighteenth century, of scientific endeavour, of botanical collection or of medical discovery.

Introduction: New Imperial and Environmental Histories 5

But as these examples indicate, these various networks often intersect. Actors within them can play roles in various analytically distinguishable projects simultaneously. Networked approaches have been increasingly adopted within environmental histories. As James Beattie puts it in a recent review piece, 'British imperialism shifted flora, fauna and commodities around the world'.[10] Historians of science and historical geographers among others have, developed Bruno Latour's Actor Network Theory (ANT) to model how such things (actants) and people (actors) participated in networks of exchange.[11] ANT's approach, as Eric Pawson notes, is particularly effective at analysing plant exchanges.[12] Beattie praises in particular imperial historian Tony Ballantyne's 'metaphor of a spider's web to capture changing connections between different people and places'. The concept 'presents a flexible, non-linear model applicable to any kind of exchange, and challenges earlier models upholding one-way transfers of knowledge from Britain to its colonies'. Ballantyne's model

> also acknowledges shifting centres of knowledge or nodes (as he terms them). The key point is that Ballantyne's model does not rely on a priori identification of Europe as the metropolis. Depending on topic, a webbed model can decentre Europe as the main site of knowledge-production. Focusing on webs has helped to reveal exchange of conservation ideas, demonstrating, for example, the importance of India, as well as France and Germany, as models for forest conservation in Empire.[13]

Beattie goes on to suggest that the notion of 'imperial careering' is also helpful to environmental historians 'because so many individuals travelled around Empire introducing ideas from one place to another'. 'Adapted for our purposes', he argues, 'imperial careering stresses at once the importance of accumulated colonial experiences in shaping environmental views and the sometimes haphazard way this knowledge was gleaned and transferred.' Such a perspective can enrich the study of scientific bureaucracies (like German-trained scientists or educated Scots) and their environmental impacts. 'Rather than viewing such groups as having introduced ideas directly from Europe to the colonies ... we can see their experiences, their policies and their attitudes having been accumulated through movement from one place to another'.[14] We need only look at Henry Noltie's study of Robert Wight and his collaborators in Europe and India in this volume to appreciate the vital role that knowledge and experience embodied in a well-networked particular individual can play in the governance of environmental exchanges. Wight's trajectory also serves to remind us of how individual actors can play multiple roles as they orient themselves in relation to differently aligned networks simultaneously, for this surgeon acted as the embodied nexus of scientific, artistic and commercial projects at one and the same time.

It is not just the biographies of human individuals, of course, that connect imperial and environmental histories. Intrinsic to both are the mobilites, the 'life stories' as it were, of other organisms, and of material objects. One of this book's major contributions is intended to be its 'more than human' approach to the imperial world. Timothy Barnard's chapter on the significance of *Rafflesia* within schemes of imperial imagination and control in the East Indies and Anna Winterbottom's on the transmission of *materia medica* through Madras, both demonstrate that the careers of plants were not only intimately bound up with those of colonial power-brokers, but were also constitutive of new patterns of knowledge and power in an imperial world. At the same time, Geoff Quilley's chapter establishes that it is not only the mobilities of organisms that reshape place and society, but also those of art. Accompanying navigational and natural scientific data, the particular movements of engravings and their deployments by variously located individuals, were vital components of the knowledge of the 'East' that East India Company networks created and transmitted.

Finally, aside from the mobilities of individual humans, other organisms and objects, Beattie notes that '*institutional* ... analyses can open up fascinating new vistas onto imperial environmental history', rightly seeing Richard Drayton's examination of imperial interactions through Kew, as having 're-invigorated investigation of colonial institutions'.[15] This volume deepens our understanding of the extent of interconnection between botanic gardens not just in metropolitan Britain but in those other significant institutional nodal points of empire in the Indian Ocean, including its own botanic gardens, enhancing Ballantyne's notion of the webs of empire at large. In particular, Beattie's chapter here reorientates New Zealand's botanical history, seeing it as developing less through an axis of connection with Europe and more through links with India.[16]

Each of the contributors to this book adopts a networked, rather than merely comparative approach, not only to their *interpretations* of the past, but also to their *methodologies*. Such networked analysis is becoming much easier than it was. With large-scale digitisation, scholars need no longer spend weeks poring through hard copies of

Introduction: New Imperial and Environmental Histories   7

colonial newspapers in archives in London, Sydney and Wellington, for instance, to write about the ways that settler communities in the British Empire used their 'parochial' newspapers to stage a conversation on Britishness.[17] However, networked historical investigation remains particularly challenging compared to nationally oriented history writing. Developing a multi-sited study involves an awful lot of reading, first to comprehend the historiographies of each place which, after many decades of nation-bound history writing tend to lack cross-referencing, and then to track the webs of correspondence across separate state archives. The mobility required of the researcher means that it can be prohibitive at certain stages of an academic career. This renders the multi-sited collaboration manifested in this collection especially welcome.

It is not only such collaboration that represents a methodological advance though. So too does the integration of human and non-human research methodologies manifested in this volume. As Rohan D'Souza's chapter on water management in Bengal, and George Adamson's chapter on colonial weather diaries in particular show, bringing the human and the non-human together in new ways through networked analyses enables the integration of various different types of sources for the study of climatic and environmental change across the Indian Ocean World. We know that the ecological reshaping of the region was closely documented and it remains traceable in both colonial and indigenous documents of various types. However, the relevant records remain dispersed, meaning that it is still difficult for relatively immobile scholars to escape a national frame of reference. Neither is it easy to integrate documentary records with physical sources such as the specimens of plants, animals and geological materials that remain in herbaria and museum collections. But Adamson's sensitive examination of East India Company surgeons' diaries speaks both to those historians interested in the scientific culture of the colonial community and to the climate scientists investigating historical climatology, while D'Souza's examination of East India Company attempts to separate land and water in Bengal contains valuable lessons for those confronting the consequences of climate change in the region today.

A further key methodological problem for historical networked accounts, apart from the nature and location of sources, is the predominance of elite voices and representations. Until recently, networked analyses have tended to privilege the most empowered subjects of empire – those able to write the texts which circulated around maritime and then telegraphic and aerial circuits; those able to travel to London to testify before Select Committees; those able to pursue a

8 *Alan Lester*

career in colonial governance that took them from one colonial site to another, and those who managed botanic gardens, for example.[18] And it is not just British elites in empire who are privileged in this way. As Vinita Damodaran's chapter on famines in Bengal demonstrates, the East India Company certainly exacerbated rent gathering practices that undermined flexible 'subaltern' forms of resilience in the face of periodic scarcity, but they built upon foundations laid by previous imperial regimes. The East India Company elite's characterisation of banditry within the region was tied up with the coping strategies of those dispossessed through such measures.

A few recent works have started to show that 'subaltern' subjects too followed (or were forced to take) certain trajectories across empire, both physically and imaginatively. In the mid nineteenth century Indigenous peoples interacted with the newspaper networks of British settlers, sometimes directly through publication of a press in their own language, or more often indirectly.[19] More expansively, Kerry Ward and Clare Anderson have recently told the stories of convicts forced into exile across the Indian Ocean circuits of the Dutch and English East India Companies.[20] Despite these meticulously researched attempts to recover the experiences of subaltern groups within networked colonial worlds, however, the problem of one-sided archival traces remains. The most sustained works rely upon subaltern individuals being caught up in webs of governmental surveillance, as a result of which their movements and signs of their resistance were recorded – hence the preponderance of convicts. What the existence and power of trans-imperial projects, discourses and networks meant for those subaltern individuals who were never entrapped within such governmental archives, or who sought to remain in situ remains elusive.[21]

However, this book not only adds a more-than-human dimension to networked imperial studies, but it also fleshes out that human dimension by adding subaltern, Indigenous and non-Western engagements with environmental change. As Beattie notes, recent environmental history scholarship has moved beyond a model holding imperialism solely responsible for the destruction of a fragile pre-colonial golden age of environmental balance. Michael Stevens' work on southern New Zealand Māori, for example, emphasises his hapu's agency in retaining access to some of their islands (and their resources) at the same time as selectively using aspects of European technology.[22] Studies in India have stressed the continuing agency of tribes in their resistance to the colonial state on a range of environmental issues.[23] Aside from Damodaran's analysis of the Bengal famine here, scholarship like that of Jeyamalar

Kathirithamby-Wells, showing how indigenous and European networks of biological understanding interacted to shape a pharmaceutical trade differentially from the fifteenth century to the nineteenth, reveals a far more complex picture of how non-Europeans engaged in widespread environmental modification and understanding, both before and after colonisation. Kathirithamby-Wells also includes the voices of Eurasian people, which are seldom heard in historical writing about South Asia. By integrating the documentary records of both colonisers and colonised, as well as those 'in-between', this collection as a whole aims to enhance humanities' scholars attempts to attend to 'subaltern' voices as much as it does natural scientists' appreciation of past climate change in the region.

Place

Because of their indeterminate fixing of spatial frameworks, some critics have argued that networked analyses are more about space than place. This tends to be because they associate space with mobility and specific places with stasis. However, any division between things that move through networks and things that remain static is problematic, and places are defined no more authentically by stasis than by mobility. In any sophisticated networked account, specific places are seen as rich and complex intersections of components with varying trajectories and mobilities. Much of the move towards a networked view of space has been propelled precisely by the desire to capture that elusive and dynamic bundle of characteristics that define specific places.

We can begin by redefining what we mean by immobility. If we take a long view, there is actually no such thing. As Doreen Massey points out, even those characteristics of any given place that are most immutable, such as mountains, hills, lakes and rivers, are temporally limited assemblages of mobile components.[24] Going beyond Heraclitus' supposed observation that 'no man ever steps in the same river twice', we can observe that in the longer term it is not only the moving body of water that renders a river, for example, a dynamic entity, but also the course of its channel as sediment is eroded and deposited in ever-shifting patterns (this is to let alone the point that the 'man' himself will have changed between immersions). Massey is driven to make this point about the mutability of both human society and what we conventionally see as geographical context partly to fulfil a desire to bridge the disciplinary divide between 'human' and 'physical' geographies. However, the point that all of the characteristics of place are comprised of mobilities of one kind or another, even if they may be imperceptible to the inhabitants at any given time, is well known to environmental historians and has relevance to historians of the imperial world too.

Working both with and against the available sources, we need to see invading settlers and imperial sojourners conjoining with indigenous peoples and immigrants from elsewhere to form new assemblages of people, organisms, materials, places and landscapes. In this volume, Dick Grove's analysis of St Helena, Winterbottom's of Madras and, at a larger scale, Beattie's of New Zealand, all envision these places as nodal points shaped as much by the traffic in people, ideas, organisms and texts through them as by the seemingly more fixed determinants of their physical and social environments. As Grove in particular demonstrates, even the most isolated, remote and seemingly self-contained of places, a place politically useful to the British state when exiling Napoleon precisely because of the difficulty of communication with it, St Helena, was constituted in part by the East India Company's trans-global networks of connection.[25] We need to appreciate that colonial places and societies became distinct through the very juxtapositions, encounters and accommodations that linked them to other places, whilst remaining interrelated components of the larger-scale assemblage that was empire.

However, this is not to mean that, as we collaborate on bringing our various sources together, we need lose sight of the detail that comes from their localised production. We must not lose the sense of that specificity of relations between people, organisms and objects that defined the precise context in which materials and texts were collected, produced, stored and preserved. As Winterbottom's chapter highlights by meticulously examining the provenance as well as the exchange of specimens and texts between surgeons in different regions of Asia and Africa as well as Britain, only by capturing the specificity of temporally and spatially specific local contexts as we connect them, can we enhance our networked view of the Indian Ocean World and our understanding of the co-constitutive transformation of the places comprising it.

Scale

At first glance, a networked approach to empire might seem to by-pass the question of scale. If we follow trajectories across space and through points of intersection regardless of where they lead us, we might weave at will through conventional scalar units ranging from the household to the globe. In much of the literature the concept of the network is seen to operate horizontally, while scale is considered to be more vertical and hierarchical. I want to conclude by making a case for considering scale rather as the product of networked relations.

Scales are frequently seen as simply existing, naturally occurring entities in their own right. Within geography and broader political economy, however, it is only since the 1970s that a shift has occurred from a broadly horizontal imagination of global divisions, informed by Immanuel Wallerstein's model of core – semi-periphery – periphery, to a vertical, and more scalar understanding of the local – urban – regional – national – global. Furthermore, new scales of relevant analysis have been added, for example by feminist historians and geographers drawing attention to the home as a significant site of social reproduction.

This malleability of thinking about scale has been explicitly examined of late in work inspired by Latour. In a range of disciplines, what might seem to be naturally occurring scales of analysis, from the household to the global, are being seen as the products of particular projects, pursued through networks of varying geographical reach, and involving combinations of human and non-human agency. Scales are being understood as 'the provisionally stabilized outcomes of scaling and rescaling processes; the former can be grasped only through an analysis of the latter'.[26]

In recent imperial history, there has been considerable attention to networks that operated at a 'global' scale, connecting disparate nodal points around the world. But there has been relatively little examination of the concept of the 'global' scale itself. If we consider the emergence of this apparently natural, but actually manufactured, scale as something worthy of investigation in its own right, it is obvious that imperial forms of government had much to do with it. In Stephen Legg's analysis of the divisions of sovereignty between British India and the League of Nations, institutions like states, leagues and federations are 'considered as assemblages kept together by the practices of scalar apparatuses [while] the impression is created that these scales are exclusive (non-overlapping), hierarchical (nested and tiered) and ahistorical'.[27] It is not only governmental projects that create scale in this way. Legg gives the further examples of postal organisations and private and public bureaucracies of various kinds that create tiers of internal regulation which become common-sense scalar units such as the postcode, the county and the region. The apparatuses of capital accumulation and civil society also manufacture and sustain such scalar activity.

Rather than assuming that networked analyses render scalar analysis redundant, then, we need to appreciate that scale is 'so normativized ... as to make it impossible to think space without it'.[28] Like gender, race and class in post-structuralist historical thinking, we might productively think of scales as entities constructed through particular projects with real effects in the world. These are the 'effects of networked practices'.[29]

Perhaps the most influential of analytical scales in imperial history is that of the nation. Indeed, so influential is the assumption that the nation is the 'natural' scale of most historical analysis that much of the recent work pursuing long-distance trajectories across constructed borders is described as 'transnational', even when it concerns periods and places where there was no nation. Massey conveys both the constructed nature of this national scale and its real effects:

> The boundaries of nation-states are temporary, shifting phenomena which enclose, not simply 'spaces', but relatively ephemeral envelopes of space-time. The boundaries, and the naming of the space-time within them, are the reflections of power, and their existence has effects. Within them there is an active attempt to 'make places'.[30]

There is perhaps no better example of the way that the constructed spatial delimitations of the nation can have very real effects than the partition of India. Chester's study of the processes through which Radcliffe's partition line came to be drawn across the Punjab in 1947 is an example of the development of 'a human geography with scale', as she moves back and forth between imperial concerns at one extreme and intra-village contestation along the dividing line at the other. But she is explicit that, for her, scale is 'critically considered as a narrative device, a measure of distance and a technique of governmentalities ... rather than a plane at which structural processes operate'. The book shows how, at the end, as well as at the beginning of empire, historians must move across space, up and down through constructed but effective scales from the household to the global, becoming intimate with selected and often dispersed locations, to tell the most meaningful stories. The resulting narrative can combine 'the intrigue of high politics with the tragedies experienced by those on the ground and the influence of the rapidly transforming international scene with the role of local society, culture and tradition'.[31]

Those acts of long-distance environmental exchange, knowledge and preservation that are the substance of this book were, I would suggest, crucial to the very idea of the Indian Ocean World as a scalar unit – they

Introduction: New Imperial and Environmental Histories   13

helped to manufacture such an Oceanic scale and hence are best pursued through that scale of analysis, but without losing sight of those local scales of interaction upon which such a large-scale imagination is layered. This book serves as one way in, then, to human and non-human assemblages of varying scale and duration across the Indian Ocean World and beyond.

Notes

1. A more general and extensive treatment of ideas of space in imperial history writing is A. Lester (2013), 'Spatial Concepts and the Historical Geographies of British Colonialism', in A. Thompson (ed.) *Writing Imperial Histories*. Manchester: Manchester University Press, pp. 118–42.
2. F. Mort (1987), *Dangerous Sexualities: Medico-Moral Politics in England since 1830*. London: Routledge and Kegan Paul, quoted by R. Phillips (2006), *Sex, Politics and Empire: A Postcolonial Geography*. Manchester: Manchester University Press, p. 6; A. Burton (2011), *Empire in Question: Reading, Writing and Teaching British Imperialism*. Durham, NC and London: Duke University Press, pp. 14–15.
3. J. MacKenzie (1989), *Imperialism and Popular Culture*. Manchester: Manchester University Press; S. Howe (ed.) (2010), *The New Imperial Histories Reader*. London and New York: Routledge.
4. C. Hall (1992), *White, Male and Middle Class: Explorations in Feminism and History*. London: Routledge; C. Hall (2002) *Civilising Subjects: Metropole and Colony in the English Imagination 1830–1867*. Cambridge: Verso; K. Wilson (2004), *A New Imperial History: Culture, Identity and Modernity in Britain and the Empire, 1660–1840*. Cambridge: Cambridge University Press; A. Burton (1994), *Burdens of History: British Feminists, Indian Women and Imperial Culture*. Chapel Hill: University of North Carolina Press; S. Marks (1990) 'History, the Nation and Empire: Sniping from the Periphery', *History Workshop Journal*, 29(1): 111–19.
5. R. Grove (1996), *Green Imperialism: Colonial Expansion, Tropical Island Edens and the Origins of Environmentalism, 1600–1860*. Cambridge: Cambridge University Press. More recently, see H. Cook (2008), *Matters of Exchange: Commerce, Medicine, and Science in the Dutch Golden Age*. New Haven: Yale University Press; K. Raj (2010), *Relocating Modern Science: Circulation and the Construction of Knowledge in South Asia and Europe, 1650–1900*. Basingstoke: Palgrave Macmillan, and S. Sivasundaram (2013), *Islanded: Britain, Sri Lanka, and the Bounds of an Indian Ocean Colony*. Chicago: University of Chicago Press.
6. D. Massey (1995), 'Places and Their Pasts', *History Workshop Journal*, 39: 186.
7. F. Driver and R. Samuel (1995) 'Rethinking The Idea of Place', *History Workshop Journal*, 39: vi.
8. In fiction see A. Ghosh (2009), *Sea of Poppies*. London: John Murray, and (2012), *River of Smoke*. London: Picador, and among historians, for example, K. McPherson (1998), *The Indian Ocean: A History of People and The Sea*. Delhi: Oxford University Press; T. Mecalf (2008), *Imperial Connections: India in the Indian Ocean Arena, 1860–1920*. Berkeley: University of California Press;

and most recently, S. Amrith (2013), *Crossing the Bay of Bengal: The Furies of Nature and the Fortunes of Migrants*. Cambridge, MA: Harvard University Press.
9. T. Ballantyne (2002), *Orientalism and Race: Aryanism in the British Empire*. Basingstoke: Palgrave Macmillan.
10. J. Beattie (2012), 'Recent Themes in the Environmental History of the British Empire', *History Compass*, 10(2): 131.
11. B. Latour (2007), *Reassembling the Social: An Introduction to Actor-Network-Theory*. Oxford: Oxford University Press.
12. E. Pawson (2008), 'Plants, Mobilities and Landscapes: Environmental Histories of Botanical Exchange', *Geography Compass*, 2(5): 1466.
13. Beattie, 'Recent Themes', 131-3.
14. Beattie, 'Recent Themes', 131-3, citing D. Lambert and A. Lester (eds.) (2006), *Colonial Lives Across the British Empire: Imperial Careering in the Long Nineteenth Century*. Cambridge: Cambridge University Press.
15. Beattie, 'Recent Themes', 131-3; R. Drayton (2000), *Nature's Government: Science, British Imperialism and the Improvement of the World*. New Haven: Yale University Press. My emphasis.
16. See also K. Ward (2012), *Networks of Empire: Forced Migration in the Dutch East India Company*. Cambridge: Cambridge University Press.
17. Something that was necessary, for instance, to write. A. Lester (2002) 'British Settler Discourse and the Circuits of Empire', *History Workshop Journal*, 54: 27-50.
18. See Lambert and Lester, *Colonial Lives Across the British Empire*.
19. L. Paterson (2006), *Colonial Discourses: Nuipepa Māori 1855-1863*. Dunedin: University of Otago Press; E. Elbourne (2005), 'Indigenous Peoples and Imperial Networks in the Early Nineteenth Century: The Politics of Knowledge', in P. Buckner and R. Douglas Francis (eds.) *Rediscovering the British World*. Calgary: University of Calgary Press, pp. 59-86, R. Ross (1999), *Status and Respectability in the Cape Colony, 1750-1870*. Cambridge: Cambridge University Press, p. 156.
20. Ward, *Networks of Empire*; C. Anderson (2012), *Subaltern Lives: Biographies of Colonialism in the Indian Ocean World*. Cambridge: Cambridge University Press.
21. For a valiant effort to track an individual 'subaltern' who appeared only once and fleetingly in the colonial archive, see C. Van Onselen (1996), *The Seed is Mine*. New York: Hill and Wang. See also J. Carey and J. Lydon (eds.) (2014), *Indigenous Networks: Mobility, Connections and Exchange*. London: Routledge.
22. M. Stevens (2009), 'Mutonbirds and Modernity in Murihiku: Continuity and Change in Kai Tahu Knowledge', unpublished PhD thesis, University of Otago.
23. See D. Kumar, V. Damodaran and Rohan D'Souza (eds.) (2011), *The British Empire and the Natural World: Environmental Encounters in South Asia*. Delhi: Oxford University Press.
24. D. Massey (2005), *For Space*. London: Sage.
25. In *River of Smoke*, Ghosh also manages to link Napoleon's exile on the island to trans-Indian Ocean mobilities.
26. Latour, *Reassembling the Social*; N. Brenner (2009), 'Restructuring, Rescaling and the Urban Question', *Critical Planning*, 16: 71.

27. S. Legg (2009), 'Of Scales, Networks and Assemblages: The League of Nations Apparatus and the Scalar Sovereignty of the Government of India', *Transactions of the Institute of British Geographers*, 34(2): 238.
28. J. P. Jones III, K. Woodward and S. A. Marston (2007), 'Situating Flatness', *Transactions of the Institute of British Geographers*, 32(2): 271.
29. Legg, 'Of Scales, Networks and Assemblages', 234.
30. Massey, 'Places and their Pasts', 189.
31. L. P. Chester (2009), *Borders and Conflict in South Asia: The Radcliffe Boundary Commission and the Partition of the Punjab*. Manchester: Manchester University Press, p. 235.

1
Botanical Explorations and the East India Company: Revisiting 'Plant Colonialism'

Deepak Kumar

The concepts and the practices of colonialism and imperialism have fascinated scholars for almost a century and their relevance continues. They have myriad shades and have shaped human life as nothing else has done so far. Concepts such as modernity, new socio-economic forces, techno-scientific changes and globalization are in some way or another related to these phenomena. It is no coincidence that during the era of the Scientific Revolution, different trading companies were established to undertake colonial expansion. Flag followed trade and both recognized the relevance of techno-scientific knowledge. The era of exploration had its own romance. Later on, institutions were established and professionalization gradually came. It was a long and arduous process. The colonizer and the colonized cannot be seen only in terms of binaries. How should one characterize this delicate and dialectic relationship: in terms of core–periphery, network, web, circuits, persuasion – coercion, 'gentlemanly', 'traditional' imperial history or 'new' imperial history? Historical facts, dug honestly from different sites, do not seem to support deterministic or essentializing understandings. The very nature of historical construction invites one to look at cross-currents and fluidity. Colonialism as a process is no exception to this. Similarly, scientific knowledge, like colonialism itself, is no monolith: both needed and aided each other.

One can ask how a science like botany or geology functioned in a colonial setting or how far it succeeded in 'straddling the spatial and epistemological divide' between the metropolis and the colony. Was this a one-way transfer? One can add, was this merely knowledge or largely derivative? Did peripheral creativity lead to peripheral enrichment? Could it produce autodidacts or intellectual-migrants who could hold their own? How should one link the local and particular (both metropolitan and colonial) with the general and universal (e.g. imperialism)? How should one conceive of both the differences and the connections between Britain and its various colonies?[1] What was the indigenous component? Is indigenous 'original and unsullied' to be seen mostly in opposition to modern/scientific knowledge? Could they interact? Could they change? Was a synthesis or co-production possible?

Numerous such questions have long engaged the attention of scholars and several plausible explanations have been offered. The seminar at which this chapter was originally presented talked of 'trans-cultural cooperation under the premise of imperialism'. Some scholars deny the idea of cooperation; they argue things were imposed from above. Many others try to soften the sting of imperialism and try to project it in terms of collaboration. This chapter will try to address these questions with the help of some relevant examples from botanical explorations in early British India. It is not without reason that colonies were often referred to as plantations. After all, it was the knowledge of and commerce in botany that propelled the growth of merchant capitalism.

The discursive terrain

Discussions on colonialism are probably as old as the colonial process itself. Shakespeare had reflected upon it in the early seventeenth century. His *Tempest* has all the ingredients of the real drama that colonization played in different parts of the world. It has voyage, discovery, oppression, collaboration, intrigues and, above all, the magic of knowledge. Till the end of the eighteenth century, the travellers, the traders, the officials, the military and the missionaries remained busy in building up the colonial project, and they emerge as the major, if not, the sole informants on what was happening. Later, the recipients also became very curious of what was happening around them. They were no longer passive and, at least in some areas, colonialism became a joint project. Out of this encounter, the seeds of decolonization sprouted and this was followed by long years of contestations, struggle and, finally, independence for the colonized. In the postcolonial decades, scholarly attention has naturally reverted to the fascinating and penetrative game-changer that colonialism was. Its myriad shades have now been dissected in terms of power, culture, imposition, contestation, metropolis, periphery and what not. The diffusionist perspective and the centre–periphery model had held sway for a long time. The model had its own advantages and did succeed in explaining the phenomenon to a large extent. The relationship between the metropolis and the colony was not merely geographical or political; it was also socially constituted, and as such 'represented the combined effects of social, political, and economic relations among different cultures and peoples'.[2] So to discard the core–periphery explanation would be like throwing the baby out with the bathwater! But the new post-colonial scholarship rightly points out the disjunctions, the ruptures and the ambivalences that the earlier explanations had left out or ignored. Can both be taken together?

In January 1985 an international seminar was held in Delhi under the broad umbrella title Science and Empire. It was hailed as a kind of 'Delhi Declaration asking for re-examination of the role of the West in the scientific and technological backwardness of nations which in our world have been sadly divided into the rich and the poor'.[3] The emphasis appeared to be more on the negative side of colonialism. Five years later a bigger conference on this theme was organized in Paris.[4] Here a global context was taken into account without sacrificing the local. By this time many articles and books had already appeared delineating the different strands of the science–colonization links.[5] The seeds of numerous future works were being sown simultaneously.

In undertaking such researches, the first port of call was obviously the archives pertaining to the trading companies who had initiated the colonial process in early modern times. These form an almost inexhaustible source of historical reconstruction. Next came the travellers' and missionary accounts. And then of course were the numerous tracts, pamphlets, journals and reports written in both colonial and indigenous languages. Later researches, probably under the influence of postcolonial essayists, tend to undermine the significance of the so-called official sources even though they came from the horse's mouth. To me, personally, it was rewarding to go through numerous, often contradictory, notes written by lower-rung officials filed between dusty covers. They give an idea of how a decision was arrived at, the tensions involved and the perceived threats. The files preserved in the colonial archives lay bare the inner thoughts of the official mind and show what went into the making of a particular decision. It may be erroneous to believe that the official sources give only a particular picture. Through them it is possible to know about the 'other' side as well. This, however, is not to underestimate the importance of 'local' sources, especially those written in their indigenous languages. In them one gets sharp critique of official policies and actions. Similarly, in private papers, several official participants appeared critical, outspoken and forthright. The letters written by colonial scientists to their peers in London and the replies they received make exceptionally interesting reading and reveal what is not normally available in official documents or contemporary publications. They often contradict what one finds in official records and give new insights.

This brief discussion on sources is important because they provide the foundation for a valid discursive terrain. Literary people and even anthropologists may have the liberty to 'imagine', but poor historians cannot afford such luxuries. So all our talk about 'web', 'network', 'circulation', 'calculation' and the like needs to be based on solid primary evidence. We would also be ill-advised to make generalizations on the basis of one or two solitary manuscripts or sources. On the basis of the available sources and the works published so far, one can reasonably assume that scientific and technological knowledge was closely woven into the whole fabric of colonialism. The colonial state claimed superiority in terms of structure, power and race, while modern science claimed superiority in terms of new knowledge. Both needed each other and moved hand-in-hand. Thanks to this relationship, the concept of a 'state scientist' emerged under which its practitioner would have the dual mandate to serve both the state and science simultaneously. The Jesuit missionaries also did the same. In China, they skillfully served the interests of both Versailles and the Forbidden City.[6] In India, they moved with the Bible in one hand and an improvised telescope or microscope in the other. Both could be used convincingly to shatter or change the world views and cosmologies of the indigenous. Major exploratory works were undertaken by the medical men who travelled on every boat as 'surgeon-naturalists'. In the initial years of colonization, the colonial scientist was, to a large extent, the master of his own agenda; and a whole new world of flora, fauna and minerals was open to him. This was a period when it was possible to forge a network or a web connecting them despite the tyranny of distance and initiate a far more liberal though limited circulation of ideas and materials. These 'web-masters' understood the significance of local knowledge. Bontius, for example, considered the knowledge of the Javanese superior to that of Greek and Roman authorities. He objected to the epithet 'barbarians' given to the locals in Batavia and argued that their knowledge of herbs 'leaves our own far behind'.[7] Similarly, many influential Europeans in India felt that local knowledge and its techniques could be put to constructive use. Except for a few, like Macaulay, they sought help from the old intellectual elite in their own work. Wilkinson in central India and Ballantyne in Banaras are illustrious examples. They were so respectful that they refused to sweep away the old hierarchies, but they did honestly try to replace them with new, syncretic Anglo-Indian precepts.[8]

But in many cases, dismissal of the local was quick and sharp. The colonizers were genuinely convinced of their epistemological superiority. In such a scenario, Lewis Pyenson claims a 'distinct' and 'insular' status for the exact sciences like physics and astronomy.[9] Scientific works in the colonial outpost no doubt 'lit the wilderness for metropolitan travellers', but whether they 'illuminated local residents with the light of superior learning', as claimed by Pyenson, is doubtful. Scholars have talked about the different ways of the transmission and reception of scientific ideas which were not always consumed 'neat' by the recipients. Tomes have been written on the encounter, struggle and so forth. But struggle against whom? Can the different parties of an encounter or struggle be studied separately? The imperial and subaltern materials are not like grain and chaff to be winnowed. A comprehensive trajectory should include, highlight and analyse both.[10]

Colonization was never a linear or a smooth process; it had its own hazards. It involved knowing the local terrain, its inhabitants and their knowledge systems. The colonizers could condemn local knowledge and its practices but could never ignore them. In fact, in some cases the local knowledge of the indigens gradually became universal knowledge, and in many cases the universal was internalized by the locals with open hearts. Similarly, rejections also took place with great disdain. A lot must have been lost in the process of translation and delivery of course, but different societies developed their own strategies and mechanisms to deal with this process.[11] Numerous individual and thematic instances can be cited which bear witness to this loss-and-gain drama. Scholars have also talked of 'another reason'; after all, the colonized societies had a rationality and a world-view of their own.[12] Colonial discourse, it is true, is neither dictated nor possessed entirely by the colonizers. Postcolonial theorists find ample instances of 'ambivalence', 'hybridization' and 'mimicry' within it.[13] It is these subtle yet inherent notions which made the colonizer think of the colonized simultaneously as an unknowable 'other' and knowable. Similarly, it is this ambivalence which explains the predicament of a 'native' intellectual whether to own or discard his own traditional notion or text, and how. Though produced as an 'other', he is also a 'producer' because his actions would invariably provoke reactions from different quarters. No one denies the existence and significance of cooperation. But the question remains: cooperation on whose terms and under what conditions? This qualification is exceptionally significant and may blow up several tall claims of collaboration and cooperation. Numerous explanations have thus been given and scholars have tried several new approaches. John Darwin, for example, has given an exciting explanation in terms of 'multiple bridgeheads'.[14] One thing, however, seems certain; all agree on the complexity of the phenomenon! In my opinion no model or heuristic device can encapsulate such a complex and Janus-faced relationship.

On the eve of colonization

One finds an early example of such interface in the works of Garcia da Orta in Goa, Heinrich van Rheede in Malabar, J. G. Koenig in Tranquebar and Robert Wight in Madras. These early European pioneers were studying Asia, its flora and its knowledge not as 'an extension of its construction in Europe but as a phenomenon in its own right'.[15] Heinrich van Rheede, who produced the magisterial *Hortus Indicus Malabaricus* (1678–1693), requested all governors in Holland's colonial outposts – Bengal, Surat, Persia and the Cape – to send 'annually' by the homeward-bound ship all kinds of seeds, bulbs, roots, plants, trees, flowers and the like for the sake of 'curiosity and also medicine'.[16] Travellers were advised to observe indigenous practices and collect materials to extend the European *materia medica*.[17] As Grove argues, fifteenth-century voyages had already begun to transform the science of botany and to enlarge 'medical ambitions for the scope of pharmacology and natural history'.[18] To this Grove adds an interesting dimension. He examines the role of caste in structuring European knowledge of the colonized society. Caste is a unique Indian system and the power of Brahmanical influence is well known and understood. In contrast, 'the diffusion of medico-botanical knowledge tended to privilege non-Brahmanical epistemologies and impose an indigenous technical logic'. This is a highly perceptive and valid angle. But could it transform European botanical science, as Grove claims?[19] Probably we need move evidence. Here one may also ask, could botanical science in Europe have progressed without inputs from Van Rheede or Rumphius? In an influential work, Richard Drayton shares Grove's Edenic imagery but would not accept his thesis on the origins of conservationism in the colonies. He is too convinced of 'constructive imperialism'. The title of his book, *Nature's Government*, is significant.[20] But did 'Nature's Government' condition or change the 'Government's Nature'?

Colonial developments cannot be understood solely in terms of politics or trade. There was indeed a strong cultural context to all that was happening on the eve of colonization. These were the formative years in which one can find the seeds of future transformations. It was an exciting time of transition. Formidable Asiatic empires from the Ottomans to the Manchus had begun to show signs of decline. The old order was crumbling; the new was yet to emerge, and when it did, it came via new routes and with new knowledge. It is not difficult to see fluidity in such a situation. Exchange in terms of both materials and ideas was possible and even visible. There were some who evoked a sympathetic chord but there were many who condemned Indian traditions and practices as most primitive, crude, clumsy and unscientific. This condemnation may be part of the process of hegemonization as well. It is also possible that, for European observers, there may also have been some genuine difficulties in understanding an abstruse treatise or in appreciating a simple technical device which would appear 'appropriate' only when viewed against the existing socio-economic context.

Was there anything like a science of botany in pre-colonial India? Probably not; there are of course references to *Krishitantra*, *Vrikshayurveda* and *Bhesajvidya* in the works of Kasyapa, Parasar, Saraswata and Kautilya, but this knowledge was definitely made subservient to philosophy, science of medicine or the science and techniques of agriculture. Majumdar attributes this neglect to the fact that scientific cognition and the results of observations were not kept sufficiently distinct from popular notions, guesses and superstitions. He adheres to a familiar trajectory: a brilliant beginning, marked progress to a certain stage, and a tragic stagnation, thanks to the Muslim invaders.[21] It is difficult to believe in the stagnation theory but the area is certainly underresearched. The Mughals are known for their keen interest in plants and gardens. A seventeenth-century text, *Dar Fann-i-Falahat*, describes the various methods of grafting, preparation of soil, harvesting techniques, water and manure requirements and the like. Interestingly, it also refers to male and female plants! Later, several tracts on various useful plants were written in Persian, for example, *Nakhl-bandiya* by Ahmed Ali in 1790 and *Nuskha-i-Kukh-bad* by Amanullah Husain.[22] Yet it may be correct to infer that the 'oriental' learning had no 'state of the art' knowledge.

Bridgeheads galore

The second half of the eighteenth century saw numerous bridgeheads and a gradual intensification in their activities. During this period the East India Company had secured a firm grip at least over Bengal and Madras, and its rivals were on the wane. The Company appreciated the significance of botanical and geographical investigations and encouraged its interested employees to undertake such activities. An early example is of James Anderson who joined the East India Company in 1759. In 1778, he obtained from the Madras Government a large piece of land near Fort St George which he developed as a botanical garden where he experimented with introduction of cochineal insects, silkworms and plants of commercial value such as sugar cane, coffee, American cotton and also European apples.[23] In Bengal, another military official, Robert Kyd, conceived of the idea of supplying the Company's navy with teak timber grown near the port where it could be used in shipbuilding. So, in June 1786, he submitted a scheme for the establishment of what he appropriately called a 'Garden of Acclimatization' near Calcutta which was promptly accepted. It is a treat to read this 'Memorandum on Agriculture Productions, Commerce, Population and Manufactures'. Kyd obviously took a long view and worked on a huge canvas. He defines policy which reflects a deep insight and muses on what the government should do. He wrote:

> Policy in its genuine signification being the art of ordering all things for the benefit of the citizens of the state ... is the common sense of Government, or rather common sense as applied to Government; is everywhere requisite serving in some nations to restrain, in others to excite, in all to methodize, and direct the endeavours of a Nation.[24]

This statement coming from an army officer and an amateur botanist stationed in a colonial outpost is significant and is quite characteristic of the early explorers who came as an integral part of the colonial process.[25] Later, in1791, he wrote about the use of coconut coir for navigation purposes and about how teak plantations were necessary to meet naval requirements, particularly in times of war. His successor Roxburgh also showed great interest in timber for shipbuilding and promoted teak plantations on a large scale at Sylhet and Bankura. The Company was quick to realize these advantages. In fact, while approving Kyd's proposals, the Court of the East India Company acknowledged: 'So sensible are we of the vast importance of the objects in view that it is by no means our intention to restrict you, in point of expense, in the pursuit of it.'[26] Thus what had hitherto been a private and unofficial enterprise became a part of government policy which led to what Sangwan terms 'plant colonialism'.[27]

These developments would not have taken place only because of the commercial acumen of a trading company. Unlike their explorer predecessors, the new breed of colonial scientists solicited and received support from their peers in England. Joseph Banks, for example, was a patriarch – perhaps the most formidable pillar on which numerous scientific workers scattered all over the globe tried to lean at some point or the other. For him, exploration did not only mean geographical discovery, but the study of plants and animals and mineral wealth found in the colonies and their bearing on the welfare of Great Britain in particular. He maintained enormous correspondences and these make a truly fascinating study.[28] In 1794, the mathematician John Leslie (1766–1832), for example, expresses his ambition to go to India as an astronomer; asks for Banks' influence and support and regrets that regular astronomical observations are not made 'under the fine climatic conditions of India', and the loss to science it entailed.[29] Another correspondent endeavours to answer the questions put by Cavendish as to the scientific knowledge of the Brahmins, mentions the great difficulties of learning Sanskrit, and desires to be elected FRS![30] Banks seems to have dealt with so many with great charm and finesse. But sometimes he does show irritation with the East India Company. Once he advised Roxburgh not to address plants meant for Kew to the Directors of the Company 'as they have sometimes claimed them'. He regrets that the Directors of the Company were always changing and he was tired of urging schemes on 'such an unstable body'.[31] On another occasion be remarked: 'I cannot say that in general the Military pay so much attention to us poor Philosophers as I am sure they will do when our value is better understood.'[32] Banks sometimes showed over-enthusiasm about the dynamics of trade and the topography and resources of territories he had never visited. His 'Memorial on Tea', submitted to the Company in December 1788, is one such example:

> Black tea may certainly be cultivated with success in the northern parts of the Province of Behar, Rungpoor and Coosbeyhar, for instance, where the latitude and the cooling influence of the neighbouring mountains of Boutan give every reason to expect a climate eminently similar to the ports of China in which black tea at present are manufactured.
>
> The mountains of Boutan afford in a short distance all the climates that are found in the cooler parts of the Empire of China and consequently every variety necessary for the product of the green teas, if then the culture of the black tea is once established in the neighbouring provinces of Behar and the inhabitants of Boutan are invited by proper inducements, they will certainly undertake that of the green,

and by a gradual change the whole of the tea trade will be transferred into that quarter. The inhabitants of Canton are now in the habit of shipping themselves on board over Indiamen whenever hands are wanted, we may therefore with safety conclude that their neighbours at Honan may be induced by the offers of liberal terms to follow their example and moreover to embark their tea shrubs and all their tools of culture and manufacture and migrate with them to Calcutta where they will find the Botanic Garden ready to receive them.[33]

Banks had obviously gone overboard and his wish could never be fulfilled. In contrast, his Indian collaborators like Roxburgh were seldom swayed and were grounded in reality. While at Samalcotta near Madras, Roxburgh was moved by the poverty of the people and called for the introduction of plants (like jackfruit) that would furnish sustenance to the poor in times of scarcity. For scarcities he frankly blamed the system and administration.[34] But his superiors appreciated more that part of his activity that had a commercial bearing and sent him to Calcutta. Roxburgh added to the Calcutta botanic garden 2200 species of plants, besides more than 800 species of trees. Evaluating his contributions a century later, one of his successors wrote:

> As regards economic botany Roxburgh's Flora is a perfect mine of wealth ... so greatly were his researches into the sources of fibers and other useful substances esteemed in England that on no fewer than three occasions were gold medals awarded to him by the Society of Arts ... I have worked a good deal with Roxburgh's Flora and among Indian plants, and it takes a good deal to convince me of a Roxburghian blunder![35]

A very distinguished and better-known contemporary was William Jones. As an amateur plant-lover, he collected Sanskrit names of a thousand plants and sought in Sanskrit medical texts their medicinal or religious value.[36] Remarkably enough, he denounced the Linnaeus sexual system of classification as insulting to women and also found 'childish' Linnaeus' penchant for naming plants after the persons who first described them or those whom be liked. For Jones the names *Champaca* and *Hinna* were not only more elegant but far more proper for an Indian or an Arabian plant than the Linnaean Michelia or Lawsonia.[37] Ironically, Roxburgh named the famous Asoka tree the Jonesia Asoka!

Well, Jones was virtually a bridge straddling several disciplinary and other boundaries. Roxburgh and his successor Wallich were important bridgeheads. They were pioneers who contributed immensely to both knowledge and trade. As Buchanan noted later, 'there is no article of trade connected with the vegetable kingdom that Dr. Roxburgh has left unnoticed or unimproved'.[38] Wallich was a surgeon at the Danish settlement of Serampore and he was taken a prisoner in the wake of the Napoleonic wars. Roxburgh pleaded Wallich's case: 'he may be advantageously employed should Government think proper in exploring the unknown productions in Botany as well as in Zoology and Mineralogy'.[39] Wallich helped by saying that his object was knowledge, not money and that 'he will be satisfied with whatever allowance Government may be pleased to grant'.[40] He got an assistantship and he would have been the ideal successor to Roxburgh. But being a Dane, and given the politics of personal contacts and intrigues, he lost out and even had to leave the garden.[41] Later Carey came to his rescue, lobbied with several officials in high posts, including the Governor-General, and Wallich returned to the garden as its superintendent.[42] Thereafter he went into plant-specimen collection in a big way. He had little time or patience for theorization.[43] His greatest virtue was that he not only collected but also tried to distribute his specimens as widely as possible, even at the risk of offending his superiors.

By 1828, Wallich had prepared a manuscript (still unpublished) which has more than 9000 specimen entries.[44] The same year he took these specimens to England in thirty barrels. It was the first time such a huge collection had reached the metropolis and it required careful sifting and analysis. Wallich was in no mood to share his 'riches' only with his compatriots 'who would be either incapable or too busy (as Lindley and Hooker) or would accept and do nothing (like Brown)'.[45] He wanted to assert his independence as a botanist and share his collections with his continental counterparts as well. This was not liked by the British Admiralty and the Court itself. But Wallich had his way, thanks to support from several European botanists. The diary of an Italian botanist, de Candolle, who worked with Wallich in London, gives interesting observations:

> Wallich is really the most generous, liberal, expansive and muddle-headed man I have ever met ... I am not surprised that he alone has achieved more than all his predecessors put together for he is a man of amazing activity ... The Wallich couple entertained us very well while apologizing for their meagre possibilities as they have only

4 servants instead of 30 or 40 in India ... He always speaks of his position as head of the Garden in Calcutta as a very outstanding one.[46]

Victor Jacquemont, a French naturalist who travelled in India during the period 1828–31, refers to Wallich as 'a Danish botanist of ordinary talents, but who passes here for the first in the world, is the director of this establishment, and he certainly has the best income of any savant in existence'.[47] Mutual suspicions were thus rife. Wallich's able assistants McLelland and Griffith also differed with him. Wallich wanted to preserve the Linnaean garden which Roxburgh had laid out, but Griffith wanted a garden exposing the natural system flanked by rows of medicinal plants. Taking advantage of Wallich's long absence, Griffith once destroyed the Roxburghian layout and in the process much was lost.[48]

It seems the Company had gradually withdrawn its patronage.[49] Griffith wanted to visit Burma, but the Court said no.[50] Probably it preferred to bank on individual contributions which botanists like Forbes Royle and, a little later, J. D. Hooker were to provide. Hooker had definitely received adequate support and his *Flora-Indica* was ranked as 'the most valuable botanical publication of this or any other day'.[51] Even before this work, a number of local 'floras' had appeared which speak volumes of the indefatigable nature and utility of the botanical 'soldiers'. Significant among them were Roxburgh on the Coromandel Coast (1795), A. Moon on Ceylon (1824), Wallich on Nepal (1824), J. F. Royle on Kashmir (1833), J. Graham on Bombay (1839), W. Munor on Agra (1844), M. P. Edgeworth on Banda (1852), J. Long on Bengal (1857) and F. Mason on Burma (1851).[52] Private societies like the Agriculture and Horticulture Society of India were also doing their bit by announcing an award of hundred rupees or a gold medal to the most successful cultivator of coffee, or superior cotton, or 'any esteemed species of European fruits'.[53] An interesting innovation as the end of the Company period is that of photography, and in 1855 the Court sent a despatch asking to 'discontinue the employment of draughtsmen and artists' and to encourage 'accurate photographs of the most important commercial products'.[54] There was also pressure from above to ascertain whether supplies from Europe could be minimized or replaced by indigenous produces and this was the motive behind Forbes Royle's *Manual of Materia Medica*.[55]

Inferences

The Company not doubt had an agenda and was strong enough to implement it, but the implementors were not passive or meek agents.

They had a dual mandate, one to serve the state, the other to extend the frontiers of knowledge. The state claimed superiority in terms of structure, power, race and so on. Science claimed superiority or precedence in terms of knowledge and, *inter alia*, helped the colonial state 'appropriate', 'assimilate' or 'dismiss' other epistemologies. In the initial stages (as in the Company period), a colonial scientist was, to a large extent, the master of his own agenda and a whole new world of flora, fauna and minerals was open to him. But as the colonial arteries hardened, science came under the purview of official knowledge with its official hierarchies and rituals.[56] Some scholars are unduly worried that the work of colonial naturalists or botanists was considered 'low' science.[57] It was not. As Richard Grove has convincingly shown, ideas like conservation and even modern environmentalism 'rather than being exclusively a product of European or North American predicaments and philosophies, emerged as a direct response to the destructive social and ecological conditions of colonial rule'.[58]

Here are important questions which still beg more attention and exploration. Was this process influenced by non-European epistemologies of nature? Was there little or substantial incorporation of local knowledge into mainstream or metropolitan science? Was the network or web of knowledge largely a one-way process? Does a divide exist between 'indigenous' and the 'other'? Is the divide artificial, as Arun Agrawal would like us to believe, given the changing nature of all forms of knowledge and the frequent connections and borrowings between them?[59] Connections were definitely there. How about the borrowings? As a well-meaning surgeon wrote:

> The indigenous system of India has been a cause of disappointment to us not because they are successful rivals of modern medicine, but because we have been able to borrow or steal from them so little that is of real value.[60]

In the numerous accounts of colonial interactions during the eighteenth and nineteenth centuries, how many Indians are referred to as botanists? One reference is to Murdan Ali, a Munshi at Saharanpur who is described as 'a very intelligent and respectable Syyud, the first of his race who addicted himself to Natural History and in whose honour Dr. Royle established the genus Murdannia'.[61] He was said to be preparing a vernacular flora of north India using the natural system but the manuscript in Urdu could not be published for want of support and seems lost. Indians appear mostly as artists and illustrators and even in this regard carried the blame for any 'imperfections'.[62] 'Local' help was always taken. There are many examples of the early colonial medical men collecting medicinal plants from the neighbouring forests and discussing their virtues with the 'locals' and these were even published in the *Philosophical Transactions*.[63] But the locals remained unnamed. Such mediation could never flower. The colonists and settlers were definitely not 'ciphers in the arithmetic of imperialism', as Saul Dubow rightly argues,[64] but the 'natives' were.

The local 'interface' was not always with the literati class. Van Rheede learnt perhaps more from the non-Brahminical Ezhavas. The 'oriental bazaars' were great learning places. L'Empereur, a French botanist who compiled *Jardin De Loxia* (Flora of Orissa), wrote to his friend, 'The *fakirs* who have the best remedies come every winter to bathe in the Ganges. By giving them something and speaking to them in Hindustani directly without interpreters, they let you into their secrets. It was a *fakir* who thus taught me the great remedy for epilepsy.'[65] The fakir remains anonymous. Yet the scholar who first explored this text feels that such enterprise was to have 'a long-term effect on the local communities with which they interacted'.[66] We need to ask, what kind of effect did it have? Maybe as the botanical gardens sprouted and geographical surveys were undertaken, some Indians got jobs as painters and draughtsmen. Does this constitute collaboration in the right sense of the term? Henry Noltie has produced four remarkable volumes on the botanical works of Alexander Gibson in Bombay and Robert Wight in Madras presidencies. He has brought to life not only these colonial botanists but also their Indian artists like Luchman Singh, Rungiah and Govindoo who did true-to-life drawings and paintings but about whom very little is known.[67] Most of the Company artists remained anonymous. Was it because of the low pay (Gibson got more than Rs. 2000 per month while his artist was paid Rs. 20 per month) or social status of the artists or was it because of racial feelings? Can these be taken as instances of collaboration?

The situation changes during Victorian times; one finds more instances of collaboration in the areas of surveys, medicine and astronomy, but in geology, botany and other sciences, such instances remain rare. To Medllicott, a geologist, the Indians appeared 'utterly incapable of any original work in natural science'. He wanted to wait until 'the scientific chord among the natives' was touched, and added, almost contemptuously, 'if indeed it exists as yet in this variety of the human race'.[68] A recent work agrees that there is very little information on the social backgrounds of the individuals ('natives'?) who possessed scientific and technical knowledge or the conditions under which they worked. Next to nothing is known about their education, or the networks in which they operated and exchanged information. Still enthused by the instances offered by Raj and Grove, it surmizes that there was a vibrant scientific community in the Indian subcontinent in the seventeenth and eighteenth centuries.[69] Pratik Chakrabarti rightly argues that eighteenth-century history tends to suffer from an exoticization of networks and collections as hybrid exchanges. There is a tendency to see in these exchanges an agenda that blunted the violent edge of colonial modernity.[70]

In a study of colonial science and its relationship to indigenous cultures, MacLeod finds new ways of seeing science in action – or rather 'in inter-action' – as a highly textured activity, serving to celebrate the diversity of knowledge among peoples, of places and over time.[71] Textured it definitely was, but we need to look for the marginal and faded threads. Ballantyne gives a more appropriate imagery: 'Empires, like webs, were fragile (prone to crises where important threads are broken) yet also dynamic, being constantly remade and reconfigured through concerted thought and effort; the image of the web reminds that empires were not just structures but processes as well.'[72]

The imperial account, in its myriad ways and shades, provides numerous important lessons. One which I learnt while writing this chapter came from Buchanan, who in a letter addressed to the Government of Bengal (22 February 1816) wrote: 'a few may be enriched by the trade, it will be of minor importance to the native, till the poor, who require it most, can season their cruder diet at a price within their reach'.[73] Hopeful, the post-colonial state, no less powerful than the colonial one and much more enamoured with market and trade, realizes its significance.

Notes

This chapter was originally presented as a paper at the Cooperation and Empire Conference, University of Berne, 27–29 June 2013. I am grateful to the organizers for the opportunity. Help and encouragement received from Vinita Damodaran and Rohan D' Souza is gratefully acknowledged.

1. A. Lester (2006), 'Imperial Circuits and Networks: Geographies of the British Empire', *History Compass*, 4(1): 124–141.
2. R. MacLeod (2000), 'Introduction: Nature and Empire', *Osiris*, 15: 5.
3. D. Kumar (ed.) (1991), *Science and Empire*. Delhi: Anamika Pub.
4. P. Petitjean (ed.) (1992), *Science and Empires: Historical Studies about Scientific Development and European Expansion*. Dordrecht: Springer.

5. D. R. Headrick (1981), *The Tools of Empire: Technology and European Imperialism in the Nineteenth Century*. New York: Oxford University Press; R. MacLeod (1982), 'On Visiting the Moving Metropolis: Reflections on the Architecture of Imperial Science', *Historical Records of Australian Science*, 3: n.p.; I. Inkster (1985), 'Scientific Enterprise and the Colonial Model', *Social Studies of Science*, XV: 677–704.
6. As Harris points out, 'in both the linguistic and Latourian sense, Jesuits were masters of translation'. S. J. Harris (2005), 'Jesuit Scientific Activity in the Overseas Missions 1540-1773', *Isis*, 96(1): 71–79.
7. L. Schiebinger and C. Swan (2005), *Colonial Botany*. Philadelphia: University of Pennsylvania Press, p. 12.
8. C. A. Bayly (1999), *Empire and Information*. Cambridge: Cambridge University Press, p. 260.
9. L. Pyenson (1989), *The Empire of Reason: Exact Sciences in Indonesia, 1850–1950*. Leiden: E. J. Brill.
10. D. Kumar (2006), *Science and the Raj*, 2nd edn. Delhi: Oxford University Press, p. 17.
11. Latour defines translation as 'a stronghold established in such a way that, whatever people do and wherever they go, they have the pass through the contender's position and to help him further his own interests'. B. Latour (1988), *The Pasteurization of France*. Cambridge, MA: Harvard University Press, pp. 65–66.
12. For stimulating details, see G. Prakash (1999), *Another Reason: Science and the Imagination of Modern India*. Delhi: Oxford University Press.
13. For details, see, H. K. Bhabha (ed.) (1990), *Nation and Narration*. London: Routledge.
14. Bridgehead is a 'hinge or interface between the metropole and a local periphery ... it might be a commercial, settler, missionary or proconsul presence or a combination of all four. It might be a decaying factory on a torrid coast or, at its grandest, the Company Behadur.' J. Darwin (1997) 'Imperialism and the Victorians: The Dynamics of Territorial Expansion', *English Historical Review*, 112(447): 629–642.
15. K. Raj (2006), *Relocating Modern Science*. Delhi: Permanent Black, p. 58. Raj cites the example of Rumphius who clearly mentioned in his Herbarium Amboinense (1663–1697) that his work was meant for the 'use and service to those who live in the East Indies'.
16. L. Schiebinger (2004), *Plants and Empire*. Cambridge, MA: Harvard University Press, pp. 15, 27.
17. An excellent account of the travellers' perceptions is given in S. Sangwan (1985), 'European Impressions and Interpretation of Indian Science and Technology', *Social Science Probings*, II(3): 353–377.
18. R. Grove (1988), 'Indigenous Knowledge and the Significance of South-West India for Portuguese and Dutch Constructions of Tropical Nature', in R. Grove, V. Damodaran and S. Sangwan, *Nature and the Orient: The Environmental History of South and Southeast Asia*. Delhi and New York: Oxford University Press, pp. 187–207.
19. Grove, 'Indigenous Knowledge', p. 193.
20. R. Drayton (2000), *Nature's Government: Science, Imperial Britain, and the 'Improvement' of the World*. New Haven: Yale University Press.

21. G. P. Majumdar (1927), *Vanaspati: Plants and Plant Life as in Indian Treatises and Traditions*. Calcutta: Calcutta University, pp. 220–224. See also G. P. Majumdar (1935), *Upavana Vinoda: a Sanskrit Treatise on Arbori and Horticulture*. Calcutta: Calcutta University.
22. I. Wladimir (1926), *Concise Descriptive Catalogue of the Persian Manuscripts in the Curzon Collection of the Asiatic Society of Bengal*. Calcutta: Calcutta University.
23. British Library Anderson Papers, OIOC, Photo. Eur. 85.
24. National Archive of India (NAI), Home, Public, nos. 13–14, June 16, 1786.
25. Robert Kyd (1746–1793) had a military career, appointed ensign in Bengal infantry in 1764; on the staff of the first Brigade at Monghyr during the Batta Mutiny; Fort Major and Barrack Master at Fort William till 1785, founded the botanical garden at Sibpur in 1786. British Library, Robert Kyd Papers, OIOC, Mss. Eur. F.95.
26. Quoted by Buchanan, NAI, Home, Public, no. 94, April 15, 1816.
27. S. Sangwan (1983), 'Plant Colonialism', *Proc. of the XLIV Session of the Indian History Congress*. Burdwan, pp. 414–424.
28. W. R. Dawson (1958), *The Banks Letters*. London: British Museum.
29. John Leslie to J. Banks, Aug. 18, 1794; Dawson, *Banks Letters*, p. 531.
30. Samuel Davis, Accountant General, Bengal, to Banks, March 10, 1791, Royal Botanic Garden Library, Kew, Banks Correspondence, 2.38.
31. British Museum Add. Mss. 33980. ff. 159–160, J. Banks to Roxburgh, Aug. 9, 1798.
32. British Museum Add. Mss. 33980, f. 170, J. Banks to Roxburgh, Jan. 7, 1799.
33. British Library, OIOC, Mss. Eur. D.993, J. Banks, Tea Memorial, Dec. 27, 1788.
34. NAI, Home, Public, no. 10, Dec. 5, 1799.
35. G. King (1895), 'A Brief Memoir of W. Roxburgh', *Annals of the Royal Botanic Garden of Calcutta*, V: Calcutta, pp. 6–7.
36. G. Cannon (1964), *Oriental Jones*. Delhi: Asia Pub. House, pp. 125, 148, 182.
37. Schiebinger, *Plants and Empire*, p. 223.
38. NAI, Home, Public, no. 94, Buchanan to Secy. to Govt., Feb. 22, 1816, April 15, 1816.
39. NAI, Home, Public, no. 26, Roxburgh to Secy. to Govt., Feb. 1, 1809, Feb. 10, 1809.
40. NAI, Home, Public, no. 52, March 10, 1809.
41. British Museum, Hardwick Papers, Mss. Add. 9869, Hardwick to Banks, May 15, 1817, T.
42. British Library, OIOC, Carey Papers, Eur. Mss. B.230.
43. A David Arnold puts it, 'Wallich was no grand theorizer. He showed little interest in plant geography, or anatomy, or in the more philosophical issue of the distribution or variation of species that later intrigued Joseph Hooker and fuelled his discussions with Darwin and Lyell. Wallich's significance was as a key figure in the patronage networks ... as a scientific entrepreneur, the man who, more than any other single individual, controlled and delivered to the West, India's vast botanical riches.' D. Arnold (2005), *The Tropics and the Travelling Gaze: India, Landscape, and Science 1800–1856*. Delhi: Permanent Black, p. 155.
44. Preserved with the Keeper of Herbarium at the Botanical Survey of India, Shibpur, Kolkata.

45. British Museum (Natural History), Candolle Papers, BMSS. CAN, Diary of Alphonse de Candolle, May 13, 1830.
46. British Museum (Natural History), Candolle Papers, BMSS. CAN, Diary of Alphonse de Candolle, May 13, 1830.
47. V. Jacquemont (1835), *Letters from India*, vol. I. London: Edward Churton, p. 114.
48. I. H. Burkill (1965), *Chapters on the History of Botany in India*. Delhi: Govt. Press, p. 91.
49. In 1855, the Superintendent of Calcutta Garden, Dr. T. Thomson, wrote: 'Library, herbarium and museum have been starved from want of funds, and in consequence, the scientific character of the Establishment has been so entirely, lost, that its existence is scarcely known in Europe.' (1857), *Selections from the Records of the Bengal Government*, no. XXV. Calcutta, p. 63.
50. British Library, OIOC, E/4/752, Bengal Despatches, XII, Aug. 23, 1837, pp. 408–409.
51. Anon. (1856), *Calcutta Review*, 26 (June), pp. 363–365. As a plant-hunter, J. D. Hooker was supreme. He became the most outstanding geo-botanist of the century. P. Raby (1996), *Bright Paradise: Victorian Scientific Travellers*. Princeton: Yale University Press, pp. 122–147.
52. H. Santapau (1958), *History of Botanical Researches in India, Burma and Ceylon*, Pt. II. Bangalore, p. 5.
53. Anon (1822), *Records of the Agri-Horti: Society of India*, March 20, p. 9.
54. NAI, Home, Public, no. 35, May 1, 1856.
55. J. F. Royle (1847), *A Manual of Materia Medica and Therapeutics*. London: John Churchill.
56. For more details see, Kumar, *Science and the Raj*.
57. One scholar, for example, attempts a lame defence: 'in reality it was more on account of problem of logistics, rather than professional incompetence on the part of colonial scientists, that the balance of their labours were categorized as "practical results" rather than accorded the distinction of research papers.' S. Sangwan (1998), 'From Gentlemen Amateur to Professionals', in Grove et. al., *Nature and the Orient*, p. 224. Data gathering *per se* is no low activity; conversely it requires great deal of competence. Roxburgh and Wallich were no great theorizers but enjoyed enormous reputations. Moreover, 'logistics' alone could not have converted data into analysis!
58. R. Grove (1995), *Green Imperialism*. Cambridge: Cambridge University Press, p. 486.
59. Arun Agrawal (1995), 'Dismantling the Divide between Indigenous and Scientific Knowledge', *Development and Change*, 26: 413–439.
60. Rockefeller Archive Centre, NY, IHD, 1.1, 464, India, Box 5, f.34J, W. D. Megaw, 'Confidential Note on the Working of the Panjab Medical Dept.', Sept. 6, 1928.
61. Edward Madden cited in Arnold, *The Tropics and the Travelling Gaze*, p. 183.
62. When Wallich published his *Plantae Asiaticae* in London in the early 1830s, he prefaced the work by apologizing that the 1,200 illustrations had been made by Indian artists in Calcutta, adding, p. 184, that 'this will at once explain any imperfections in the figures'.
63. P. Chakrabarti (2006), 'Medicine Amidst War and Commerce in Eighteenth Century Madras', *Bulletin of History of Medicine*, 80: 1–38.

64. S. Dubow (2006), *A Commonwealth of Knowledge*. Oxford: Oxford University Press, pp. 14, 99.
65. Raj, *Relocating Modern Science*, p. 41.
66. Raj, *Relocating Modern Science*, p. 59.
67. H. J. Noltie (2002), *The Dapuri Drawings: Alexander Gibson and the Bombay Botanic Gardens*. Edinburgh: Royal Botanic Garden, pp. 79–80; H. J. Noltie (2007), *Robert Wight and the Botanic Drawings of Rungiah and Govindoo*. Edinburgh: Royal Botanic Garden.
68. NAI, Revenue, Agriculture, Surveys, no. 25, Sept. 1880.
69. P. Parthasarathi (2011), *Why Europe Grew Rich and Asia Did Not*. Cambridge: Cambridge University Press, pp. 187–192.
70. P. Chakrabarti (2010), 'Networks of Medicine', in A. Bandyopadhyay (ed.), *Science and Society in India 1750–2000*. Delhi: Manohar, p. 65.
71. MacLeod, 'Introduction to Nature and Empire', p. 10.
72. T. Ballantyne (2002), *Orientalism and Race*. London: Palgrave Macmillan, p. 39.
73. NAI, Home, Public, no. 94, April 15, 1816.

2
Medicine and Botany in the Making of Madras, 1680–1720

Anna Winterbottom

Introduction

Over the last fifty years, historians of science and medicine have demonstrated that natural knowledge was central to the process of early modern European expansion. Networks of botanical gardens, plant collectors and plantations eventually aided European powers in increasing their control over colonial territories by using exotic plants as food, medicine and valuable articles of trade.[1] However, with some exceptions, such studies have emphasized the importance of European capitals and the scientists working within them as what Bruno Latour calls 'centres of calculation'.[2] While the role of colonial collectors, naturalists, doctors and surgeons working on the ground is recognised by Latour and others, their immediate contexts have often been neglected and their interests in collecting subordinated to those of the metropolitan collector.[3] However, the activities that made up the 'scientific revolution': the assiduous collection and detailed study of natural objects, the amassing of libraries and 'repositories' of curiosities and books of dried plants, the exchange of information through networks of scholarly correspondence and the formulation of theories about the natural world also took place in colonial settlements and outposts. Furthermore, each settlement was embedded within webs of local and international connections and the collection and deployment of natural knowledge had immediate political consequences on the ground as well as distant ones in Europe. In this chapter, I will examine the process of collecting, describing and using plants in Madras: the English East India Company (EIC)'s most important settlement on India's Coromandel Coast with the substantial population of 8,000 by the late seventeenth century.[4] I will demonstrate that the town's survival as an

EIC colony often depended on the deployment of medical and natural historical knowledge in regional diplomacy during a critical period of its existence. I will examine the natural and political networks within which the city was embedded and their interaction through the collections and correspondence of two English EIC surgeons stationed at the Fort. As these materials reveal, spaces for the exchange of natural and medical knowledge included the courts of the rulers of Golconda and Arcot; the army camps of the EIC and the Mughal and Maratha armies; the city hospital; the bazaars and apothecaries' shops; the physic gardens that dotted the city; and the ships that carried drugs and ideas to and from the town. The natural knowledge that was created in these experimental arenas was used in medical missions, which formed a key part of local diplomacy, as well as to provision the hospital and supply ships calling at the harbour with fresh drugs. *Materia medica* and information about its uses was marketed to apothecaries in European capitals and exchanged for patronage, both locally and internationally. I will argue that rather than being dictated by the priorities of the European collector, local and personal priorities took precedence in shaping such collections.

The surgeons and their collections

The evidence for this reconstruction is drawn largely from the correspondence of Samuel Browne and Edward Bulkley with the apothecary and fellow of the Royal Society James Petiver and from collections they sent him and other correspondents in London. Samuel Browne was appointed to the position of surgeon of Madras in 1688, after serving as a ship's surgeon.[5] Petiver became acquainted with Browne through another collector in 1689, and the two corresponded until Browne's death in 1698.[6] Edward Bulkley, formerly the surgeon at Pettipoli, first joined Browne at Fort St George in 1692 then replaced him in 1697, remaining in the position until 1709, when he resigned and became a 'land customer', member of the Madras Council, and Justice of the Peace until his death in 1713.[7] Substantial collections of plant and animal specimens made by these two surgeons remain in the Sloane Herbarium of London's Natural History Museum.[8] Significant collections also remain in the herbaria of EIC cashier-general Charles Dubois (*bap*. 1685–d. 1740) at the University of Oxford and the Royal Botanical Gardens in Edinburgh.[9] However, it is clear that these materials represent a fraction of the total amount of what each surgeon sent to London, let alone of their total collections in Madras.

Medicine and Botany in Madras, 1680–1720   37

Among many other specimens, the collections Browne sent to England include seven large bound volumes of dried and labelled plants (*hortus sicci*), many with their Tamil names written on bark in the original script and in transliterated form. These volumes also contain accounts of their medicinal virtues, usually written next to the dried plant.[10] The contents of these volumes, originally sent to the EIC but loaned to the Royal Society, were partially transcribed and published by Petiver in the journal *Philosophical Transactions*.[11] The published articles contain comments and cross-references to other contemporary works of botany, particularly Hendrik van Rheede tot Drakenstein's *Hortus Malabaricus* (1678–1703).[12] The comparisons were made by Petiver in some cases, but in other cases supplied by Browne, who maintained a library including van Rheede's monumental work as well as many other works of contemporary European science such as Prosper Alpinus' 1591 *De medicina Aegyptiorum*, one of the earliest European studies of non-Western medicine; publications of the Royal Society including John Ray's *Historia Plantarum* (1686–1704) and Robert Hooke's *Micrographia* (1665), and Parkinson's well-known herbal of 1640, *Theatrum botanicum*. He also had works on the East Indies, including Garcia da Orta's *Colloquies* (1563) and Christoval Acosta's *Tractado* (1578) and the collections of the Dutch botanists Carol Clusius and Jacob Bontius.[13]

Browne's seven volumes reveal the types of medical problems that the surgeons encountered. Unsurprisingly, fever emerges as a major problem: 34 of the 226 plants mentioned in the first five books are febrifuges. Smallpox is mentioned several times: often the plants described as useful in treating it are the same as those used against fevers.[14] Treatments for 'bloody flux' (dysentery),[15] gonorrhea,[16] leprosy[17] and poison[18] are mentioned several times. However, the collections also refer to more everyday practices including children's medicine[19] and remedies used by women during childbirth, postpartum recovery or menstruation.[20] References to the treatment of mental problems such as melancholy, hysteria and even hypochondria, also appear.[21] While the extensive comparisons to the *Hortus Malabaricus* made by the surgeons may be erroneous in some cases, a high degree of similarity was perceived by the surgeons and their informants between the pharmacopeias of Kerala recorded by van Rheede and of Tamil Nadu recorded by Browne. Just over one-third (115) of the 317 plants Browne mentions in the seven volumes are identified with those which occur in the *Hortus Malabaricus*.[22]

It is clear from an examination of Browne's volumes that they were produced in close collaboration with a Tamil practitioner of medicine who was travelling with him and was closely involved with the process of selecting and collecting as well as naming the specimens and relating their virtues. Like the *Hortus Malabaricus*, they must therefore be regarded as collaborative works. In contrast to the prominent authorial role granted to the Indian authors of the *Hortus Malabaricus*, however, the name of Browne's co-worker is never mentioned. Nonetheless, his central role is clear from internal features of the volumes, such as their organisation according to the Tamil names given at the beginning of the volume,[23] as well as from references in Browne's correspondence. In 1698, at which time Browne decided to give up his botanical work, he wrote to Petiver: 'I have also sent to [Edward Bulkley] one of the Malabar Doctors who is well skilled in the nature of Indian Plants from whome he or his people may transcribe their virtues.'[24] In cooperation with this physician, Bulkley embarked on the process of transliterating the Tamil names of plants and gathering accounts of their medicinal properties. He wrote to Petiver in 1700 promising accounts of both Tamil and Telugu names as well as of the medicinal properties of the plants,[25] and in 1701 reported 'I have lately contracted a friendship with the principall of the Gentue [Hindu] Doctors who promises to be very communicative and give a large account of known plants of these parts'.[26] He sent the results of this collaboration to Petiver in 1703.[27] Bulkley also sent drawings and paintings copied from or by local artists (Figure 2.1), some of which were eventually included in Petiver's printed works.[28]

Bulkley also relied on local people with natural and medical knowledge to make the collections of plants and fossils and illustrations he sent to Petiver and others. In a peevish letter in which he complains that Petiver has not sent him requested plants and books, he writes: 'it is a greater charge & trouble to make collections than you suppose, there are very few that understand it and they will have extraordinary pay to goe 40 or 50 miles and be a moneth absent from their families and businesse'.[29] In the same letter, Bulkley reports that he had employed a man to travel from Madras to Bengal, making plant collections on the way, but that his collecting activities were being impeded by the conflict between the Mughals and Marathas and the fear of meeting tigers in the woods. Nevertheless, some collections made by this man do survive in the Sloane Herbarium.[30] Bulkley also reports sending his servants to make collections in Aceh (Sumatra) and Pegu (Burma/Myanmar).[31]

As Bulkley's letters reveal, making collections was not an activity that the two doctors undertook in leisured hours, but was a costly and time-consuming exercise, often conducted in woods and fields over which lay the shadows of marauding armies and wild beasts. In the next sections I will ask why it was considered so important by the two doctors to make such extensive collections of natural materials during a time of political crisis.

Figure 2.1 © British Library Board *Icones Avium Maderaspatanarum* (BL ADD MS 5266, ff. 91–2)

Medicine and politics

Established in 1639, the English East India Company's settlement at Madras (also known as Madraspatam or Chinapatam, now Chennai) had quickly become the focal point of EIC operations on the Coromandel Coast. By 1695, Samuel Baron described it as 'the most considerable to the English nation of all their settlements in India whether ... in reference to the trade to and from Europe, or the Commerce from one part of India to the other'.[32] The late attempts to establish trades to China and Japan, to resettle the Indonesian archipelago, and to gain a foothold in Bengal, were all directed from Fort St George. With the decline of Masulipatnam after c.1700, the town also become important to regional trade conducted by both Asians and Europeans, including members of the medical profession.[33] As Chakrabarti notes, Madras was the centre of military power from which the Company fought the territorial conflicts known as the Carnatic and Mysore Wars later in the eighteenth century.[34]

Nevertheless, during the late seventeenth and early eighteenth centuries, Madras was in a difficult position. Since 1657, the settlers had been subjects of the rulers of Golconda, the Quṭb Shah dynasty, who had regained independence from the Mughal Empire after a war of succession.[35] Despite nominally accepting Mughal overlordship in 1677, the same year, Abul Hasan of Golconda negotiated a military alliance with the Maratha leader Śivaji, based on the annexation of land in Bijapur and Karnataka. The conflict continued, until the final defeat of Golconda in 1687. The East India Company had thrown in their lot with these enemies of the Mughal Empire. However, the war proved so disastrous that the English parliament granted a charter to a rival company in 1698, which fought and petitioned the Emperor against the old Company until a final merger of the two took place in 1702–9. The Madras factory was therefore under great pressure to form a new alliance with Zu'lfiqar Khan and Daud Khan, leaders of a powerful faction of the Mughal nobility, who had been sent by Aurangzeb to defeat the Marathas and had consolidated Arcot as a centre by the early 1690s. The network of surgeons played an important part in the diplomatic negotiations between Madras and the new Nawabs of the Carnatic.

In 1693, Samuel Browne was sent to treat a wound of a Mughal general named Qasim Khan. Khan must have been satisfied with his treatment, for he appointed the surgeon as the *havildār* (a position with military as well as civil responsibilities)[36] of six towns adjoining Madras. Whether Browne did take up this Mughal administrative post is unclear – the EIC were apparently unhappy about it because of uncertainty regarding Qasim Khan's official position at the time.[37] In ordering Browne to choose between their employment and that of the Mughals, the Governors might also have had in mind the defection the previous year of another doctor, Richard Blackwall, the surgeon at Fort St David from 1693, who was said to have 'by his profession, access to the Mughal's camp'.[38] Blackwall had taken on the government of Porto Novo under the Mughals and supported attacks on the Company factories. Despite the uncertainty surrounding his personal position, Browne made a useful contact for the EIC during this visit, by establishing friendly relations with the Armenian physician to the Nawabs of Arcot, through whom he was able to procure a grant confirming the Company's settlements in Madras and Cuddalore, in exchange for gifts of 'curiosities'.

Browne's involvement in local politics caused the Company some headaches. In 1697, Browne was fined for robbing, attacking and – to add insult to injury – pulling the beard of a Mughal customs official.[39] Nevertheless, shortly afterwards he was mediating in a dispute with the very same official, who had cut off the roads between Fort St George and nearby San Thomé after a dispute concerning land rents.[40] Despite such hiccups, Browne used his patrons in the Mughal establishment and the Company hierarchy to build up a lucrative business supplying drugs to the camps of the Mughal generals. Browne's contacts in the Mughal army were also useful for the Company: he could inform them about goings-on and, as he did in 1695, recover errant servants who had defected to the Mughal camp.[41] The tours of duty that Browne undertook with the Mughal army also allowed him to collect plants. One of the books of grasses he sent to Petiver is recorded as having been collected en route to Tirupati in 1696. This was shortly after the Mughal conquest of the region after the killing in 1694 by Zu'lfiqar Khan of the raja Yācham Na'ir and the instalment of his eldest son, Kumaru Yachama Naidu as an obedient Mugahl mansabdār.[42] Once again, therefore, Browne's trip was probably intended as an exercise in diplomacy. As this example demonstrates, collecting was part of the everyday practice of military medicine. The plants that became dried specimens in the herbarium would also have been tucked into the doctor's bag for immediate use in medicine.

Despite the accommodation reached in 1693, relations between the English settlers and the rulers of Arcot remained tense. Selim Khan attacked Cuddalore during 1698 and Zul'fiqar Khan's deputy Daud Khan repeatedly threatened Madras, blockading it for an extended period in 1702. Again, Company officials turned to the network of surgeons with access to the Mughal hierarchy: on this occasion, they appealed to the self-made Italian medic Manucci, then living in Madras, to negotiate with Daud Khan.[43] The need for political awareness as well as medical skill might partly explain the Company's decision in 1697 to replace Browne with Bulkley in the position of surgeon. Bulkley, they wrote, was 'fit to serve us by his large experience of India ... and as fit for prescribing physic as for manuall operation [surgery]'.[44] In 1707, the year of the Emperor Aurangzeb's death and a time of political unrest in the Mughal Empire, Bulkley was sent to Arcot on a mission that combined medical and diplomatic aims. While there, he also collected several volumes of plants and information about their medicinal virtues.[45]

Despite its growing wealth and size, Madras was in a precarious position. Poised between Mughal expansionism, the rebel Marathas and Golconda, it was regularly threatened with extinction. The network of contacts that could be built up between physicians, who had the advantage of close personal access to those at the centre of power, was an important way to exchange information and gifts. It was therefore crucial for the surgeons to acquire a good reputation: this would have entailed becoming acquainted with the protocols of Mughal court life and medicine and being able to employ the plants they gathered on their travels in their cures. Knowledge of plants and the means of employing them was thus crucial to establishing the East India Company's position in India in terms of their relationship with the Mughal hierarchy.

Spaces of experimentation: hospital, bazaar and garden

When they were not on tours of duty with the EIC or Mughal armies, the surgeons were based at the Madras hospital. Originally founded in 1664, the hospital was relocated in 1688 to a large building described by Lockyer:

> The Hospital joins the New-House by the Water-Gate to the Northward, is a long building and has a piazza with a paved Court before it: at one end of the Court is the Plaister-Room, and at the other end an Apothecaries Shop, where the Medicines are prepared after the Prescriptions of the ingenious Dr. B[ulkle]y.[46]

Regional medical conventions appear to have had some influence on Bulkley; for example, when he wrote to request changes to the hospital, he recommended the appointment of a dubash (interpreter and general manager) and a conicoply (accountant or registrar) as well as four 'coolies' (workmen).[47] Although the EIC's hospitals' intake was probably restricted to Europeans, it appears to have been common for Europeans to turn to Asian doctors and sometimes vice versa in the early Company settlements: Fryer noted that in Surat, 'the Brahmin comes every day and feels every man's pulse in the factory, and is often made use of for a powder for agues, which is as infallible as the Peruvian Bark'.[48] The exchanges that took place in the informal medical marketplaces of Madras also often spilled over boundaries of nationality or race. For example, the minutes of the early Mayor's court in Madras record a case Manucci brought against a patient Cojee Bauba – probably an Armenian – for non-payment of fees,[49] while Browne gossips about a Muslim inhabitant of Madras believed to be in possession of a stock of a now-rare type of medicinal myrobalans (*Terminalia chebula*).[50]

Like their Dutch counterparts, the VOC, the EIC relied on local drugs to circumvent problems of expense and spoiling associated with sending drugs from Europe to settlements abroad.[51] The apothecaries' shop in the hospital constituted an English equivalent to the 'medical shop' in the castle at Batavia[52] and it played a crucial role in provisioning the ships' surgeons who passed through Madras. For Browne and Bulkley it was also a place of experimentation where they used the knowledge they gained from their surroundings to prepare and market simple and compound drugs. Selling these preparations locally was profitable for the doctors; sometimes more so than collecting for their international contacts: in 1698, Browne wrote to Petiver that he was retiring from the pursuit of botany to focus on his 'physick practise' as well as the office of assay master.[53] Bulkley was able to assume his positions at Council and as Justice of the Peace after similarly retiring from medicine some years later.

Among the doctors' duties were to procure drugs and equipment from the bazaars to furnish the hospital as well as for their own activities as apothecaries. Browne mentions the drugs available in the bazaar in several of his letters and appears knowledgeable about their origins. The origins that are mentioned give us a taste of the global and regional trade networks through which the drugs available around Madras in this period were supplied. For example, Browne writes that tutia – an argillaceous ore of zinc, the powder of which is an ophthalmic – similar to that available in England can be procured locally, but that its source is Persia.[54] Bulkley was similarly able to inform Petiver that the fragrant black sandal or agallochum available in the Madras bazaar was acquired from Cape Comorin.[55]

Both Browne and Bulkley clearly spent time observing the work of their Indian counterparts in practice, adopting the practices they saw into their own routines, and reporting them to their correspondents in Europe. For example, in a letter to Petiver discusses the two types of assa foetida (*Ferula assa-foetida*) that were sold there, giving details of their application to palsy with instructions on preparation.[56] Another interesting example relates to plant products used to clean water, including the seeds of the Moringa tree.[57] Some of these beans were demonstrated at a meeting of the Royal Society in 1696 by Dr Havers, a fellow of the Society and another of Bulkley's correspondents, where it was decided that they worked by sticking to the dirt and dragging it down to the bottom of the container. After the meeting, Petiver wrote to Bulkley about the properties of the seeds, and the surgeon replied, giving the names of the plant in 'Malabar' and 'Gentue' (Tamil and Telugu), and noting their preparation and use in medicine, including against dysentery, as well as their antiseptic properties.[58]

As well as gathering drugs in the forest and purchasing them in bazaars, the inhabitants of Madras cultivated them in their gardens.[59] As several authors have pointed out, gardens designed to introduce new crops and to provide *materia medica* for local hospitals had existed for a long time in both Hindu and Muslim traditions and had spread to Europe in the form of the 'physic gardens' and 'acclimatisation gardens' that emerged in Italy, Portugal, later Holland, and finally England and France and their colonies.[60] In Mughal towns of the period, 'householder gardens' were common, along with royal gardens and tomb gardens and the leasing of gardens could provide civic revenue.[61] The Company's gardens were thus only part of several long and overlapping traditions. As commercial and experimental spaces, the gardens also revealed, in their beds and borders, the networks that Madras was embedded within, as ships brought seeds and plants from other Company settlements, the territories of the rival European powers, and places of regional trade and religious pilgrimage.

The surgeons used their space in the Company gardens to experiment with local plants and to introduce crops from around the world. For example, Browne describes the 'Country Plants I have collected into a Square of the Company's gardens'.[62] Both Browne and Bulkley also raised plants they received from their networks of correspondents overseas: Browne describes growing China root, a popular medicinal substance normally identified with *Smilax China*, rhubarb, cinnamon trees from Ceylon (Sri Lanka), and wild agallo, benjamin[63] and camphor from Manilla. Edward Bulkley received plants from as far off as West Africa: with one letter he enclosed a drawing of a small sort of Gourd 'gathered on the Coast of Guinea & presented to me by name of the everlasting apple'.[64] He cut the gourd open and extracted a seed, which he planted in his garden, where the plant flourished. Bulkley also despatched seeds to be planted in other East India Company settlements: for example he sent rhubarb roots to the factory in Bencoulen (modern Bengkulu in Sumatra) to see whether they would grow better there than they had in his garden.[65]

The Company surgeons also attempted to introduce European and American plants into their gardens: Bulkley made several requests for Petiver to send him seeds for plants yielding food or medicine.[66] Some introduced crops had a clear commercial value for the Company. By the late seventeenth century, several factories had become involved in the cultivation and vending of tobacco,[67] a plant that in 1693 Petiver still listed as completely unknown in London. Meanwhile, the Company were also renting licences to grow and sell it, along with other mild stimulants or intoxicants including betel and cannabis (*Cannabis sativa*).[68] An interest in what might be called 'narcobotany' appears in the collections sent by Browne to Petiver, which include both these specimens. The opium poppy, which later became so important in the trade to China, was also discussed by Petiver and Browne.[69]

Gardens were also spaces for diplomacy: Mughal gardens were symbolic of the legitimacy of territorial claims: 'microcosms of spatial order within a more tumultuous and uncertain landscape', an idea that would not have been lost on many contemporary English readers of Shakespeare or Marvell.[70] They were also spaces where armies might rest, cures be performed and diplomatic negotiations take place.[71] Mughal visitors to Fort St George were liable to demand to inspect the Company's gardens as well as its armies, as Daud Khan did on a 1701 visit to the settlement, and thus they were a crucial source of prestige.[72] Perhaps prompted by this visit, the Governor had by the early eighteenth century transformed the Madras garden from a barren space to a pleasure ground complete with 'Bowling-Green, spacious Walks, Teal pond, and Curiosities preserv'd in several divisions'.[73] In 1708, Governor Thomas Pitt received a grant confirming the city's privileges from the *diwan* Zia-ud-din Khan in the garden's 'Great Walk'.[74]

One of the aims that I set out at the beginning of this chapter was to demonstrate that the activities associated with the 'scientific revolution', did not occur only in European capitals, but also in colonial settings. Experimentation is perhaps the most emblematic of these activities. As the example of the Moringa seeds demonstrates, the colonial metropolis and its institutions were often 'peripheral' in terms of access to both materials and information. The hospital provides an example of an experimental space, but far from being a solely European institution transferred to alien soil, both its staff and the practices of medicine carried on within it demonstrate hybridity of practice, drawing on Mughal conventions of layout and staffing and regional medical ideas. Furthermore, in terms of the networks that joined the experimental spaces of Madras to those of other settlements and supplied the items to the bazaars which formed the basis of the compound medicines mixed by the surgeons in the apothecaries' shop, they were often dictated more by regional trades independent of colonial control than by the priorities of the East India Company itself.

Although the two surgeons sometimes made use of Petiver's instructions for collecting, the materials they gathered from the field or purchased in the bazaar were not dictated primarily by the demands of the metropolitan collector, but by their immediate networks of trade and politics.[75] The actor-network theory of Latour has been modified in recent years by a number of studies that demonstrate that scientific knowledge is created not only in the laboratory, but also 'in the field and the forest, on ships at sea and on mountaintops, in the course of exploration and trade'.[76] The needs that shaped collections of naturalia were those of the field hospital, the foreign court and the ship's surgeon rather than the priorities of the distant gentlemanly experimenter.

International networks

The attempt that I have made here to stress the local and regional priorities shaping the surgeons' collections does not mean that their international connections were unimportant: indeed it was through these links that they acquired the curiosities that they exchanged in the courts of Golconda and Arcot and the works of reference that enabled them to compare their own environment with others around the world. The surgeons received books, dried specimens, seeds and botanical information from a range of international correspondents. As Madras was a usual calling point for all EIC ships heading further East or returning home, the surgeons were able to distribute instructions and materials for collecting – some of which they received from Petiver[77] – and receive collections on the return journeys. Bulkley sent collecting instructions to the Company surgeons in Bencoulen[78] and Vizagapatam[79] and refers to acquiring collections from Cochin China from James Cunningham, who was a surgeon in Chusan,[80] and in the short-lived settlement of Pulo Condore, where he was imprisoned.[81] These men, in turn, were embedded in other networks. James Cunningham and Henry Smith in Melaka, for example, corresponded with and sent collections to Petiver and Charles Dubois.[82] The go-betweens in these networks of land-based surgeons and collectors were the ships' surgeons, employed by the EIC.

As well as the other EIC settlements, contacts included the agents of other European companies – with whom the surgeons' relationships ranged from friendly exchange to rivalry. Among the Dutch company surgeons, Oldenhand at the Cape was known as an avid collector and botanist.[83] The plant collections of celebrated collectors were fought for within the East Indies. For example, in 1702, Bulkley's correspondence reveals a scrabble for the remaining collections of Wilhem ten Rhijne and Rumphius in Batavia.[84] One of the most important of the international relationships of the Madras surgeons was with the Jesuit George Kamel or Camelli, a lay father who made the first in-depth study of the wildlife of the Philippines. Bulkley exchanged frequent gifts of plants and seeds with Kamel and discussed the local uses of the plants in their respective regions.[85] Bulkley also acted as a conduit for the Jesuit's correspondence with James Petiver, with whom he published articles in the *Philosophical Transactions*.[86] Camelli sent specimens and drawings to Petiver and Ray.[87] Camelli, as well as Browne's patients among the Portuguese of San Thomé, adjoining Madras, also appear to have provided a means for the Madras surgeons to acquire further contacts among Jesuit missionaries. In 1696, Browne wrote concerning his objective of obtaining medicinal aloe species: 'I have written by way of the French and Portuguese padres to their brethren in the vast woods about three months journey to the northwards of Bengal towards Pegu.'[88]

The discussions that the surgeons took part in over particular plants or remedies with Jesuit missionaries and the Dutch Company's surgeons and botanists[89] demonstrate the closeness of the scholarly investigations taking place among the different European traders and missionaries in Asia at this time. The close connections between the Spanish Jesuit botanist Kamel and the Protestant surgeons remind us that the allied interests of science and trade were sometimes more important in such friendships than the dictates of faith. At the same time, the scramble for the manuscripts or collections of Rumphius and Ten Rhijne reminds us that the acquisition of natural knowledge was a crucial part of the competition between the European trading companies to acquire and exploit the wealth of the Indies.[90]

Each of the two surgeons I have focused on also sent a huge amount of plant materials to various correspondents in Europe and that which survives in the Natural History Museum represents only a tiny sample. For example, Bulkley refers in one letter to having sent twenty volumes of specimens to Petiver.[91] Among the contacts that the surgeons maintained in England were several London apothecaries including his brother-in-law, who ran a shop in Bread Street, and Mr Porter, a druggist in Cornhill Street.[92] The circle of botanists who received collections from the East Indies formed a close, though not always friendly,[93] group of experimenters and gardeners who constituted the overlapping membership of the East India Company, the Royal Society, and the Society of Apothecaries.

The web of contacts that the two surgeons maintain within the colonial world of the Indian Ocean were invaluable because they provided them with the materials necessary to make Madras a 'centre of calculation' by supplying them with materials on which comparisons and connections to their own collections could be drawn.[94] European contacts were important for the surgeons because they could provide them with patronage. This could come in the form of books, seeds, dried plant materials, and selling and marketing the exotic drugs that the surgeon supplied. In other cases, the surgeons asked their correspondents to exert their influence to improve their positions within the East India Company, as when Edward Bulkley lent on Charles Dubois to procure him additional funds and a palanquin in return for gifts of plants and seeds.[95]

Conclusions

In October 1698, Edward Bulkley sent to Charles du Bois five volumes of plants, four with 'a catalogue of their names in Malabar', two parcels of seeds, a gourd from Pegu, two pickled fruits with their names in Tamil and Telugu, and a litany of woes. His collections were being impeded by the 'trouble the Moor has given us of late' on the pretext of the acts of piracy lately committed against their shipping. These, he admitted, 'have been divers', but he blamed the agents of the 'new' East India Company for the 'mischief we feele and fear', adding 'I pray God direct you to some speedy redress of the grievances your trade labours under, which are truely very great'.[96] This letter gives a sense of the conditions under which the collections I have discussed were made. Plants provided cheap and readily available sources of medicine that could be used in treatments performed in the Madras hospital and the Mughal army camps and courts. Botanical collections were also intended to generate profit through sales, whether locally or internationally, and win favour for their purveyors within the shifting and competing hierarchies of the 'old' and 'new' Companies and regional powers. Browne and Bulkley's skilful deployment of their collections could win them favour in both Europe and in Asia.

Bulkley wrote at a time of transition in both England and India. The 'Glorious Revolution' had just swept King James from power, spelling trouble for many of his former allies within the Company's ranks. Meanwhile, the Mughal Empire looked to be at its height of its powers after the death of Śhivaji's successor Śambaji in 1688. In 1702, Aurangzeb ordered the suspension of trade with all the European companies and a survey of Madras was commissioned with the intention of occupation.[97] Meanwhile, the conflict with the 'new' Company continued until the final merger in 1709. In the following decades, the situation in England gradually became somewhat less precarious and the introduction of 'Dutch finance' ended the fiscal crisis. Theories of Mughal 'decline' and the significance of European powers in India during the eighteenth century remain contentious.[98] However, it is clear at least that by the time Bulkley died in 1713, being buried at the end of his garden,[99] the United Company was more securely established at Madras, as expressed in its now immaculate gardens. The networks of doctors had been crucial diplomatic actors in a critical period during which many believed that Madras was fated to be eclipsed altogether. In fact, the settlement could be said to have survived more by the performance of healing in regional courts than by wounds inflicted on the battlefield. It was the new relationship with the rulers of Arcot established by these doctors that eventually enabled the Company to consolidate its base at Calcutta.[100]

The surgeons' collections reflect the hybrid environment of early modern Madras and the networks – maritime, military and diplomatic – that the doctors were embedded in and which facilitated their creation. Many details are missing from this reconstruction of the practice of medicine and botany in the early colonial city. Unlike the contributors to the *Hortus Malabaricus*, we never learn so much as the names of the Tamil and Telugu-speaking doctors who were so crucial in collecting and revealing the medicinal uses of the specimens the surgeons sent to London. Nevertheless, the role of these collaborators was clearly crucial. Locating the process of collecting within the immediate environment of Madras allows us to regard the collections that Browne and Bulkley sent Petiver must be regarded as complex amalgams of both Asian and European natural and botanical knowledge. They are neither simple reflections of the *siddha* medicine of Tamil Nadu nor works that merely draw Asian *materia medica* into a European pharmacopoeia. Instead, they were the product of different allegiances and influences that were in tension within their works. The collections of these two surgeons, who were key players in the transformation of politics and botany in the region, straddling local and international concerns, in many ways provide the perfect portal through which to view Madras as it was transformed from a trading post subservient to the interests of regional powers to a major player in British colonial expansion.

Notes

1. Among others, Richard H. Drayton (2000), *Nature's Government: Science, Imperial Britain, and the 'Improvement' of the World*. New Haven: Yale University Press; Richard Grove (1995), *Green Imperialism: Colonial Expansion, Tropical Island Edens, and the Origins of Environmentalism, 1600–1860*. Cambridge and New York: Cambridge University Press. Londa Schiebinger and Claudia Swan (eds.) (2005), *Colonial Botany: Science, Commerce and Politics in the Early Modern World*. Philadelphia: University of Pennsylvania Press:, p. 19; E. W. Herbert (2011), *Flora's Empire: British Gardens in India*. Philadelphia: University of Pennsylvania Press.
2. Savithri Preetha Nair (2005), 'Native collecting and natural knowledge (1798–1832): Raja Serfoji of Tanjore as a "Centre of Calculation"', *Journal of the Royal Asiatic Society*, 15(3): 279–302 contests the Eurocentric ways in which the term 'centre of calculation' (from Bruno Latour (1987), *Science in Action*. Cambridge, MA: Harvard University Press, Chapter 6) has typically been employed.
3. Latour, *Science in Action*, p. 217. Critiques include Kapil Raj (2007), *Relocating Modern Science: Circulation and the Construction of Knowledge in South Asia and Europe, 1650–1900*. Basingstoke and New York: Palgrave Macmillan.
4. Chaudhuri, *The Trading World of Asia and the East India Company*, pp. 49–51.
5. D. G. Crawford (1914), *History of the Indian Medical Service, 1600–1913*, 2 vols. London: W. Thacker & Co., vol. 1, p. 91. Browne was previously the surgeon of a ship called the *Dragon*.
6. The first letter from Petiver to Brown is dated 61 March 1689, British Library (hereafter BL) MS Sloane 3332, fols. 6–7. Petiver sends a book on English botany and requests a correspondence. Browne's burial on 22 December 1698 is recorded in the manuscript 'Book of Marriages, Burials and Christenings' kept in the museum at the Fort in Chennai.
7. Crawford, *History of the Indian Medical Service*, vol. 1, p. 245.
8. I am very grateful to Drs Charlie Jarvis and Mark Spencer for their great help in accessing and navigating the Sloane Herbarium and to Dr James Delbourgo for pointing out Browne and Bulkley's collections there to me.
9. The Edinburgh collection came through a former keeper, Isaac Bayley Balfour (Sherardian Professor at Oxford from 1884 to 1888) and according to G. C. Druce (1927), 'British plants contained in the Du Bois herbarium at Oxford, 1690–1723', *Rep. Botanical Exchange Club*: 463–66, Balfour ordered

the chopping up of the original '80 [elsewhere given as 74] elephant folio volumes' and separate mounting of the sheets of the du Bois herbarium. So clearly it was through Balfour that some of the 'duplicates' to come to RBGE either before or after he became Regius Keeper in 1888. I am grateful to Henry Noltie at the Royal Botanical Gardens for this information, and also to both Dr Noltie and to Dr Stephen Harris and several of the staff of the Plant Sciences library and herbarium for their great help in accessing these collections.

10. The specimens are kept in the Sloane Herbarium in the Natural History Museum and described in J. E. Dandy (1958), *The Sloane Herbarium: An Annotated List of the Horti Sicci Composing It*. London: British Museum. Manuscript notes in the front of the first Browne volume in the Sloane Herbarium note that the seven books were borrowed by James Petiver and Hans Sloane during 1699 from the Royal Society's repository, to which they had been transferred after a request to the East India Company. A note by Fra[ncis] Hawskbee reads 'The 1 2 3 & 4 books are in the Society's house, the rest are missing.' Presumably the rest were returned to the repository at a later stage.

11. The seven articles are all published in *Philosophical Transactions*, 22 (1700/1): 579–94, 699–721, 843–58, 933–46, 1007–22, and 23 (1702/3): 1055–6, 1251–65. Petiver refers to each of the specimens as 'SB' followed by the number of the specimens in the seven volumes of the Sloane Herbarium. I have adopted Petiver's system in the references below. As Dandy, *The Sloane Herbarium*, p. 101 notes, an eighth book is also described in *Philosophical Transactions*, 23: 1450–60, but this was sent after Browne's death and also contains specimens from Bulkley. For other volumes containing specimens collected by Brown, see Dandy, *The Sloane Herbarium*, p. 102.

12. H. A. van Rheede tot Drakenstein (1678–1703), *Hortus Indicus malabaricus, continens regioni malabarici apud Indos celeberrimi omnis generis plantas rariones*, 12 vols. Amsterdam, Johannis van Someren and Joannis van Dyck. For an English translation, K. S. Manilal (2003), *Van Rheede's Hortus Malabaricus. English Edition, with Annotations and Modern Botanical Nomenclature* (12 vols.). University of Kerala, Trivandrum. See also H. Y. Mohan Ram (2005), 'On the English edition of Van Rheede's Hortus Malabaricus by K. S. Manilal (2003)', *Current Science*, 89(10): 1672–80.

13. For example SB 107 (Tamil transliterated as 'Corutree') cross-references Garcia da Orta and Christoval Acosta, *Tractado de las drogas y medicinas de las Indias Orientales* (Burgos: Martin de Victoria, 1578) and Carolus Clusius (1605), Pierre Belon, Cristóbal Acosta, Nicolás Monardes and Garcia Orta, *Caroli Clusii ... Exoticorum Libri Decem: Quibus Animalium, Plantarum, Aromatum, Aliorumque Peregrinorum Fructuum Historiae Describuntur*. Leyden: Ex Officina Plantiniana Raphelengii. SB 131 (Tamil, 'Noona chedde') refers to Jacob Bontius (1642), *De medicina indorum* (Franciscus Hackius, 1642).

14. SB 2 (Tamil: 'Avaree'); SB 15 (Tamil, 'Coata-corundee'; SB 16 (Tamil: 'Mucotarre'); SB 75 (Tamil: 'Cungee'); SB 86 (Tamil: 'Perrepan-chedde', 'chedde' meaning plant or bush); SB 119 (Tamil: 'Coadevelle', Telugu: 'Chittra-Mullum'); SB 161 *Jasminum augustifolium* OLEACEAE (53: Manilal, 2003, 6:53, p. 187); SB 189 *Toddalia asiatica* RUTACEAE (Manilal 2003, 5:41, p. 159); SB 211 (Tamil: 'Vulerha'); SB 234 (Tamil: 'Tumba maraum or Carpa maraum').

15. SB 64 (Tamil, 'Caut Yellendae') and SB 129 (Tamil, 'Ponau verre poondoo').

16. Gonorrhoea: SB 66 (Tamil, 'Clachedde'), SB 112 (Tamil, 'Adundee'), SB 120 (Tamil, 'Nelle-carambee'), SB 126 ('Coola guttee'), SB 211 (Tamil, 'Vulerha').
17. SB 167 ('Chedde mel chedde', meaning a creeper); SB 179 (Tamil, 'Waapa maraum', Browne identifies it with 'nimbo' the Portuguese name for *Azadirachta indica* MELIACEAE).
18. SB 238 (Tamil, 'Shevanar calunga'). Used as a general counterpoison. Browne reports trying it against the bite of the Cobree de Capello (*Naja tripudians*) without success.
19. SB 70 (Tamil: 'Codeseru-paulado') cures the whooping cough and SB 189 (Tamil, 'Visne crantee') is a cure for scabs and itches in young children.
20. For example, SB 126 (Tamil: 'Coola guttee') is listed as a cure for period pains.
21. SB 212 (Tamil: 'Coattakai') 'cures hypocondriack melancoly and hysterick passion'.
22. This is a bibliographic rather than scientific identification based on the cross-references given by the surgeons and Petiver. Botanical identification of most of the specimens has not yet been carried out.
23. For discussion of the extent of mutual comprehensibility between European and South Asian systems of plant classification see Henry Noltie's chapter in this volume.
24. BL MS Sloane 4062, fol. 290, Browne to Petiver, FSG, 30 September 1698. It is clear that Bulkley had previously assisted Browne in making some of the collections the latter sent to Petiver, see for example, James Petiver and Samuel Browne, 'An Account of Mr Sam. Brown His Second Book of East India Plants, with Their Names, Vertues, Description, etc. By James Petiver...', *Philosophical Transactions*, 22 (1700/1), p. 708.
25. BL MS Sloane 3321, fol. 28, Bulkley to Petiver, 23 February 1700.
26. Ibid., fol. 67, Bulkley to Petiver, FSG, 30 January 1701.
27. Ibid., fol. 110-11, Bulkley to Petiver, FSG, 12 February 1703.
28. Ibid., fol. 211 – From Bulkley to Petiver with no date [Recd. 9 Dec 1706 from Ireland]. The original paintings are in Add MS 5266, fols. 91–2. The inscription reads 'Icones Aurium Maderaspatannarum aevi incisarum, pro Synopsi Avium Rajana, uti & vide descriptionem p. 193, & seq. coloribus depictae ad oringales Icones, quas ab Arce S. Georgii misit Edwardus Bulkley'. They were copied again by the engraver of four pages towards the back of the BL's copy of Petiver's Opera (Shelfmark 443.i.1.(8) K. Birds.).
29. BL MS Sloane 3321, fols. 84–5, Bulkley, FSG, 9 November 1701.
30. Sloane Herbarium, vol. 32, fols. 135–50 contain plants gathered in Bengal. Bulkley reports sending them in BL MS Sloane 3321, fol. 169 – An unsigned letter to Petiver from 'your humble servant' at Fort St George 7 February 1705.
31. BL MS Sloane 3321, fol. 171 – 1 March 1704/5. It is in this letter that the reference to tigers occurs. Collections from Pegu sent to Petiver by Bulkley are in the Natural History Musem, Hortus Sicci (HS) 32, fols. 119–153. None of these specimens is named.
32. BL MS Add 34123 – 'Copybook of Henry Vansittart, Governor of Bombay, 1756', fols. 40–2: 'Samuel Baron's account of the trade of India, written from Fort St George in 1695'.
33. Pratik Chakrabarti (2010), *Materials and Medicine: Trade, Conquest, and Therapeutics in the Eighteenth Century*. Manchester: Manchester University

Press, pp. 33–4. John F. Richards (1975), *Mughal Administration in Golconda*. Oxford: Clarendon Press, p. 72.
34. Chakrabarti, *Materials and Medicine*.
35. Richards, *Mughal Administration in Golconda*.
36. Sir Henry Yule, *Hobson-Jobson: A glossary of colloquial Anglo-Indian words and phrases, and of kindred terms, etymological, historical, geographical and discursive*. New ed. edited by William Crooke, B.A. (London: J. Murray, 1903). Digital edition published by Digital Dictionaries of South Asia, University of Chicago, URL: http://dsal.uchicago.edu/dictionaries/hobsonjobson/ (last accessed 16 September 2014). See pp. 412–13 for the use of the word in the military and as the holder of a *hawāla*, a tenure between zemindar and ryot. See also Francis Joseph Steingass, *A Comprehensive Persian–English Dictionary*. London: Routledge & K. Paul, 1892. Digital edition also available from Digital Dictionaries of South Asia. University of Chicago, URL: http://dsal.uchicago.edu/dictionaries/ (last accessed 21 May 2014). I am grateful to Drs Minakshi Menon and Prashant Keshavmurthy for their advice about this term.
37. Letter from Sir John Goldsborough at Chuttanutti, dated 14 October 1693, *Letters to Fort St George* (Tamil Nadu State Archives), Vol. V, pp. 164–8.
38. John Bruce (1810), *Annals of the Honourable East India Company*, London: Black, Parry and Kingsbury, vol. III, p. 154, reproduced in Crawford, *History of the Indian Medical Service*, vol. 1, pp. 94–5, who notes that Blackwall was later sent as a surgeon to Bencoulen. Love and Crawford note an episode previous to this in which Browne drunkenly challenged Blackwall to a duel.
39. *Letters from Fort St George*, Tamil Nadu State Archives (hereafter TNSA), vol. VIII, pp. 99–100, fol. 882, 23 April 1698 and pp. 111–14, 13 May 1698. Higginson sends a letter in Persian appealing on the doctor's behalf and 2000 fanams: and 4 Gold mohurs to pay the debt.
40. *Public Consultations*, TNSA, vol. 26, pp. 43–4, 11 October1697. The incident is also noted in Crawford, *History of the Indian Medical Service*, vol. 1, pp. 91–2.
41. *Public Consultations*, TNSA, vol. 20, pp. 43–4, 1 August 1693, Browne returns from the Mughal camp with a defected French soldier and procures a pardon for him.
42. J. F. Richards (1975), 'The Hyderabad Karnatik, 1687–1707', *Modern Asian Studies*, 9(2): 241–60, 248.
43. See Rao Bahadur K. V. Rangaswami Iyangar (1994), 'Manucci in Madras', in *The Madras Centenary Commemoration Volume*. Delhi: Asian Educational Services, p. 150. Letter, undated but c. 1699 from John Pitt (of new Company) to Manuchi – BL, India Office Records (IOR) Original Correspondence 6685 and 6790. Muzaffar Alam and Sanjay Subrahmanyam (2012), *Writing the Mughal World: Studies on Culture and Politics*. New York: Columbia University Press, p. 351 for an account of Manucci's mission to Daud Khan.
44. Despatch from England dated 16 April 1697 and quoted in Henry J. Love (1913), *Vestiges of Old Madras, 1640–1800: Traced from the East India Company's Records Preserved at Fort St. George and the India Office, and from Other Sources*. London, J. Murray, vol. II, p. 88.
45. BL MS Sloane 3321 fol. 213, Bulkley FSG, 12 February 1707. The letter implies that this was his first visit.
46. Lockyer, cf. Love, *Vestiges*, vol. 1, pp. 83–4.

47. Love, *Vestiges*, vol. 1, p. 564. A dubash (from *do bhāśī* lit. 'two languages') also has the meaning of secretary or representative (*Hobson-Jobson*, p. 328). See S. Neild-Basu (1984), 'The Dubashes of Madras', *Modern Asian Studies*, 18(1): 1–31. 'Conicoply' is probably from Tamil *kanakkapillari*. Several references to 'the warehouse conicoply' appear in the FSG records. Public hospitals were established by the Emperor Jahangir and were apparently common even in smaller towns during the reign of Aurangzeb. I. A. Khan (1979), 'The Middle Classes in the Mughal Empire', *Social Scientist*, 5: 28–49.
48. Cf. D.V. Subba Reddy [ed., author not given] (1964), 'John Fryer – A Traveller Of XVII Century', *Bulletin of the Department of the History of Medicine* (later *Bulletin of the Indian Institute for the History of Medicine*), 2. 'Peruvian bark' refers to cinchona, the source of quinine.
49. Mayoral Court Records (TNSA), vol. 2, fol. 197, 3 December 1718.
50. SB 228.
51. Pratik Chakrabarti (2006), 'Neither Meate nor Drinke but what the doctor alloweth', *Bulletin of the History of Medicine*, 80(1): 1–38, p. 7.
52. Cook, *Matters of Exchange*, p. 306.
53. BL MS Sloane 4062, fol. 290, Browne to Petiver, FSG, 30 September 1698.
54. BL MS Sloane 3333 fol. 201, Samuel Browne, FSG 17 October 1696. The definition of tutia is from William Lewis (1791), *An Experimental History of the Materia Medica*. London: J. Johnson. Further discussions of the identity of tutia occur in BL MS Sloane 3332, fol. 67 – 'An abstract of Bontius his Animadversions upon Garcia da Orta with some additional remarks by Mr Alexander Brown', 12 June 1695.
55. SB 709. Cape Comorin or Kanyakumari is on the southern-most point of the India peninsula. Agallochum is a fragrant wood used as incense since ancient times (H. H. Wilson (1843), 'Notes on the Sabhá Parva of the Mahábhárata, Illustrative of Some Ancient Usages and Articles of Traffic of the Hindus', *Journal of the Royal Asiatic Society of Great Britain and Ireland*, 7(1): 137–44).
56. BL MS Sloane 3333, fol. 201, Samuel Browne to James Petiver, FSG, 17 October 1696. Assa foetida is much used in Ayurveda in the treatment of simple digestive problems such as wind, bloating, indigestion and constipation, and also for respiratory problems such as bronchitis, bronchial asthma and whooping cough. It is also used as a circulatory stimulant, lowering blood pressure and thinning the blood. (Information from 'Ferula assa-foetida', Plants for a Future: Edible, medicinal and useful plants for a healthier world, URL: http://www.pfaf.org/database/plants.php?Ferula+assa-foetida, accessed 14 October 2009). Assa Foetida had been known in the West for some time by the seventeenth century: it appears in Garcia da Orta's seventh colloquy who in turn refers to Avicenna's descriptions.
57. *Moringa pterygosperma* MORINGACEAE. Parkinson, *Theatrum Botanicum*, p. 1650. The *Hortus Malabaricus*, vol. 10, Tab. 11 describes the use of the Moringa in the preparation of vegetables and to treat various types of inflammation. Marshall mentions the use of the seeds of nirmalī (*Strychnos potatorum*) to clean water (Khan, p. 337. Khan notes this use appears in Suśruta).
58. BL MS Sloane 3321, fol. 28 – Bulkley to Petiver, 23 February 1699/1700.
59. For medicinal gardening in Kerala, see Francis Zimmermann (1989), *Le Discours Des Remèdes Au Pays Des Épices: Enquête Sur La Médecine Hindoue*. Paris: Payot.

60. P. Bowe (1999), 'The Indian Gardening Tradition and the Sajjan Niwas Bagh, Udaipur', *Garden History*, 27(2): 189–205; J. Brookes (1987), *Gardens of Paradise: The History and Design of the Great Islamic Gardens*. London: Weidenfeld and Nicolson; Grove, *Green Imperialism*, pp. 73–94; J. L. Wescoat and J. Wolschke-Bulmahn (eds.) (1996), *Mughal Gardens: Sources, Places, Representations, and Prospects*. Washington, DC: Dumbarton Oaks Research Library and Collection.
61. Irfan Habib, 'Economic and Social Aspects of Mughal Gardens', in Wescoat and Wolschke-Bulmahn (eds.), *Mughal Gardens*, pp. 127–38.
62. BL MS Sloane 4062, f. 290.
63. See Jeya Kathirithamby-Wells, this volume.
64. BL MS Sloane 3321, fol. 185 Bulkley to Petiver, FSG, 24 January 1706. As he noted in an earlier letter (fol. 172, 15 March 1705), the gourds were gathered by sailors on the ship *Abingdon*.
65. BL MS Sloane 3321, fols. 84–5, Bulkley to Petiver, FSG, 9 November 1701.
66. Ibid., fol. 19 – Bulkley to Petiver, FSG, 13 October 1699: 'I desire that you will send me as many medicinall seeds as you thinke may be like to growe here, I should like to raise some Europe plants here.'
67. Tobacco cultivation was established in the Deccan by 1605. WHO India, 'Economic History of Tobacco Production: From Colonial Origins to Contemporary Trends', URL: http://www.whoindia.org/SCN/Tobacco/Report/03-Chapter-02.2.pdf (accessed 19 June 2010). Petiver notes in a commonplace book, BL MS Sloane 4020 fol. 216, 'Tobacco certainly is a proper native of America, though now it is gott in to the Easte Indies also where (in the province of Guzarat [Gujarat] especially) they sow it in abundance'. As J. Crawford (1869), 'On the History and Migration of Cultivated Narcotic Plants in Reference to Ethnology', *Transactions of the Ethnological Society of London*, 7: 78–91, notes, both Emperor Jahangir and King James issued edicts or tracts attempting to curb the consumption of tobacco in their realms.
68. SB 8.14–15. Cannabis is also described in the eighth book of plants sent to Petiver from Fort St George (Brown and Petiver (1702/3), *Philosophical Transactions*, 23: 1454).
69. BL MS Sloane 3333, fol. 195, Petiver, 'A return to Mr Samuel Browne's remarks on the 4th book of Bontius his animadversions on Garcia da Orta' (undated).
70. Wescoat and Wolschke-Bulmahn (eds.), *Mughal Gardens*. See also Chandra Mukerji (2005), 'Dominion, Demonstration and Domination: Religious Doctrine, Territorial Politics and French Plant Collection', in Schiebinger and Swan (eds.), *Colonial Botany*, p. 19.
71. Herbert, *Flora's Empire*, Chapter 4, 'Eastward in Eden: Botanical Imperialism and Imperialists'.
72. Madras 'Public Consultations', vol. 30, 12–15 July 1701, cf. Love, *Vestiges*, vol. II, p. 16. The Council were alarmed by this request since at the time the gardens left exposed the weakest defences of the city. Fortunately for them, Khan was dissuaded with the aid of a lavish dinner, 'dancing wenches' and much alcohol.
73. Cf. Love, *Vestiges*, vol. ii, p. 84.
74. Stern, *Company State*, p. 199.
75. For example, BL MS Sloane 3321, f. 19 – Bulkley to Petiver, FSG, 8 [October] 13th 1699, Bulkley requests instructions for collecting, asks for European

seeds and for Petiver to popularise some roots and ground pearl, and sends a coffee plant from Mocha, collections from Vizigapatnam.
76. J. Golinski (2005), *Making Natural Knowledge: Constructivism and the History of Science*. Chicago: University of Chicago Press, pp. xii–xiii.
77. BL MS Sloane 3321, fol. 19, Bulkley to Petiver, FSG, 13 October 1699, 'pray send store of instructions for collecting &c.'.
78. Ibid., fol. 104, Bulkley, FSG, 17 August 1702, Bulkley reports sending instructions to Alexander Read at Bencoulen.
79. Ibid., fol. 19, Bulkley to Petiver, FSG, 13 October 1699.
80. Ibid., fol. 112, Cunningham to Petiver dated Chusan 12 February 1702/3. He mentions sending collections to Sloane.
81. Ibid., fol. 117, [Cunningham – a copy, not in his hand] 'Recd the 4th Aug of a China man att Emoy that came from Cochin his name Watteo Aneos nephew the following letter directed to The Supracargoes & Capts in the service of ye Hon[oura]ble Comp[an]y trading to the East Indies'. Describes his capture. fol. 132 – Cunningham to Petiver dated Pulo Condore, 8 January 1703/4 sends collections from Chusan and Pulo Condore to Petiver and Sloane. Collections from Cunningham in Pulo Condore include H.S. 278, 279, and 280.
82. H.S. 59 (Dandy, *The Sloane Herbarium*, p. 32) contains Cunningham's collections from China made in 1698 and at the Cape of Good Hope in 1699 and H.S. 252 from Amoy, Chusan and the Crocodile Isles (Dandy p. 62). Plants from Batavia and Pulo Condore are in H.S. 253 (Dandy, p. 63) and from the Cape in H.S. 257 (Dandy, p. 64), more plants from Batavia are in HS 289 (Dandy p. 70).
83. The British Library's collection of Petiver's works with MS notes [443.i.1.] contains a picture of a plant 'Ageratum' that Petiver acquired from Oldenhand, 'a learned physician and very curious botanist at the Cape'. The journals of Alexander Brown and Isaac Pyke, both of whom report meeting him, are BL MS Sloane 1689 and IOR MS Mss Eur D 5 respectively.
84. BL MS Sloane 3321, fol. 103, Bulkley, FSG, 9 October 1702. See Cook, *Matters of Exchange*, pp. 315–17.
85. BL MS Sloane 3321, fol. 133, Bulkley to Petiver 10 February 1703/4 where he reports a discussion of the 'Punsaloy or fruit of the Panitsjaka mer', *Hortus Malabaricus* vol. 3, Tab 41, p. 45; given as 'Panitsjika-Maram'. Bulkley follows the *Hortus Malabaricus* in noting the use of the fruit as glue, and adds Camelli's report of successfully using it to treat fever.
86. G. Camelli (1699), 'A Description and Figure of the True Amomum, or Tugus. Sent from the Reverend Father George Camelli, at the Phillipine Isles, to Mr. John Ray and Mr. James Petiver, Fellows of the Royal Society', *Philosophical Transactions*, 21: 2–4. See also R. A. Reyes (2009), 'Botany and Zoology in the Late Seventeenth-Century Philippines: The Work of Georg Josef Camel SJ (1661–1706)', *Archives of Natural History*, 36: 262–76.
87. Petiver notes in the discussion of SB 57 that Camelli sent a drawing of indigo to him and Ray. There are several of Camelli's drawings among Petiver's published collections – e.g. *Opera*, Tab. XXVIII (6). Petiver mentions Cunningham sending him a specimen from 'the island of Mischowahi' in the discussion of SB 106 (book 3). *Phyllanthus emblica* EUPHORBIACEAE (Manilal, *Hortus Malabaricus*, 1:38).

88. BL MS Sloane 3321, fols. 84–5, Bulkley, FSG, 9 November 1701 and MS Sloane 3333 fol. 201, FSG, 17 October 1696. I. Habib (1982), *An Atlas of the Mughal Empire*. Delhi: Oxford University Press, map 0B 'The Mughal Empire, Economic' marks the 'aloe-wood forests' and 'lac-forests'.
89. BL MS Sloane 1689, fol. 11v.
90. Cook, *Matters of Exchange*.
91. BL MS Sloane 3321, fol. 133, Bulkley to Petiver, 10 February 1704.
92. BL MS Sloane 3321, fol. 18, Edward Bulkley to James Petiver, FSG 12 October 1699.
93. Petiver uses much of his commentary on Browne's collections to level criticism at his rival Leonard Plucknet.
94. Latour, *Science in Action*, p. 223 for discussion of control at a distance.
95. BL IOR O.C. 7880, Bulkley to du Bois, 28 October 1698, transcribed in Henry Yule (1887–89), *Diary of William Hedges*. London: Printed for the Hakluyt Society, vol. 2, p. cccxx.
96. Ibid.
97. J. Richards, *The Mughal Empire*, New Cambridge History of India, I. 5. Cambridge: Cambridge University Press 1993, Chapter 10.
98. For an overview of recent debates see R. Travers (2007), 'The Eighteenth Century in Indian History: A Review Essay', *Eighteenth-Century Studies*, 40(3): 492–508.
99. Habib, 'Economic and Social Aspects of Mughal Gardens', p. 135 notes that garden tombs were common for Mughal noblemen. While Rheede tot Drakenstein's and other Dutchmen's tombs mirrored Indian styles, Bulkley's is an English-style gravestone. Love, *Vestiges*, vol. II, p. 90. See also Julian James Cotton (1945), *List of Inscriptions of Tombs or Monuments in Madras Possessing Historical or Archaeological Interest*. Government Press: Madras. Entry 68 is for Edward Bulkley 'from his monument on the South Esplanade, near the hospital' who died on 8 August 1714. For the position of Bulkley's garden see Figure 2, 'd'. For the current location of Bulkley's tomb, V. Sriram, 'Lost and Found: the Bulkley Tomb', *Madras Heritage and Carnatic Music*, URL: http://sriramv.wordpress.com/2012/09/28/lost-and-found-the-bulkley-tomb/ (accessed 2 May 2014). The tombstone bears the coat of arms of the Bulkley family of Cheshire, showing three bull's heads between a chevron. I am grateful to Henry Noltie for pointing this out.
100. Brown was offered but declined the position of surgeon in Chutanuti (Calcutta) (Crawford, *History of the Indian Medical Service*, p. 246).

3
Robert Wight and his European Botanical Collaborators

H. J. Noltie

Introduction

The Scottish-born East India Company surgeon and botanist Robert Wight, who spent his working life in southern India, is used as an example to show some of the botanical networks operating between India and Europe (and to a lesser extent within India) in the period 1820 to 1850. The information in this chapter[1] is taken from a recent series of monographs on Wight's life and work,[2] to which readers are directed for further detail and background.

Wight was involved in numerous networks, including those of the patronage necessary for entry into Company service and his subsequent career within the Madras Presidency. Also involved were networks of 'subaltern' Indians whom he employed as plant collectors and artists – but due to their status and the conventions of the time, Wight's relations with Indians are almost entirely undocumented. By contrast, his links with European collectors and scientists (whether in India or Europe) are rather well documented and it is these scientific networks that will be outlined here: he used these to the full, and only by doing so could he have achieved what he did in the field of descriptive and taxonomic botany. While originating as a practical necessity, I consider that these contacts were a significant factor in enabling a major contribution to the accumulation of global scientific knowledge, and formed part of a process that continues to this day. These scientific relationships are summarised in Figure 3.1, which, while not meant to be taken too seriously (many connections and minor names have been omitted, and the differing thicknesses of lines give only approximate ideas of the relative importance of the interactions), nevertheless serves to convey an impression of the extent and complexity of this network and its geographical distribution.

It is necessary to start by putting my cards on the table. I am not, by profession, an historian of science, my background is that of a practising plant taxonomist. My initial interest in Robert Wight came through the prolific collections he amassed in southern India – dried plant specimens and botanical drawings, a significant proportion of which (about 23,000 herbarium specimens and 700 drawings) are held in the institution where I work, the herbarium of the Royal Botanic Garden Edinburgh. The primary intention of my work on Wight was to make these collections better known, to identify which of the specimens were nomenclatural types for the many new genera and species that he described, and to try to understand more about where and why they were made.

I have not read deeply in the historical or theoretical literature on Colonial Science, but, of what I have, it seems to me that historians have not always fully understood the taxonomic method in their 'discourses' of colonialism. In an attempt to form 'theory' (more accurately general principles: for unlike theories in science they are not susceptible to experimental verification) there too often appears something approaching scorn for empiricism and unadorned facts, and an obsession with the reduction of science to being merely a tool of imperial control. Such searches for principles are frequently tinged by the political beliefs of the 'theoriser' (and to all practical purposes, 'post-colonial' can be read as 'anti-colonial'), which is by no means to denigrate attempts to reconstruct the largely unrecorded voice of the 'subaltern' as a long-overdue corollary to this agenda. Of late a more nuanced approach has begun to make a welcome appearance, for example in the work of scholars like Kapil Raj,[3] and Deepak Kumar in Chapter 1 of the present book. The search for general principles – for example the copious ink shed on the question of the relative roles of the 'metropolis' and 'periphery' in the diffusion of scientific knowledge – is fraught with difficulty, not least because so many cases result from unique sets of circumstances, and individual (frequently eccentric) personalities.

Much of the post-colonial approach, including the orthodox and tenacious Saidian view, diminishes the motive of intellectual, or even aesthetic, curiosity as an end in itself, and in the present case-study it does not seem unduly naïve to see Wight's descriptive taxonomic work (in contrast to his economic botanical work, which is not discussed here), on which he expended enormous amounts of personal effort, time and money, primarily in this light. There is a deep current in the British psyche that loves the study of natural history for its own sake,[4] but in this context it is also worth recalling Sir William Jones's motivation for establishing and setting an agenda for the Asiatic Society in Calcutta in the 1780s. In the words of Michael Franklin, Jones's 'grandiose research project' was to shape and direct the exhaustive research of a small but dedicated group of Company employees undertaken purely (and incredibly) in their own leisure time ... undertaken on the egalitarian basis of individual merit and scholarly zeal ... Motivated by a desire to provide some sort of intellectual justification for the British presence in India.[5]

Within Jones's life-time William Roxburgh was a member of the Asiatic Society and as Wight, if forty years later, dedicated one of his major illustrated works to Roxburgh's memory, and took 'Roxburgh' as his *cognomen* for membership of the illustrious Academia Leopoldina, it seems likely that he identified his own contribution in terms of a continuation of this Jonesian tradition of scholarship.

In an intriguing study of 'Indian Botany and the British' Theresa Kelley has boldly claimed that the commissioning of drawings from Indian artists by Company surgeons including Wight was 'an intriguing quid pro quo: in exchange for an exotic, inexhaustible array of Indian plants, the British gave back in the kind that was theirs to give'.[6] Without necessarily going quite so far (not least as the drawings remain largely in British collections), this certainly pays tribute to the Indian artistic contribution to botanical documentation and such reciprocity, even if asymmetrical, seems to me one of the brighter patches in the fields of colonial history and global exploration. This positive element, 'complex and multilayered interactions between the vastly disparate natural and historical practices of various peoples', in Wight's work has recently been affirmed by Kapil Raj.[7] Having stated my own prejudices, I make no apology for outlining in some detail an example for which there is abundant documentary evidence for a more reciprocal view of at least one aspect of colonial science.

The universal taxonomic project

Before looking at Wight's work it seems useful to give a brief statement of some of the basic rules for the valid description of plant species, as initiated by Linnaeus and subsequently greatly elaborated and refined by means of a set of internationally agreed, and regularly updated, rules, which started with De Candolle's *Lois de la Nomenclature Botanique* of 1867.[8]

1. Priority of publication (to give credit to the first person who recognised and made a [Western] scientific description of a particular species), the starting point being taken as the publication of Linnaeus' *Species Plantarum* in 1753.

2. Concise diagnostic descriptions, which are extremely difficult to interpret without comparison with correctly named voucher specimens, or, failing these, with high quality, analytical illustrations.
3. Progressive refinement of the nomenclatural 'type' method, which evolved through the nineteenth century, but was formalised only in 1930[9] – so that when first described every species name must now have a specimen (or, failing that, an analytical illustration) designated that fixes and stabilises its usage. (These rules are applied retrospectively, to allow linkage of an author's application of a name with an original specimen or illustration.)

Plants are no respecters of political boundaries, and the purpose of this methodology is to ensure a stable system of taxonomy and nomenclature across such artificial limits. Furthermore, and partly the result of communication difficulties (including the distribution and circulation of literature), the same species has often been described under different names at different times and in different parts of the world. With careful comparison of specimens and literature, such duplication is sooner or later elucidated and the necessary synonymy made. Until recently, such work could only be done with reference to books and collections, which, for historical reasons, were housed largely in Europe, or with the help of active collaborators based there. In response to a challenge by the English botanist John Lindley – that field workers in India should do more – Robert Wight clearly expressed the problems involved:

> European botanists ... enjoy greater advantages for this [taxonomic] work than Indian ones ... Indian Botanists are few, and very remote from each other, with but little intercourse [i.e., other than by letter], and generally having other duties [those of the EIC] to engage their attention, whence Botany, in place of a professional pursuit becomes with them a mere recreation. So situated, few enjoy the opportunities required for the successful elucidation of a difficult natural order [i.e., plant family], even when well qualified for the work; each, only becoming acquainted with the species within his own limited circle, generally too few to admit of his attempting from them anything like a comprehensive examination of a complex [natural] order. He therefore, in place of attempting the nearly hopeless task here assigned to him, more frequently when possessed of a scientific friend in Europe, sends specimens there to have them examined and named, and but too frequently is disappointed in his expectations. In this way large collections of all kinds of plants, from all parts of India, have gradually

found their way to Europe and been brought together in the large European collections. Let these in the first instance be well investigated by a scientific Botanist, the genera and species clearly defined, their present confused synonymy unravelled, and such descriptions as can be made from dried specimens drawn up and published, to put the less qualified Indian Botanist in possession of the information thence attainable, and then he will have a firm foundation on which to build his observations made on growing plants. It is true that equally perfect descriptions cannot be made from dried specimens, as from growing plants, but I feel assured, from my own experience, that even with this most disheartening order [the family Guttiferae], much more might have been done [by European botanists] than has been yet effected.[10]

It was not a question of botanists from the 'periphery' being put down; rather an inevitable consequence of an enormously successful methodology. The aim, as it remains to this day, was for a universal classification system covering the plants of the whole world – in Wight's time the aim was to construct a classification that was believed to represent a divinely created order. Today, botanists think more in terms of a single 'frame' of the ongoing 'movie' of the evolution of life – the current aim/belief being that the classification system should represent this evolutionary history. Now, by analysing the structure of DNA, it is possible for the first time in history to prove whether morphological similarities between taxa (or more accurately individuals) are due to genetic relationships rather than convergent evolution. During the late nineteenth and early twentieth centuries, as libraries and herbaria in India improved and, above all, as more and more accurate illustrations were published, the dependence in such matters on the resources and intellect of the West gradually lessened, as Wight very much intended. In 1845 Wight, and his Ceylon colleague George Gardner, expressed the hope of being able to do what they could 'towards placing Indian Botany as nearly as we are able on a par with English ... [and that they would] be able to satisfy European Botanists that the *Calcutta Journal of Natural History* is the proper source to which all must apply who wish to be informed regarding the progress of Botanical Science in India'.[11] This dependency on Europe has in the last decade become very substantially lessened as Western collections (both herbarium specimens and botanical literature) have been digitised and made available through the internet on a hitherto unimaginable scale.

From an interest in Wight's life and work that, as already explained, arose largely from the perspective of his collections, it became apparent that there is an almost complete dearth of book-length biographies of EIC surgeon-naturalists, including accounts of their taxonomic philosophy, methodology, sources of inspiration and motivation. Such a lack has inevitably had a limiting effect on the value of the sorts of generalisations and theorising criticised above. A biography of William Roxburgh has recently been published,[12] but there is still nothing remotely substantial on key figures such as Francis Buchanan-Hamilton, William Griffith, John Forbes Royle or Hugh F. C. Cleghorn, and recent attempts in Copenhagen to produce a biography of Nathaniel Wallich appear to have foundered. Wight was not an innovative scientist (any more than was Wallich), nor as important over as wide a range of fields as Roxburgh or Buchanan-Hamilton, but he certainly merited a traditional biography, told as much as possible in his own words, with detailed references to sources and avoiding unprovable theoretical speculation. Although born in 1796, and thus belonging to a later generation than Roxburgh (born 1751) or Buchanan-Hamilton (born 1762), and (leaving India in 1853) living into the era of high Imperialism and of Darwinism, Wight is best understood as a latter-day participant in the Scottish Enlightenment tradition, with beliefs underpinned by natural theology. This he imbibed in his upbringing (his mother's cousin was Allan Maconochie, first Lord Meadowbank, an important figure in Enlightenment Edinburgh and a founding member of the Royal Society of Edinburgh), and education at the High School and University of Edinburgh in the period 1807–18. Wight therefore subscribed (probably unquestioningly) to the principles of 'improvement' and the gathering of 'statistical' data as had Roxburgh and Buchanan-Hamilton before him, but concentrating largely on the documentation of flowering plants. Richard Grove has drawn attention to the humanitarian strain in the work of Scottish EIC surgeons,[13] and it should be remembered that Sir John Sinclair in the *Statistical Account of Scotland*, which he co-ordinated and edited, rather remarkably gave as his reason for the acquisition of such 'statistical' data as: 'an inquiry into the state of a country, for the purpose of ascertaining the quantum of happiness enjoyed by its inhabitants, and the means of its future improvement'.[14]

Wight's geographical field of activity (the present-day states of Tamil Nadu, and parts of Kerala and Andhra Pradesh) happened to coincide with an area where extensive primary documentation of its rich flora still remained to be undertaken in the period 1830–50, accounting for the very large number of new species (1262) and genera (100) that he described, many of which have stood the test of time, being still recognised today. It is worth noting that of these new species apparently only a single one appears to have a potential medicinal use: in other words, most were purely of academic interest, or in helping to fill gaps in the continuum of nature that was also an important part of Wight's belief system.

This is sufficient by way of introduction to the main theme of the chapter: Wight's botanical networks and their geographical location. These started in Edinburgh, where he studied botany under the aged Professor Daniel Rutherford (1749–1819), and a young 'extra-academical' lecturer John Stewart (1792–1820). Rutherford was better known as a chemist, but in his botanical lectures his teaching of natural classification (as well as the artificial Sexual System of Linnaeus) was of some significance as it also influenced the greatest of Wight's near-contemporaries, the botanist Robert Brown. Wight also adopted a natural classification as soon as a practical scheme was published by A. P. de Candolle from the late 1820s onwards, using the Candollean system for arranging his herbarium and taxonomic publications. By means of his publications, starting from 1838, Wight actively promoted the natural system for a largely European audience in India ('Anglo-Indians') in his *Illustrations of Indian Botany* (1839–50) and *Spicilegium Neilgherrense* (1845–51). It was also during his Edinburgh education that Wight first got to know George Walker-Arnott (hereafter 'Arnott'), who would later become an important botanical collaborator both to himself and to W. J. Hooker, but whose significance has been nothing like adequately recognised. Robert Kaye Greville was another university contemporary of Wight, who became an important cryptogamic botanist (and anti-slavery campaigner).

Wight's subsequent life and career can be divided into four parts. First Indian period 1819–26; Madras Naturalist 1826–8; Furlough in Britain 1831–4; Second Indian period 1834–53.

First Indian period 1819–26

When Wight arrived in Madras in September 1819 as an army surgeon, but determined to develop his botanical interests, he faced almost insuperable difficulties. The first came from a lack of relevant literature. He had the Lichfield Botanical Society's 1787 translation of Linnaeus' *Genera Plantarum*; Karl Ludwig Willdenow's edition of *Species Plantarum* (1797–1803) – effectively the latest 'world Flora'; and a copy of Christiaan Hendrik Persoon's *Synopsis Plantarum* (1805–6) – a masterpiece of Parisian typographical compression, 20,000 species covered in two sexto-decimo volumes. He therefore had no choice but to name and arrange his early collections according to the Linnaean system. Descriptions of Indian plant species lay embedded in Willdenow and Persoon – if only they could be found. Very few illustrations of Indian plants were available to help to interpret the brief specific Latin descriptions included in such works. From the seventeenth century were uncoloured engravings in the Dutch works of Hendrik van Rheede and Johannes Burman, and the English publications of Leonard Plukenet. At the turn of the eighteenth and nineteenth centuries William Roxburgh had worked hard to supplement this scanty body of illustrated literature. Banks's efforts to publish the related drawings by Roxburgh's Indian artists was limited to the three, prohibitively expensive (and inaccessible) elephant-folio volumes of the *Plants of the Coast of Coromandel*,[15] but Roxburgh's unillustrated *Flora Indica* was entirely unpublished when Wight arrived in India.[16] Wight concisely and eloquently expressed such difficulties in a letter to the Madras Medical Board in 1828:

> The naming of its objects from definitions only [i.e., written descriptions] has always been a difficult department of Natural History. This difficulty is daily increasing from the increased number of objects to be named and in this Country [India] it is greater than in most others from their being no separate descriptive Catalogue of its natural productions [i.e., a Flora of India], and from the number of nondescript species [ones not yet named] which it contains. The want of such a Catalogue renders it necessary to select the name of each plant from among forty or fifty thousand [in works such as Willdenow], in place of from four to five thousand, the estimated number of described Indian plants.[17]

No-one who has not tried it can imagine the sheer difficulty of accurately identifying tropical plants (or, for that matter, any other living organism). Wight, therefore, was in desperate need of a European collaborator with access to books and well-named reference collections in order to identify his specimens and determine which were 'nondescript'. He first tried Robert Graham, who had succeeded Rutherford as Regius Keeper and Professor at Edinburgh in 1820, sending him copious specimens, which Graham ignored – being more concerned with his medical practice and summer botanical lecture course (and excursions).

Madras Naturalist 1826–8

Wight's first stroke of luck came in 1826 when, due to ill health, James Shuter left the official EIC post of Madras Naturalist. Wight was appointed to replace him by the great Governor of Madras, Sir Thomas Munro. The fifty-year history of this post (1778–1828) links European Linnaean with Scottish Enlightenment traditions – of the eight holders, no fewer than five were Edinburgh medical graduates, including Roxburgh and Patrick Russell; the Europeans included Johann Gerhard König – a pupil (and unofficial 'Apostle') of Linnaeus and Benjamin Heyne. This appointment led to the only extensive field trip of Wight's entire Indian career. This lasted nine months in 1826/7, accompanied by an Indian draftsman he collected plants, birds, rocks and even 'Hindoo antiquities'. The Naturalist's post, however, was abolished in 1828, under the governorship of Stephen Lushington, in a period of retrenchment and symptomatic of struggles within the Company – between Madras, Calcutta and London – over the support of broad-ranging scientific (as opposed to strictly commercial) activities. Similar arguments would resurface in 1838 over a later, and more expressly economic-botanical post, held by Wight.

Of potential collaborators in India – to help with, or share in, Wight's natural history activities – there were none in Madras. Nathaniel Wallich, Superintendent of the Company's garden at Calcutta, was at least in India, and they started to correspond in April 1826, but their three early letters have not survived. It was also during this period that Wight, following the tradition of Roxburgh and Heyne, started commissioning botanical drawings from a Telugu-speaking artist called Rungiah, who appears to have been of the Tanjore school of painters. Whereas the influence of indigenous *classifications* (as opposed to *species concepts*) on Western taxonomies seems to me to have been misunderstood by some authors including Richard Grove,[18] the contribution of Indian artists to the descriptive-scientific agenda is unquestionable. Wight (unlike, for example, Roxburgh) was particularly appreciative of the individuality of this contribution, and printed the artist's name on almost every one of the more than two thousand illustrations of Indian plants that he published – he even named an orchid genus *Govindooia* after Govindoo, the second of the artists he employed.

In March 1828, from Negapatam at the southern end of the Coromandel Coast, Wight started a correspondence with William Jackson Hooker, Professor of Botany at the University of Glasgow in distant Scotland. The key role played by Hooker during his Scottish period, long before he moved south to Kew, has often been forgotten, but it was in Glasgow that he established himself as, effectively, Banks's successor, and in 1836 was knighted by King William IV effectively for this role as leading botanical *savant*. Following in the Linnaean and Banksian tradition, Hooker built up huge personal collections (manuscripts, portraits, botanical illustrations, herbarium specimens and books). When he moved to the Royal Botanic Gardens Kew in 1841 (as its first Director as a National, rather than a merely Royal, establishment) the collections were still Hooker's personal property, though he allowed generous access to them to scholars during his lifetime. The collections were sold to the nation by his son Joseph only after the death of his father which occurred in 1865. It was from Glasgow that the elder Hooker, using a slow and expensive postal system, developed his extensive global network of contacts, including many in India (of whom Wight was but one), between his prolific lecturing, editing, illustrating and writing activities. The writing and editing included both scientific and semi-popular publications, nearly all of which were profusely illustrated (and, in this, were an important influence on Wight) – including the *Botanical Miscellany*, the *Journal of Botany*, *Curtis's Botanical Magazine* (with its *Companion*), the *Icones Plantarum*, fern monographs and the *Exotic Flora*. In return for information, specimens and drawings, Hooker offered to send Wight supplies of drying paper and funds for collecting. The former was not required and the latter was not taken up by Wight due to a diffidence of character and a worry about failing to live up to expectations. What was accepted from Hooker, with huge gratitude, was the gift of botanical books, and, more particularly, the identification of specimens, the latter specifically acknowledged by Wight as 'the greatest compliment you [Hooker] could have paid'.[19]

Furlough in Britain 1831–4

Between 1831 and 1834 Wight spent a busy and productive furlough in Britain, especially in Scotland, making personal contact for the first time with his correspondents Hooker and Graham, effectively the only 'professional' (i.e., salaried) botanists in Scotland, holding, respectively, the botanical chairs at Glasgow and Edinburgh. Wight attended two of Graham's pioneering summer undergraduate excursions to the Scottish Highlands. But there was at this time also a strong 'gentleman-amateur' botanical tradition in Scotland, represented by Wight's former fellow-students Arnott and Greville – the 'amateur' referring strictly to their non-stipendary status, the academic abilities of both being of an exceptional order. All four of these Scottish-based botanists had private herbaria and libraries, the best of which, by far, was Hooker's in his house at 7 West Bath Street, Glasgow. There was much toing-and-froing of specimens, books and manuscripts by mail coach between Glasgow, Arlary (Arnott's country seat in Kinross-shire), and to Wight's various places of temporary residence, which included spells in Edinburgh and at his sister's house in Blair Atholl in highland Perthshire. At this time there was also one 'semi-public' herbarium in Scotland, that of Edinburgh

University, which had recently (1829) been enriched by the bequest of his herbarium of Bengal plants by Francis Buchanan-Hamilton. Despite the help and encouragement of Hooker (who first published Wight's taxonomic work, and – anonymously – Rungiah's drawings), it was Arnott who came to be Wight's botanical saviour and greatest collaborator. Arnott's was an unusual background for a botanist – he trained as lawyer and mathematician rather than medically. But this, together with European travels, and visits to A. L. de Jussieu in Paris and A. P. de Candolle in Geneva during the 1820s, partly in collaboration with George Bentham (the outstanding English 'amateur' botanist of his generation), gave Arnott unique skills and a firm grounding in natural classification – as expounded in his influential article on 'Botany' for the seventh edition of the *Encyclopaedia Britannica* (1831). As a result of this personal contact with Arnott, Candolle worked on and published descriptions of Wight's specimens of the family Compositae both for a separate publication edited by Wight,[20] and for the fifth and sixth volumes (1836, 1838) of his own great world Flora, the *Prodromus Systematis Naturalis Regni Vegetabilis*. It was also through Graham and Arnott that an important German connection came about – with the taxonomist Christian Nees von Esenbeck at Breslau, through whom Wight was elected to membership of the venerable and peripatetic, imperial academy of science, the Academia Caesareae Leopoldina-Carolinae Naturae Curiosorum (founded 1653). Nees worked extensively on Wight's specimens of the families Gramineae, Cyperaceae, Lauraceae and Acanthaceae: of these the work on Gramineae remained unpublished, that on Cyperaceae appeared in Wight's *Contributions*, that on Lauraceae and Acanthaceae in Wallich's *Plantae Asiaticae Rariores* (1831, 1832).

Wight's arrival in London from Madras in June 1831 fortuitously coincided with the latter part of Wallich's similar scientific furlough from Calcutta, and the great curation/distribution of the south- and southeast-Asian herbarium that Wallich had accumulated, by means of a wide network of collectors, at the Calcutta Botanic Garden. Graham, Greville, Bentham, Lindley and Robert Brown all helped with sorting and naming the specimens in Wallich's 'botanical laboratory' at 61 Frith Street in Soho. The EIC supported this work in terms of continuing to pay Wallich's salary in India, and also by subscribing to 40 copies of *Plantae Asiaticae Rariores*, Wallich's major, and sumptuously illustrated, taxonomic work, which contains important contributions by Bentham and Nees. Wight used Wallich's method as an example, and London as a base for distributing the vast collections he himself had brought back from South India, though he failed in attempts to obtain financial support from the EIC for his botanical publications. Wight thus had to pay from his own pocket for printing his own herbarium *Catalogue* (1833-7), and for the Flora that he embarked on with Arnott's help, their *Prodromus Florae Peninsulae Indiae Orientalis* (1834). The latter work never got beyond its first volume, and, for reasons of expense, was devoid of illustrations.

In London, in efforts towards naming his collections, Wight consulted the institutional herbaria, with their important authentic (not yet called 'type') specimens. These were at the Linnean Society (the collections of Linnaeus and Sir James Edward Smith, still in Banks's house in Soho Square, curated by David Don), and at the British Museum in Montague House, Bloomsbury, where Banks's herbarium had recently been moved, curated under the direction of Robert Brown. Several individuals known to Wight also had private herbaria in London, notably John Forbes Royle, recently returned from superintending the Saharunpur Botanic Garden in North India, working (effectively) as economic botanist to the EIC, and John Lindley, the great horticultural botanist, orchid expert and populariser of systematic botany. Wight was elected to fellowship of the Linnean Society on 17 January 1832, but although he consulted its herbarium and attended meetings, its main importance to him was, perhaps, social and he never published in its journals. His proposers were the élite of British botanical society: Robert Brown, John Lindley, Francis Boott (an Edinburgh-trained, American medic), George Bentham, the wealthy amateur Aylmer Bourke Lambert, Hooker, Greville, Graham, and, of a previous generation, Archibald Menzies, who like Roxburgh had studied botany at Edinburgh under John Hope. It is likely that at this point Wight met Lindley's protégé William Griffith, just about to go as an Assistant Surgeon to Madras to start a remarkable, but all-too-short-lived, south- and southeast-Asian botanical 'career'.

The result of Wight's furlough, with extensive help from Arnott, was the curation and distribution of his pre-1831 botanical collections, the publication of its (lithographed) *Catalogue*, and, shortly after Wight's departure back to India, the two major taxonomic works already mentioned – the *Prodromus* and the *Contributions*. Wight took back to India in 1834 a set of named voucher specimens, and the hope that European monographers would continue to work on his own and on Wallich's collections (though only Bentham, Nees and Lindley would do so). Arnott was left working on a second volume of the *Prodromus*, and as receiver of vast shipments of new collections sent back by Wight from India over the next four years. Arnott, however, became swamped with this material, and then collapsed with depression when he failed to succeed Hooker in the Glasgow chair.

Second Indian period 1834–53

Many things changed as a result of Wight's experiences in Britain – he now had a more accurately named set of specimens, a much better knowledge of systematic botany and literature, and was fired up with a renewed enthusiasm. But there were other factors at play, notably a change of job description, and a desire to publish his botanical work *in India*. Initially, between 1834 and 1842, such publication was achieved through the vehicle of the periodicals of two Madras-based societies – the Agri-Horticultural Society of Madras, and the Madras Literary Society. Later, from 1838 to 1854, Wight published in two Calcutta-based periodicals – that of the Agricultural and Horticultural Society of India, and McClelland's *Calcutta Journal of Natural History*. Finally came Wight's own extensive illustrated publications executed in Madras – the uncoloured, six-volume, *Icones Plantarum Indiae Orientalis* (1838–53), the two-volume, hand-coloured, *Illustrations of Indian Botany* (1838–50) and the two-volume, hand-coloured, *Spicilegium Neilgherrense* (1845–51). Wight's desire (along with Griffith and McClelland) to publish in India was tied up with questions of 'priority' and, in Wight's case, the role of illustration in making identification easier, and for popularising botany and promoting natural classification. There were advantages in the cheaper cost of printing in India compared with Europe, especially of illustrations using the technique of lithography. A precedent in this latter matter had been set by Wallich in Calcutta as early as 1824,[21] but it was taken to new orders of magnitude by Wight, who, by the time he left India in 1853, had published illustrations of no fewer than 2645 species of flowering plant.

A major change in Wight's career came in 1836 with a commission from the Governor of Madras, Sir Frederick Adam, to work on economic botany. This arose in part from advice given to 'Sir Fred' by Robert Brown, who had been consulted before Adam left London, but also from the local advice of John Grant Malcolmson, at this time Secretary of the Madras Medical Board and an important geologist. Adam's support, and that of his cousin and successor as Governor, John, thirteenth Lord Elphinstone, for Wight's work in the field of applied natural history – as it had been with Munro in 1826–8 – can be seen in the context of a Scottish Enlightenment background. It was taken against the wishes of the penny-pinching Lushington family of the Madras Revenue Board, and also certain elements of the Calcutta Government (under the Auckland administration, who in February 1838 wrote a letter recommending that 'measures should be taken to bring the operations assigned to Surgeon Wight to an early termination').[22] This cannot, however, be denoted an English conspiracy, since Wight (as on several later occasions over his cotton work) had crucial support for his scientific work from the Court of Directors in London, probably under the influence of lobbying from scientists such as Brown, Royle, Hooker and Lindley.

The possibility of botanical links within India were by this time slightly better than they had been in Wight's early days. Frequent communications between Wight and Wallich in Calcutta largely concerned economic botany and the sending of copies of some of the Calcutta set of Roxburgh's botanical drawings, some of which were published by Wight in his *Icones*. But by this date there were more European botanists active in India who corresponded with Wight and sent him specimens and drawings. These came from various geographical areas and from individuals of various backgrounds: among the more important (see Figure 3.1) were John Ellerton Stocks, William Munro, Michael Pakenham Edgeworth, George Warren Walker and his wife Anna Maria; others (not shown on the diagram) included Nicholas A. Dalzell (a Bombay civil servant) and the Rev. Edmund Johnson, a missionary, who sent Wight specimens from Kerala. Such contacts were almost entirely epistolary, as leave and internal travel were not undertaken lightly, and it is important to note Wight's geographical isolation. From 1842 he was based in the remote town of Coimbatore working (during official hours) entirely on the introduction of American long-staple cotton; he was unable to visit either Wallich or Joseph Hooker when they called in at Madras in 1844 and 1848 respectively.[23] There was, however, a single exception to this botanical isolation. In 1844 George Gardner, a protégé of Hooker from Glasgow days, had been appointed to run the Ceylon botanic gardens, based at Peradeniya. In 1845, with considerable determination, the 36-year-old Gardner travelled to Coimbatore to retrieve the Ceylon herbarium that Wight had had on loan for nine years, for tuition in Indian botany from an old hand, and to obtain named duplicates from Wight's herbarium. Wight referred to this unique occasion as 'quite an oasis in my Indian life'.[24] It led to an excursion to the Nilgiri Hills, partly for Gardner to recover from 'lunar ague', but chiefly as an excuse for a major collecting trip. Wight, however, had failed to obtain the necessary permission for this expedition and his reward was that the Company charged him Rs 375 (about £1900 in today's terms) for being absent 'on private affairs'[25] – proving that by this stage Wight's taxonomic work was a private,

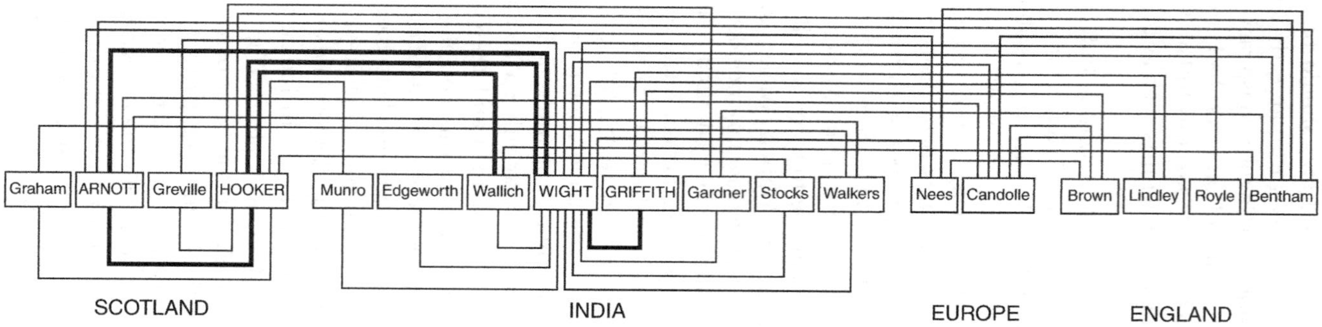

Figure 3.1. Robert Wight and his European botanical collaborators (drawn by Caroline Muir) See Key on pp. 75–6.

self-funded project, and not part of a Company agenda (or anything whatever to do with 'imperial control').

Wight's most important Indian correspondent, by far, was another EIC surgeon, William Griffith. Griffith belonged to a younger generation (born 1810) and was passionately interested in the anatomy and physiology of living plants, and what would now be called ecology. The whole question of the contribution of field studies to taxonomy is an interesting one, the changing views on which have not always been fully appreciated. In the Linnaean tradition little attention was paid to 'field characters', and Wight belonged firmly to this school. There is a revealing description by R. K. Greville (in an 1834 letter to Wallich) of Wight and Arnott as 'the deadliest fags at a pile of dried specimens I ever saw',[26] and Wight added no ecological details or additional notes (such as on growth habit or flower colour) to his specimens. Griffith, however, realised the limitations of this method: 'botanists publish too much from dried specimens' and questioned 'how people can work on dry plants I cannot imagine, I am daily convinced of the poverty of the study from such materials, unless a man has seen much of living structures'.[27] However, all that came of Griffith's labours were copious notes, drawings and specimens, made over an unparalleled geographical sweep from Afghanistan to Bhutan and Burma, as he died aged 34 before he could achieve a synthesis of his voluminous notes and materials in published form. His death, and his herbarium collections and undigested manuscripts, precipitated a crisis in Calcutta and Griffith's friends, including Lord Auckland (the Governor-General) and the Bengal surgeon John McClelland, with vicarious advice from Wight, were determined that Griffith's work should be published in India, and a set of specimens retained in Calcutta. This led to a contretemps between Wight and Wallich who had a deeply held prejudice against Griffith.[28] It was all very unfortunate, but of interest in eliciting Wight's firm opinions on the importance of the specimens and papers being claimed *for India*. The papers were published 'by order of the Government of Bengal', 'arranged' by McClelland (who was deemed to have failed to live up to British, especially Hookerian, editorial standards),[29] but the dried herbarium collections fared less well – an incomplete set was retained in Calcutta, but the majority were returned to Britain, where what Wight most feared came to pass in the damp, rat-infested cellars of the India House, where many were destroyed prior to a rescue operation mounted by Joseph Hooker in 1858. Curiously Wight conspicuously failed to take his own advice regarding his own specimens, of which he left none in India.

Postlude: retirement in Britain 1853–72

Great things were expected by the Hookers (father and son), and a by now hugely expanded scientific community, when Wight returned to Britain in 1853. He was elected FRS, but in fact failed to do any further taxonomic work. He might well have been suffering from physical and intellectual exhaustion, but from an obscure reference in a correspondence between Wight and W. J. Hooker,[30] it appears that the contretemps with Wallich reappeared over a paper written by Wight that involved a question of botanical nomenclature. Wight did, however, continue to contribute to botanical studies, if indirectly, by making his substantial herbarium, kept at his house, Grazeley Lodge, near Reading, available to all British, Indian and European botanists who wished to consult it. He then started to give vast numbers of duplicate specimens to Hooker for distribution from Kew (60,000 sheets representing 3000 species to 20 institutions from Boston to Calcutta (at last), via South Africa and Australia), and shortly before his death the 'top set' of specimens including the 'types' of his own species. Too much water had passed under the bridge – both for Wight, and for Arnott – for there ever to have been a serious possibility of completing their *Prodromus*, and Wight got sidetracked into amateur farming. The mantle of Indian taxonomy and Flora-writing passed to a younger generation, notably Joseph Hooker and Thomas Thomson, though their 1855 *Flora Indica* was also aborted after only a single volume. Only with Joseph Hooker's *Flora of British India* (1872–97) was the synthesis completed, towards which Wight's herbarium specimens from South India, and his publications, were vital ingredients. Over and above his invaluable illustrated publications, this generous sharing of specimens counts as Wight's other major contribution to botany, and these specimens continue to be used in taxonomic revisions to this day.

Afterword

The aim of this chapter has been to describe in some detail the European botanical networks of the most productive botanical taxonomist working on the flowering plants of South India in the first half of the nineteenth century. The approach has been biographical (perhaps prosopographic) and empirical, and it is hoped that it has shown why I believe that Wight primarily saw his role as being to contribute to a unified scheme of botanical classification in an eighteenth-century encyclopaedic tradition, and the reasons for why, at this date, this had to be one based in Europe.

Key to individuals in the network (Figure 3.1); their locations at time of contact with Wight; their botanical interests and 'status'.

SCOTLAND

Robert Graham (1786–1845); Scottish taxonomist and physician; Regius Professor of Botany at Edinburgh University and Regius Keeper of the Royal Botanic Garden Edinburgh 1820–45.

George Arnott Walker-Arnott (1799–1868); Scottish taxonomist; working as 'gentleman-amateur' at his Kinross-shire estate of Arlary until becoming Professor of Botany at Glasgow in 1845.

Robert Kaye Greville (1794–1866); English-born taxonomist; 'gentleman-amateur', based in Edinburgh, specialising in cryptogams (non-flowering plants, especially ferns and algae).

William Jackson Hooker (1785–1865); English-born taxonomist; Professor of Botany at Glasgow 1820–41, from 1841 Director of the Royal Botanic Gardens Kew.

INDIA

William Munro (1818–1889); English soldier based in India; 'gentleman-amateur' botanist, specialising in the grass family, Gramineae.

Michael Pakenham Edgeworth (1812–1881); Irish-born Bengal civil servant; 'gentleman-amateur' botanist who described many new plants from the Himalaya.

Nathaniel Wallich (1786–1854); Danish-born EIC surgeon; Superintendent of Calcutta Botanic Garden 1817–46.

Robert Wight (1796–1872).

William Griffith (1810–1845); English EIC surgeon and taxonomist; travelled extensively in India, Afghanistan, Bhutan, Burma and the Malay Peninsula; Acting Superintendent of Calcutta Botanic Garden 1842–4.

George Gardner (1812–1849); Scottish surgeon and taxonomist; Superintendent of Peradeniya botanic garden, Ceylon 1844–9.

John Ellerton Stocks (1822–1854); English EIC surgeon; collected plants especially in Sind.

George Warren Walker (1778–1843); English soldier; stationed in Ceylon 1819–39 as Deputy Adjutant General, 'gentleman-amateur'; keenly assisted in botanical activities by his wife Anna Maria (née Patton) (1778–1852).

EUROPE

Christian Gottfried Daniel Nees von Esenbeck (1776–1858); German taxonomist; specialising in the plant families *Acanthaceae*, *Gramineae* and *Cyperaceae*, from 1818 President of the Academia Leopoldina, and Professor of Botany at Breslau (now Wroclaw) 1831–48.

Augustin Pyramus de Candolle (1778–1841); Swiss taxonomist; based in Geneva, author of the *Prodromus Systematis Universalibus Regni Vegetabilis*, the classification system used by Wight.

ENGLAND

Robert Brown (1773–1858); pre-eminent Scottish-born taxonomist, 'Jupiter Botanicus'; from 1827 Keeper of Banksian Collection of Botany at the British Museum, London.

John Lindley (1799–1865); English taxonomist (specialising in the family Orchidaceae), horticulturist and writer of botanical text books; Assistant Secretary of the Horticultural Society of London (1827–58) and Professor of Botany at University College, London (1829–60).

John Forbes Royle (1798–1858); Indian-born East India Company surgeon; working as economic botanist for the EIC in London (having returned from the superintendence of Saharunpur Garden in 1831), from 1837 Professor of Materia Medica, King's College, London.

George Bentham (1800–1884); English taxonomist, specialising in the plant families Labiatae and Scrophulariaceae; 'gentleman-amateur', based in London.

Notes

1. This chapter is based on a presentation given at the workshop 'The East India Company and the Natural World', held at the University of Sussex, 8 June 2007.
2. H. J. Noltie (2005), *The Botany of Robert Wight*. Ruggell: A.R.G. Gantner Verlag. A catalogue of the names of flowering plants published by Wight (with details of their types). Introductory chapters include a bibliography of Wight's works, a chronology of his life, a gazetteer of his collecting localities and biographical details of his collaborators. H. J. Noltie (2007), *Robert Wight and the Botanical Drawings of Rungiah & Govindoo*. 3 vols. Edinburgh: Royal Botanic Garden Edinburgh. Vol. 1 is a biography of Wight, with emphasis on his taxonomic work, and the experiments to introduce American long-staple cotton to India. Vol. 2 is about the drawings Wight commissioned from Rungiah and Govindoo, with 137 of them reproduced in colour. Vol. 3 is a travelogue, describing the author's search of Robert Wight in India and Britain.
3. K. Raj (2006), *Relocating Modern Science*. Delhi: Permanent Black. Of particular relevance is the discussion of the work commissioned by the French surgeon Nicolas l'Empereur from an Orissan painter at the turn of the seventeenth and eighteenth centuries, but also discussed is the Indian contribution to subjects such as map making.
4. In this context it is interesting to note that Hendrik van Rheede (a soldier and Dutch East India company (VOC) administrator for a notably mercantile nation) was apparently *in the first instance* inspired to compile his great *Hortus Malabaricus*, not for commercial reasons, but by his aesthetic response to the fecundity of tropical nature (as expressed in Rheede's own preface to *Hortus Malabaricus* Vol. 3), see R. Grove, 'Indigenous Knowledge and the Significance of South-West India for Portuguese and Dutch Constructions of Tropical Nature', in R. Grove *et al.* (eds.) (1998) *Nature and the Orient*. Delhi: Oxford University Press, p. 199.
5. M. J. Franklin (1995), *Sir William Jones*. Cardiff: University of Wales Press, p. 84.
6. T. M. Kelley (2012), *Clandestine Marriage: Botany and Romantic Culture*. Baltimore: Johns Hopkins University Press, pp. 162–209.
7. In a book review of the author's 'Robert Wight and the Botanical Drawings of Rungiah and Govindoo', K. Raj (2009), *British Journal for the History of Science*, 42: 606–8.
8. This first nomenclatural 'Code' was written by Alphonse De Candolle (Paris: V. Masson et fils, 1867), partly as a result of discussions at the Third International Botanical Congress held in London in 1866 – the Congress at which Wight made his final botanical appearance reading an unpublished paper on 'On the Phenomenon of Vegetation in the Indian Spring'. The 'Code' currently in operation is: J. McNeill et. al. (eds.) (2012), *International Code of Nomenclature for Algae, Fungi, and Plants (Melbourne Code), adopted by the Eighteenth International Botanical Congress Melbourne, Australia, July 2011* (Regnum Vegetabile 154). Königstein: Koeltz Scientific Books.
9. Agreed at the International Botanical Congress, held that year in Cambridge.
10. R. Wight (1838), *Illustrations of Indian Botany* , vol. 1, p. 120. Madras: for the author by J. B. Pharoah.

11. R. Wight (1845) in a letter to John McClelland, dated Coimbatore 6 March 1845, quoted in prefatory 'Notice' [1 of 2] to *Calcutta Journal of Natural History*, 6: ii.
12. T. Robinson (2008), *William Roxburgh: The Founding Father of Indian Botany*. Chichester: Phillimore.
13. R. H. Grove (1995), *Green Imperialism*. Cambridge: Cambridge University Press.
14. J. Sinclair (ed.) (1798), *Statistical Account of Scotland*, vol. 20, p. xiii.
15. Published in London, the first part in 1795, the last not until 1820.
16. The first parts were not published until 1820 and 1824, a complete version not until 1832 – all by the Baptist Mission Press, Serampore.
17. R. Wight and G. A. W. Arnott (1834), *Prodromus Florae Peninsulae Indiae Orientalis*. London: Parbury, Allen & Co., p. xix. This number proved to be a huge underestimate, and (as a result of the work of Wight and many others) the total number of species occurring in India is today recognised as more than 15,000.
18. Grove, 'Indigenous Knowledge',p. 203. It is true that in *Hortus Malabaricus* many of the plants are arranged ('classified') in the order provided by Itti Achuden and his colleagues, as inferred from cognate Malayali names, which group together 'similar' species; but the question is 'similar in what way?' By 1771 Linnaeus had based about 350 of his own species on ones recognised in the indigenous Ezhava tradition, but Linnaeus' sexual *classification* was based almost entirely on floral structure. Due to similarities in flowers equally apparent to both Indians and Europeans, many groupings were the same in both classifications, for example four forms of 'tandale cotti' were recognised as four Linnaean species of *Crotalaria* and placed by Linnaeus in his Class Diadelphia; though in the case of 'pavel' and its variety 'pandi-pavel', recognised as distinct in Kerala, Linnaeus lumped them together as *Momordica charantia*. The example of 'onapu' cited by Grove is atypical, but instructive, as it is a member of a largely tropical group that does have a long-known representative in Europe; Linnaeus was therefore able to place it in an existing genus, with an older European generic name coined by Rembert Dodoens, 'Impatiens', as *Impatiens latifolia* (Linnaeus did not describe the two other Malayali onapus). In another case an Ezhava grouping was clearly based on plant habit: 'maravara' of vol. 12 means 'epiphyte' in Malayali, which Linnaeus could not maintain as a single group and split between orchids (*Epidendrum*) in his Class Gynandria, and ferns (*Polypodium*) in his Class Cryptogamia. These examples show the complexity of interactions possible between different classification schemes, but also (in the case of *Impatiens*) that it is possible to have a universal scheme in which species recognised in one culture can be incorporated into another that can ultimately be tested for genetic relationships, rather than similarities that reflect particular interests on the part of the classifier (e.g., for some the habit might be important, for others medicinal usage). This is not to deny that ultimately each classification has its own validity dependent on the purpose for which it is constructed.
19. Royal Botanic Gardens Kew, Director's Correspondence, vol. 52, f. 113, Wight to Hooker, 6 October 1829.

20. R. Wight (1834), *Contributions to the Botany of India*. London: Parbury, Allen & Co.
21. N. Wallich (1824), *Tentamen Florae Napalensis*, the first part with 25 plates, lithographed by the Government Lithographic Press, Calcutta, based on drawings by Wallich's Calcutta Botanic Garden artists Vishnupersaud and Gorachand.
22. British Library, APAC, EIC Board of Control Collections, F/4/1755 no. 71755 f. 91.
23. Coimbatore is 533 km by road from the Presidency headquarters of Madras. Wallich was on his way back to Calcutta from a sick leave at the Cape of Good Hope; Joseph Hooker was on the way to his great Himalayan expedition.
24. Royal Botanic Gardens Kew, Director's Correspondence, vol. 54, f. 552, Wight to Hooker, 12 February 1845.
25. British Library, APAC, EIC Correspondence with India, E/4/964.
26. Calcutta Botanic Garden, Wallich Correspondence, packet 19, Greville to Wallich, 17 March 1834.
27. W. Griffith (1848), *Posthumous Papers*. Calcutta: J. F. Bellamy. Letters to Wight, pp. xxiii, xxvii.
28. This was a result of their falling out on a tea mission to Assam in 1835, and Griffith's remodelling of the Calcutta Botanic Garden while Wallich was on sick leave at the Cape in 1842–4.
29. Six octavo volumes of text, and four folio volumes of plates, printed at the Bishop's College Press, Calcutta, 1847–54.
30. Royal Botanic Gardens Kew, Director's Correspondence, vol. 33, f. 439, vol. 55 ff. 479, 480, Wight to William Hooker, 10 and 24 November, and 30 December 1853.

4
The East India Company, Famine and Ecological Conditions in Eighteenth-Century Bengal

Vinita Damodaran

It is a well-known fact that British India was devastated by a rash of famines. According to the report of the Famine Commission, in a period of 90 years from 1765 when the British East India Company took over the *Diwani* of Bengal to 1858, Bengal experienced 12 famines and four severe scarcities. Famine research has gained ground in both Asia and Africa in recent times and it is well known that British India experienced a series of subsistence crises particularly in the latter half of the nineteenth century. However, analyses of these famines by historians have rarely included a study of environmental changes. This is unfortunate, as it is becoming increasingly clear that knowledge of the ecological basis of different peasant economies is crucial to an understanding of the capacity of certain communities to withstand drought and other famine-related hazards. From the late eighteenth century many Indian communities were disturbed by the interventions of the East India Company and their revenue and agricultural regimes which increased taxation, encouraged sedentarisation and attempted to restrict raids, hunting and nomadism. The new rulers further introduced new regimes of property and pushed the conversion of the jungle into arable land, seeing jungles as harbouring disorder and marauding tribes.[1] By the nineteenth century the advent of the railways and the inroads of private capital had further exacerbated these interventions. Such disruptions had the effect of destroying traditional economies,[2] dislocating customary patterns of living and making these communities much more vulnerable to famine and disease. To date, most studies of famine have tended to underestimate the changes made by modernisation and 'development', especially following the incursions of the East India Company in 1765.[3] This article seeks to examine the impact of processes of modernisation and development on eighteenth- and nineteenth-century India by examining famines in late eighteenth-century Bengal.

The historian Michelle Mcalpin has argued against the R. P. Dutt position that over-taxation and forced commercialisation of Indian agriculture under British rule was responsible for what he believed to be the increasing severity of famine in the eighteenth and nineteenth centuries, culminating in the widespread and devastating crop failures of 1899–1900 in which as much as one tenth of India's rural population perished. She argues instead by comparing recent Indian history with European history where with the developments of markets and trade in the sixteenth century, Western Europe saw an evolution from 'true famine' to 'famines caused by lack of purchasing power', a transition in other words from problems of scarcity to those of unequal distribution in a situation of plenty. The same transition in India, she notes, was completed by India in the late nineteenth century. If this is the case, then the late eighteenth-century famines could be seen in the Indian context as 'true famines' caused by real scarcity resulting from the failure of the monsoon. Since more than two thirds of the population was engaged in agriculture and almost wholly dependent on sufficient and well-distributed rain, any deficiency in the actual rain meant that the harvest for that year was reduced. The adverse effects of famines on a predominantly agricultural economy included not only a reduced availability of human labour because of starvation deaths but also a fall in the availability of draught power because of high cattle mortality. However, what she ignores is the affect of the incursions of the East India Company, which included a severe land revenue demand and other exactions on the peasantry after 1765 and the whittling away of the ability of the local populations in the pre-eighteenth century to cope with periods of scarcity. Careful husbandry and elaborate social and cultural systems of security and insurance were designed to counter periodic subsistence crisis in the pre-colonial period.[4] It was this ability that was systematically destroyed by the changes wrought by modernisation by the late eighteenth century. In her attempt to counter a 'nationalist' reading of famine she perhaps fails to understand the true significance of these changes wrought both by colonialism and in the immediate pre-colonial period by the integration of Bengal into a global economy.

It is important to summarise the extent and impact of the changes in Bengal wrought by colonialism in Bengal. Recent research has argued for a case of declining economic fortunes in India following the dissolution of the Mughal Empire. Challenging the more optimistic thesis of M. Alam, C. Bayly and P. Marshall, other historians such as D. Clingingsmith and J. Williamson believe that the political fragmentation of the eighteenth century following the collapse of the Mughal Empire resulted in a decline in agricultural productivity that was reinforced by a devastating climate shift and a steep upward trend in a frequency of droughts.[5] They favour the argument of aggregate economic decline following the dissolution of a strong empire into contending states. The Mughal state had showed evidence of stability and systematic revenue collection where 40% of the economic surplus was extracted. As central Mughal authority waned, the state resorted increasingly to revenue farming and the practice became even more increasingly widespread in successor states. Revenue assessment increased to 50% or more, and their work cites evidence to show that the rent burden was crushing in some places, such as Rohilla state, northern Awadh and Moradabad. With revenue assessment at 50% compared to China's 5–6% T. Raychaudhuri notes that the Indian peasant had no 'incentive to invest labour or capital'.[6] Territorial disputes by successor states also drew key resources out of agriculture and marauding armies destroyed wells and irrigation tanks that had long been the backbone of agriculture. It has been argued that the Maratha raids disrupted the stable order in the western districts of Bengal and the large-scale depopulation caused by these raids was one of the biggest problems that the British administration faced in Midnapur.[7] The key extraction of peasant surplus was revenue demand, and when the British arrived they increased the revenue burden further, almost doubling it in some places. There is also evidence in the second half of the eighteenth and early nineteenth century of worsening climatic conditions due to El Niño.[8] M. Davis usefully examines the impact of climate on famine: a theme that has long resonated in the work of Richard Grove.[9] The evidence suggests low and falling agricultural productivity in the second half of the eighteenth and early nineteenth century and the resulting soaring relative price of grains was to contribute to the scarcity that led to the 1770 famine. The effect of the famine was to enshrine free market economics as part of colonial policy all over the empire. Periodic famines were seen as a check to population growth. As Mike Davis notes, by the nineteenth century these Malthusian ideas which were voiced all through the colonial period resulted in the pursuit of free market economics and 'India like Ireland became a utilitarian laboratory where millions of lives were wagered against a dogmatic faith in omnipotent markets overcoming the "inconvenience of dearth".' This was a policy that became 'a mask for colonial genocide'.[10] The impact of these ideas on India is vital to understand in the context of the famines of the nineteenth century.

It is important to note that Bengal's ability to generate surplus that could be easily turned into cash was as attractive to the late Mughal Empire as to the British. This is not to under-estimate the scale of the changes brought by colonial rule but only to underline continuities in forms of revenue extraction. Medieval and early modern famines were not uncommon in India. Bihar, for example witnessed a severe famine in 1670–71. This famine broke out in October 1670 and lasted until 1671. The areas included Benares to the west and Rajmahal to the east and developed as a result of a drought. Contemporary observers noted that the famine resulted in the loss of thousands of human lives and there was extreme scarcity of essential commodities.[11] Migration of people from Patna and its suburbs resulted and many went to Dacca for search of food. The famine of 1670–71 also encouraged slave trading and had an important effect on the weaving industry and the shipbuilding industry.[12] From John Marshall's diary it appears that 100–300 people died daily in the region in the period.[13] From Akbar to Aurangzeb, the Mughal emperors were worried about the consequences of such famines and sought preventive measures by maintaining irrigation works. The lake at Fatehpur Sikri was constructed by Akbar for irrigation purposes and he took a personal interest in maintaining reservoirs. He also gave clear instructions to his officers to grant land remissions especially on newly cultivated lands. With the decline of the Mughal Empire in the latter half of its existence these measures were neglected, though in the reign of Aurangzeb one third of the country's irrigation was done through canals. Other measures that the Mughal Empire took included land revenue remission amounting to about 1/10, but the bulk of demand was collected. The Mughals opened free kitchens and subsidised distribution of food grains.[14] The main difficulty seems to have been the transportation of food grains in a time of drought and moving pack animals in adequate numbers without fodder or water to combat the famine. The attitude of *zamindars* and government officers was often unsympathetic and this only increased in severity in the colonial period. As noted by the historian John Mclane, the *zamindars* of Bengal almost never took an interest in how or what crops were grown. Their economic interests were confined to sharing the profits of cultivation and to the distribution of rights to their collection.[15]

The East India Company continued these forms of extraction though in a more efficient and ruthless manner. By the end of the eighteenth century the drive to enlarge revenue and the Company's investment joined to its servants' ambition of building private fortunes was the primary motive force of British colonial expansion in India.[16] As Nick

Dirks noted, the grant of the *diwani* of 1765 'became the pretext for acquiring sovereign rights over trade, revenue, law and land on the part of a joint stock company that was at the same time systematically violating the terms of its own relationship to the Crown and the parliament of England'.[17] He sees the eighteenth century as the long century of imperial scandal, a time when trade and empire led to a crisis in 'the fundaments of English politics, culture and society'. One can argue that the attitude of the Company leading up to the 1770 famine contributed to this sense of crisis. By 1788, when Burke's passionate speech at the impeachment trial of India's governor general denounced imperial excess and the profligacy of English company Nabobs, the Company had begun to be seen as 'a rogue state: waging war, administering justice, minting coin and collecting revenue over Indian territory'. Horace Walpole wrote movingly:

> The oppressions of India and even of the English settled there under the rapine and cruelties of the servants of the Company have now reached England and created general clamour here... to such monopolies were imputed the late famine in Bengal and the loss of three million of its inhabitants. A tithe of these crimes was sufficient to inspire horror.[18]

The famine left a lasting impression on the inequities of EIC rule and tormented the utilitarian administrators of India such as Lord Macaulay who, commenting several decades later, was to note that 'against the misgovernment such as afflicted Bengal it was impossible to struggle'.[19] This comment reflected the impact of British revenue extraction methods on the local population and the corruption of its officials in the late eighteenth century, the period of *Diwani* administration in Bengal and one that the British continued to be ashamed of well into the nineteenth century.

In 1765 authority over the Mughal provinces of Bengal, Bihar and Orissa was transferred to the East India Company and by the 1820s these provinces constituted the eastern wing of the great new empire in India. The impact of colonial rule varied according to the region and the agro-ecological setting. Bengal was an area whose western extremity was a segment of the Gangetic plain that extended over north India, and whose eastern extremity was the rain-forested hills of the Burmese border. In the south, it was the plateau of Chotanagpur. While the majority of the population lived on the alluvial plain, on the edges of the plains was a different world: the world of the hills and the tribals. The

Kharwars and the Cheros occupied the eastern part of Chotanagpur, the Oraons and Mundas inhabited the central plateau, the Bhuiyas were in the west and the Hos were in the further south. The hills south of Orissa were inhabited by the Konds. Bengal thus contained many physical and human environments.[20] Most of Bengal received high rainfall and much of it was irrigated by the flooding of great rivers. There was a marked difference in the eighteenth century between the old areas of highly concentrated settlement, that is, predominantly western and central Bengal and those in the north, east and south of the province which had been colonised later and more gradually.

Lowland Bengal was a predominantly agricultural economy with more than two thirds of the population was engaged in agriculture – predominantly rice – and almost wholly dependent on sufficient and well-distributed rain to the extent that any deficiency in the actual rain meant that the harvest for that year was reduced. The problem with rice cultivation was that it was extremely susceptible to drought and in case of crop failure in lean years the rice tracts had no other crops to fall back on. Rural society here cultivated the land and paid the land tax, but most of the wealth came not from direct cultivation but participation in the taxation system. Bengali society was divided between the *zamindars*, the hereditary revenue collectors of the Mughal Empire, and a broad base consisting of some landless labourers and a large number of poorer cultivators most of whom were sharecroppers. Revenue demand under the British escalated in the late eighteenth century and it is recorded in the Midnapore *zamindar*'s memorandum to the Floud commission in 1793: that the assessment was as severe as it could possibly be made, the amount realised in 1790–91 being double the assessment of Jafar Khan and Suja Khan, three times the collection of Maharaja Nand Kumar in 1764–65 and double the collections made by Reza Khan in 1765–66, though one third of the population has been swept away and half the lands remain uncultivated.[21] Low-caste Hindus occupied the lowest range in the hierarchy of the cultivators and the landless. There was also a large artisanal class, as indicated by these statistics for a village outside Calcutta in the eighteenth century, which had 19 coppersmiths, 66 carpenters, 40 silver smiths, 41 oilmen and 180 weavers.[22] Eighteenth-century Bengal was an integrated economy with a network of markets and waterways. Parts of western Bengal were rururban, though many of these artisans and merchants rested on an agrarian base and any shortage adversely affected a large section of the populace. At the top of the hierarchy was the colonial government which, as Henry Stratchey the judge and magistrate of Midnapore noted, was 'unquestionably despotic over its subjects.

The submission of the natives is perfect and unqualified; so complete as to preclude the necessity of coercion or intimidation of any kind.'[23]

By the late eighteenth century the exaction of tribute by the East India Company had had a tremendous effect on employment and commerce. Contemporary sources drew a convincing picture of large-scale artisinal and service unemployment in Bengal in 1781 and Cornwallis sombrely commented on the 'languor that the tribute had thrown upon the cultivation and the general commerce of the country'.[24] Mcclane notes that while Governor Harry Verelst, the Select Committee at Calcutta and Richard Becher Resident at Murshidabad blamed the oppressive collection practices of the *nawab*'s officers and the export of silver from Bengal for the economic decline,

> the causes were also rooted in the company's reliance on land revenue to finance its exports and its employees to divert trade into their own and dependent's hands and to remove huge sums of money taken as farming profits, trading profits and 'presents' from Bengal's economy. The 1770 famine confirmed and deepened the economic crisis, it did not create it. Even before the famine there was a marked sense of crisis in Bengal.[25]

The period of *Diwani* administration had created a dual system under which the British wielded the real power but, out of sheer self-interest, did not take responsibility for the administration of the province. The grant of *diwani* conferred on the Company the right to enjoy all the surplus revenues of the *Subah* after providing for the emperor's tribute and the Nawab's allowance. The Company became for all intents and purposes 'the sovereign of a rich and potent kingdom'.[26] As the directors of the Company noted:

> We conceive the office of *Dewan* should be exercised only in superintending the collection and disposal of revenues, which office though vested in the Company should officially be executed by our resident at the Durbar, under the control of the Governor and Select Committee ... the administration of justice, the appointment of offices of *zamindarries* in short whatever comes under the denomination of civil administration, we understand is to remain in the hands of the Nabob or his ministers.[27]

While political reasons seem to have played a part in the reckoning, what was of primary importance was the financial calculations. By avoiding the responsibilities of government it was hoped to save a huge sum annually, about 122 *lakhs* of *sikka* Rupees or £1,650,900 sterling which would pay for the Company's investment, furnish the whole of the China treasure, meet the demands of the other English settlements in India and still leave a considerable balance in the treasury.[28] The land revenue which was the basis for the finances of the state was farmed out to various classes of tax collectors. This farming system under which the Company tried to squeeze as much revenue as was harmful to the economic security of the tenantry. As Richard Becher, resident of the *Darbar*, noted in a letter to Verelst, Governor and President at Fort William on 24 May 1769: 'on this destructive plan, and with a continual demand for more revenue have the collections been made ever since the English have been in possession of the Dewannee'.[29] One of the main defects of the revenue system of this period was the over-assessment of many areas, due to the lack of exact knowledge of their real value. Clive and his successors encouraged James Rennell to complete his survey of Bengal. Arbitrary assessments under the designation of *Mathaut* in addition to normal revenue continued in this period and these included those for repairing bridges and riverbanks, paying customary fees to the *Cutcherry* (Court) and maintaining state elephants. Becher believed that these exactions were extremely harsh and one of the principal causes of distress.[30] Not only was the land revenue collected with extreme harshness, the revenue demand was itself enhanced after the assumption of the *diwani*. However, the directors' demand to increase in investments without any corresponding export of specie from England and the heavy drain of silver from Bengal forced the authorities to raise the collections even further.[31]

The 1770 famine

The famine of 1770 was preceded by partial crop failure due to the failure of the monsoon in Bengal and Bihar in 1768.[32] Hunter, commenting nearly a century later, noted that by September 1769 'the fields of rice had become like fields of dried straw'. As accounts of the famine intensified, official reports noted that 'during the 1770 famine not a drop of rain had fallen in most of the districts of Bengal for six months. In the famine which ensued the mortality and the beggary exceeded all expectation.' According to contemporary estimates, 'over one third of the inhabitants perished in the once plentiful province of Purnea and in other parts the misery is equal'.[33] Many of the surviving peasants in Purnea migrated to Nepal where the state was less confiscatory than the East India Company.[34] As the famine spread east into Bengal several districts were abandoned. The famine devastated western and northern Bengal, Bihar and Orissa (which at that time comprised only the district of Midnapur).

That the Bengal government was more concerned about the collection of revenue than for the famine-stricken people is evident from the fact that more revenue was collected in 1770–71, the year of the famine, than in 1769–70, the year of dearth which was productive of the famine.[35] The only serious intimation of the approaching famine to the court of directors in 1769 is not signed by the president Mr Verelst, but by Mr John Cartier the second in council who was to succeed him. Cartier intimated his anxieties to the Company board in January 1770, noting that in one district there was so much suffering that some form of land tax remission was advisable, but ten days later he informed the board that although the distress was undoubtedly very great, the council had not yet found any failure in the revenue or stated payments.[36] In April, astoundingly, the council acting on the advice of the Muslim minister of finance, Mohammed Reza Khan, added 10% to the land tax of the ensuing year. But the distress continued to increase at a rate that baffled official calculation. In the second week of May, the central government awoke to find itself in the midst of universal and irremediable starvation.[37] All through the summer of 1770 the people went on dying. W. W. Hunter, who looked at the record of the famine nearly a century later, wrote:

> the peasants sold their cattle; they sold their implements of agriculture, they devoured their seed grain, they sold their sons and daughters, till at length no buyer of children could be found, they ate the leaves of trees and the grass of the field and in June 1770, the resident at the *Darbar* affirmed that the living were feeding on the dead.[38]

The rain in September 1770 brought some relief, but it came too late to avert depopulation. An epidemic of disease, mainly smallpox, hit hard, killing millions. Owing to the decomposition of numerous half-putrefied dead bodies that lay unburied or unburnt along the streets and in the empty houses, the air had been contaminated and smallpox of a virulent type broke out.

Precise figures for the number who died are impossible to ascertain. The East India Company had little statistical information about its recently acquired territories and a system of dual government existed in which the Company was formally responsible only for revenue collection. Contemporary accounts give some indication of the scale of death. Ghulam Husain Khan's contemporary Persian text noted that famine and smallpox both made their appearance in the month of Mohurrum (May 1770) and they both rose to such a height and raged so violently for full three months together that entire multitudes were swept away.[39] An eyewitness account was given by John Shore, an East India Company official on whom the famine made a deep impression.[40] Another anonymous contemporary report recorded the following:

> one could not pass along the streets without seeing multitudes in their last agonies, crying out as you passed 'my god! my god! have mercy on me I am starving': whilst on other sides, numbers of dead were seen with dogs, vultures and other beasts and birds of prey feeding on their carcasses.[41]

Before the end of May 1770, one third of the population was calculated to have disappeared, in June the deaths were returned as six out of sixteen of the whole population, and it was estimated that 'one half of the cultivators and payers of revenue will perish with hunger'.[42] During the rains (July–October) the depopulation became so evident that the government wrote to the court of directors in alarm about the number of 'industrious peasants and manufacturers destroyed by the famine'. It was not till cultivation commenced for the following year 1771 that the practical consequences began to be felt. It was then discovered that the remnant of the population would not suffice to till the land. The areas affected by the famine continued to fall and were put out of tillage. Warren Hastings' account, written in 1772, also stated the loss as one third of the inhabitants[43] and this figure has often been cited by subsequent historians. The failure of a single crop, following a year of scarcity, had wiped out an estimated 10 million human beings according to some accounts. The monsoon was on time in the next few years but the economy of Bengal had been drastically transformed, as the records of the next thirty years attest.

Twenty years after the famine, the population in Bengal was estimated at 24–30 million. Six in every sixteen persons was officially admitted to have perished in 1770. The government relief measures were woefully inadequate, amounting to a contribution by the Company of 4000 pounds for six months. They also laid an embargo on the importation of rice, but these methods were woefully limited. Districts in which men were dying at the rate of 20,000 a month received allotments of 150 rupees. The provincial council gravely and magnanimously sanctioned a grant of ten shillings worth of rice per diem for a starving population numbering 400,000 souls. Local government agents were accused of carrying off the farmers' grain in 1771 under the pretext of government regulation, stopping and emptying boats and even forcing the farmers to sell the seed they needed to sow for the next harvest. Remission of the land tax was not put into effect though it was urged by local officials. In a year when 35% of the whole population and 50% of the cultivators perished, not 5% of the land tax was remitted, and 10% was added to it for the ensuing year.[44] It has also been noted that the general distress was turned by many of the government officials, English merchants and their Indian assistants or *gumasthas* into a source of illicit private profit by monopolising the grain and ensuring that the peasants had no seeds left even for the following crop.[45]

W. W. Hunter, writing a century later, while exploring the reasons for the devastation of the famine of 1770 noted that the scale and extent of the famine was determined by lack of markets and transport. There was also interference in the market by the government that did not have a good result. The government prevented private merchants from undertaking the movement of grain. The Company issued orders prohibiting the export of grain from one district to another except to the city of Murshidabad. Similar orders were issued to the authorities at Chittagong and they were asked not to export grain anywhere except to Calcutta. The government was reduced to forcing merchants to sell rice at restricted prices in the capital. The restrictions also prevented traders from importing rice from other parts of the country into the famine-affected areas. The province also had no money to give in exchange of food. The dearth of money, especially silver coins, became so acute that private traders could not carry on their commercial transactions and trade came to a standstill.[46] The absence of means of importation and government policy to prevent movement of grain meant that neighbouring districts which could have supplied the grain were not able to do so. Local transport methods, which included boats, seem to have been affected by government measures of seizing boats and preventing importation and this had the effect of exaggerating the consequences of a local famine. Sylet district in north eastern Bengal had reaped plentiful harvests in 1780 and 1781, but the next crop was destroyed by local inundation and notwithstanding the facilities for importation effected by water-carriage, one third of the people died. The same thing took place in 1784 when two thirds of the cattle perished. Criticisms of this policy had been voiced at the time by the eighteenth-century economist Adam Smith, who believed that intervening in the grain trade by the East India Company had helped exacerbate food shortages.[47] This had the effect in future of deterring the British government from ever interfering in markets in the name of free trade, which had important and often negative implications for the famines of the nineteenth century.

It can be argued that the way in which a local scarcity becomes transformed into a disastrous famine had a lot to do with transport networks, market forces and administrative policy. More importantly however, is the gradual erosion of a way of life and the whittling away of traditional means of subsistence that rural communities in Bengal went through in the eighteenth century, a process that was hastened under colonial rule. This latter factor has not been sufficiently understood by historians like Michelle Mcalpin who have argued that the effects of modernisation have tended by and large towards reducing the effects of scarcity and this transition was achieved in India much later than in Europe. It is important to note that it was these traditional methods of husbandry that were affected in the Indian context by processes of modernisation, high taxation and incorporation into the modern state apparatus which had the effect of eroding tradition systems of subsistence and pushing people over the edge.[48] In the case of Bengal, this process seems to have happened by the late eighteenth century. Furthermore, this process also included the gradual erosion of traditional systems of subsistence and its ecological basis, access to common lands, trees and so on, all of which served in the eighteenth and nineteenth centuries to regulate the effects of famine and highlight the regional variations of coping strategies in times of scarcity. Writers such as Amartya Sen do not really see famine as a process but more as an event, and he fails in his classic study *Poverty and Famines* to explore the erosion of traditional means of subsistence which made groups particularly vulnerable to famine. A. DeWaal has made the important point in his work that while starvation deaths have been the central focus of current definitions of famine, it is more important to identify the destruction of customary patterns of life leading to destitution and hunger as these form the core of any famine situation. Mortality, therefore, is not a necessary condition of famine and is only the most striking manifestation of the phenomenon. De Waal points out further that this was also the way that the local people of Dafur perceived famine in the 1980s and the increased deaths were significant to the extent that this was a different kind of famine, 'one that killed'.[49] The neglect of studies that look at traditional coping mechanisms is indeed a lacuna that needs to be addressed as such traditional systems protected village communities.

In the case of lowland Bengal and Bihar, these communities were regulated through complex networks of patrimonial obligations that were gradually supplanted by a cash nexus.[50] As Rangarajan and Sivaramakrishnan note, 'in ecological terms' the conquest of regional politics by the East India Company achieved 'localised partitioning of bioregions into a patchwork of farms and woodlands by restricting raids, hunting, nomadism and the mobility of rural labour over space and time'.[51] They argue that colonial rule 'made conditions inimical to the reproduction of mobile livelihoods and their associated mosaic of shifting landscapes',[52] tending to tie people to fixed plots of land and make revenue assessment easier. Heavy revenue exactions had the effect of eroding traditional relationships related to water harvesting and irrigation. For example, under earlier regimes in south Bihar elaborate artificial irrigation systems were in place that reduced the impact of scarcity. It was reported that famines in this area after 1770 were less known due to the survival of these traditional irrigation systems. The effect of this ingenuity was to make it possible to grow rice crops in an area that lacked water. The area also grew a variety of other crops, including wheat, millets and barley sown as *rabi* or spring crops along with oil seed, opium and poppy. A specialist gardening caste, the Koeri, cultivated this latter plant.[53] Coarse grains dominated the *bhadoi* harvest and were of vital importance to subsistence farmers. Clearly, growing a variety of crops allowed the local communities to offset the dependence on rice making them less vulnerable to monsoonal failure. Similarly in South East Bengal, Buchanan Hamilton noted an elaborate system of tank building. 'Every man who gets a few rupees perpetuates his name by digging a tank.'[54] Water here was stored in ponds, the ponds fed by diverting river water into artificial channels. Everywhere in Bengal, however, these elaborate systems of irrigation had collapsed in the face of revenue exactions at an earlier date coinciding with the decline of the Mughal Empire adding to the scarcity and exacerbating the famine. As rice came to be extensively cultivated in many areas all through the nineteenth century it increased the vulnerability of these areas to famine. Local *zamindars* had the responsibility of cleaning canals and ponds but the excessive revenue exactions irked them and they began to increasingly shirk their duties.[55] In the nineteenth century these processes further intensified,[56] and these local irrigation systems fell into disuse everywhere. Joint control over these works made maintenance difficult.

Bengal's ability to generate a surplus that could be easily turned into cash had made it attractive to the late Mughal Empire and then to the

British. The fiscal squeeze, the massive invasion of the internal trade of Bengal by private enterprise and the looting of the revenue collections by local English *nabobs* all drained the coffers of the province and put ever-increasing tax burdens on a impoverished agricultural class. These were communities who had become increasingly vulnerable to scarcity and famine. As for those classes that did not live off the land, they were also susceptible to high prices and dearth. In this context, it is important to note that particular groups were worse affected than others, for example lime workers in the 1770 famine in Birbhum, with limited access to land, were badly affected and of a hundred and fifty in one area only five were recorded as living.[57] Contemporary witnesses suggested that the mortality was exceptionally high among the non-cultivating population – weavers, spinners, silk winders, boatmen, salt and lime workers and growers of non-food products such as cotton and silk worms. The resident of Dacca reported in 1776 that the Dacca fabric for these six or seven years had declined in quality, a great part of which could be attributed to the ravages of the famine in 1770 carrying away great numbers of the best spinners and *ryots* who cultivated the cotton plant.[58]

At the beginning of 1771 local potentates unable to realise the land tax were stripped of their assets and imprisoned. The ruin of the old aristocracy of Bengal dates from this period. The maharajah of Burdwan, the proprietor of Nudeah and the lady proprietor of Rajshahi all emerged from the famine with their lands threatened with dispossession and in debt. Depopulation was followed by land falling out of tillage: Bengal lost one third of its people and one third of its cultivable area speedily became waste. In the present state of the country wrote Francis in 1776, 'the *ryot* has the advantage over the *zamindar*. Where so much land lies waste and so few hands are left for cultivation the peasant must be courted to undertake it.'[59] This created a new class of tenantry: the non-resident cultivators or the *paikhast* who threw up their previous holdings and went in search of new ones at lower rates to which depopulation had reduced the value of land.

The 1768–70 droughts and famines were a profound blow not only to the system of revenue but to the whole rationale of empire. As such, they provided an impetus for the evolution of a famine policy. Under the immediate devastating circumstances, Warren Hastings had no choice but to call for the Company to stand forth as *diwan* in 1772, ending the dual system and placing responsibility for the security, administration and economy of Bengal squarely on the Company's shoulders. Hasting's administrative overhaul of Bengal, which paved the way for the establishment of the British-run, district level administration, would continue throughout British rule in India. Having converted Calcutta to the capital of Bengal, the question which immediately demanded Hastings' attention of was the settlement of revenue. As he noted: 'it was late in the season; the lands had suffered unheard of depopulation by the famine and mortality of 1769. The collections violently kept up to the former standard and added to the distress of the country.' Hastings rapidly set about framing a new system for the assessment of revenue.[60] But not much seem to have changed, the continuing wars with the Rohillas, the Mahrattas and the British continued to put a strain on Bengal's coffers.[61] As Abbé Raynal pointed out, the famine of 1770 'had throughout Europe excited so much horror of the English',[62] causing a rethinking of imperial policy.

The response to famine conditions among the local population has been the subject of some interest among historians, who have tended to cite the passivity of the Bengali peasantry as an indication of the hold of Bengal's traditional hierarchical society.[63] However, as Mcclane notes, this is not necessarily a correct assessment of eighteenth-century Bengali society. *Raiyats* did have a strong sense of their rights when they believed their landlords were treating them unfairly:

> They assembled in rowdy crowds, complained to the government and withheld their rents frequently. In addition beneath the *jotedar* landholders were numerous low caste peasants on the margins of village society who migrated often and in the early nineteenth century joined *dakait* gangs by the thousands and terrorised their affluent neighbours.[64]

We move on to this aspect in the following section.

The recalcitrant frontier

The impact of the famine on the frontier areas of Western Bengal also bears exploration. This is where the hold of the Company was most tenuous and the scarcity and famine conditions of the 1770 pushed the already hostile population into open rebellion. For the first fifteen years after the famine, depopulation steadily increased. The death of children in the famine meant that the elderly died off without there being anyone to take their place. Various struggles broke out between landed proprietors to entice tenants. But the desertion was so general that Lord Cornwallis was to announce in 1789 that one third of the company's territories in Bengal were a jungle inhabited by wild beasts. Birbhum and Bisunpur were the worst affected areas. In Birbhum, four years before the famine, it was recorded that there were 6000 rural communities each with a village in the centre of its lands. In 1771, three years after the famine, only 4000 of these communities survived.[65] The cultivators fled from the countryside to the towns in an attempt to find food, but the towns were equally affected and it was reported by a Birbhum official in 1771 that only a quarter of the houses in towns were occupied. Depopulation continued steadily until 1785 by which time 1500 communities had disappeared of the original 6000 and their lands relapsed to jungle. Attempts to collect land tax continued, with the most harsh methods being used resulting in several farmers being thrown into debt prisons. Desertion increased as a result, with *ryots* attempting to flee the collection of the *najay* tax, which gave ample scope to the revenue collectors to oppress the *ryots*. Warren Hastings described the tax thus: 'it is called *najay* and it is an assessment upon the actual inhabitants of every inferior description of the lands to make up for the loss sustained in the rents of their neighbours who are either dead or have fled the country'.[66] In 1771, more than a third of the land was returned in the public accounts as deserted, in 1776 the figure was more than a half, 40,000 acres lying waste for every 1,000,000 in 1772, to close on 112,000 acres in 1776.[67] The villagers were dragooned into paying the land tax by Muslim troops, but notwithstanding the utmost severities, receipts seldom amounted to more than half the demand. The state of Birbhum at the end of the famine of 1770 is clear from eye-witness reports. The district had become a sequestered and impassable jungle. Earlier it had been the route for armies controlling Bengal; in 1780 a small band of sepoys could with difficulty find their way through the forest. A contemporary newspaper correspondent reported 'they marched through an extensive wood, all the way a perfect wilderness; sometimes a small village presented itself in the midst of the jungles, with a little cultivated ground around it ... these woods abound with tigers and bears'.[68] Labour was to remain the scarce factor of production in the rural economy throughout most of the eighteenth and nineteenth centuries.

By the end of the famine, 'social banditry' was on the increase in these frontier areas of Bengal as dispossesed landholders sought to sustain a livelihood through plunder. The council wrote in 1773:

> A set of lawless banditi known under the name of '*sanyasis*' or '*faquirs*' have long infested these countries; and under pretence of

religious pilgrimage, have been accustomed to traverse the chief part of Bengal, begging, stealing, and plundering wherever they go. . . . In the years subsequent to the famine, their ranks swollen by starving peasants who had neither seed, nor implements to commence cultivation with in the cold weather of 1772 brought them down on the harvest fields of lower Bengal burning, plundering and ravaging in bodies of fifty to thousand men.[69]

Land revenue remained uncollected and severe military pressure had to be used to subdue these peasant bandits. The repression of *thugee* was Warren Hastings' foremost task and he went about it assiduously, commanding that every convicted dacoit should be executed, his whole family be made slaves and that every inhabitant of the village be fined. The category of banditry was an imprecise one and could encompass phenomena right through from popular famine looting to the organised armed activities of professional dacoits.

By the end of the famine period the disorders could be called a period of rebellion. Given the past famine conditions and the terrible fiscal squeeze of the colonial state, social banditry was the only option. The dispossessed peasants made common cause with a range of other occupational groups like boatmen in conditions of acute scarcity. The Company rule of Bengal had long proved irksome and the famine sent it into a downward spiral and into rebellion. In 1761 the Rajas of Burdwan, Birbhum and Midnapur had combined their forces and moved against the English. It was feelings of hostility like this that exploded after the famine of 1770 into outright rebellion. Zamindars were the rallying points of dacoits in rural Bengal.[70] The *faujdar* of Midnapur welcomed the dacoits as he could then thwart the pressure of the Company operating from Calcutta. In 1789 the board of revenue commented on the condition of Birbhum, noting that

> the district is in great want of regulation and order ... this is in part due to the jungly situation ... but arisen more from the want of exertion and proper attention on the part of the *zamindar* ... as of all the different denominations of officers and servants employed under him who are without any sort of control and act and levy contributions from the country as they think proper.[71]

In this context, the depredations of the Chuars (aboriginal tribes) in particular is interesting. The Chuars inhabited the Jungle Terai region, an area covered by vast stretches of jungle. They were seen as making incursions into Birbhum and Ghatsheela from about the 1760s. Organised under three *sardars*, they refused to cooperate with the revenue assessments of the Company and fuelled the resistance of the frontier *zamindars*. As Forbes noted, when asked to pay their rents they declared themselves to be fighting men, 'they had never paid any rents but they were always ready to fight when called on'.[72] The famine condition intensified Chuar protest and one can conclusively state that in the frontier areas the famine successfully fuelled peasant resistance and succeeded in challenging the hold of the Company for several decades. As Sen notes, for a long time the western jungles were the habitation of the Chuars and as early as 1769 their plunder had become a settled theme of public discussion.[73]

To summarise then, the famine of 1770 was the biggest calamity of the eighteenth century in terms of the enormous loss of life and the extent of human suffering involved. The core areas of central Bengal were devastated and these included Murshidabad, Rajshahi and Hoogly. The most vulnerable were the landless labourers, artisans and boatman who were without means of laying by stores of grain. The cultivating classes were also seriously affected because the adverse effects of famines on a predominantly agricultural economy included not only a reduced availability of human labour because of starvation deaths but also a fall in the availability of draught power because of high cattle mortality. It is interesting to note that the famine did not really affect the low-lying delta areas of East Bengal though weavers and spinners died in Dacca in 1770. This was because such areas managed to retain crucial supplies of water during a dry season in the rest of the province.[74] The frontier principalities of western Bengal such as Birbhum and Bishunpur were affected by the famine in a different way. Situated on the verge of British jurisdiction and separated from headquarters by rivers and swamps they remained in the hands of hereditary princes. The hold of colonial power in these areas was weak and could be challenged in situations of scarcity and high taxation. Under conditions of famine and following it the region saw a renewed period of instability. Here banditry emerged as a response to the EIC policy of revenue assessment, sedenterisation and control. Elsewhere, as in Chotanagpur, the response was even more extreme. The 1770 famine did not affect the plateau of Chotnagpur, especially the south of the plateau in the hill tracts which was marked a distinctive agro-ecological setting being populated mainly by tribal communities who practised various forest-linked agricultural methods occupying a territory that was only gradually brought under British control. Here recalcitrant tribal groups such as the Munda and Ho resisted incorporation into British rule well into the nineteenth century. By the nineteenth century the north and central parts of districts such as Palamau contained fertile valleys inhabited mainly by plains Hindus growing rice, sugar cane, wheat and barley, while the southern part continued to be inhabited by tribals who were increasingly to come under pressure. The resistance to the revenue and agrarian regimes of the EIC continued until the 1830s. It was clear then that, as Rangarajan and Sivramakrishnan note, 'the landscape-ordering and people- sedenterizing policies' of the East India Company 'were easier to conceive and more difficult to execute throughout the modern and colonial period'.[75] It was only in the mid nineteenth century that the frontier regions and Chotanagpur came well under the control of the East India Company.

Notes

1. M. Rangarajan and K. Sivaramakrishnan (2012), *India's Environmental History: from Ancient Times to the Colonial Period*, Delhi: Permanent Black, p. 22.
2. Lance Brennan argues that behind the famine of 1896-97 in Nadia district in Bengal lay a series of ecological disasters from the drying up of some of the Ganges distributaries and the debility of the population caused by epidemics of malaria (linked to stagnant water from atrophying rivers and railway embankments) See Lance Brennan, Les Heathcote and Anton Lucas (1984), 'The causation of famine: a comparative analyses of Lombok and Bengal, 1891-1974', *South Asia*, 7(1): 1-26.
3. See Michelle Macalpin (1983), *Subject to Famine: Food Crisis and Economic Change in Western India, 1860-1920*, Princeton, NJ: Princeton University Press.
4. See David Ludden (1983), *Peasant History in South India*, Princeton, NJ: Princeton University Press and Scarlett Epstein, 'Productive efficiency and customary systems of rewards in rural south India', in R. Firth (ed.) (1967), *Themes in Economic Anthropology*, London: Tavistock, pp. 229-52.
5. D. Clingingsmith and J. G. Williamson (2008), 'Deindustrialization in 18th and 19th Century India: Mughal Decline, Climate Shocks and British Industrial Ascent', *Explorations in Economic History*, 45(3): 209-234.
6. Clingingsmith and Williamson, 'Deindustrialization in 18th and 19th Century India', 214.
7. D. Kumar (ed.) (1982), *Cambridge Economic History of India*, vol. 2, Cambridge: Cambridge University Press, p. 296.
8. Clingingsmith and Williamson, 'Deindustrialization in 18th and 19th Century India'.
9. Richard Grove (1998), 'The East India Company, the Raj and El Niño: the critical role played by colonial scientists in establishing the mechanisms of global climate teleconnections, 1770-1930', in R. Grove, V. Damodaran and S. Sangwan (eds.), *Nature and the Orient: The Environmental History of South and Southeast Asia*, Delhi: Oxford University Press, pp. 301-324.

Conditions in Eighteenth-Century Bengal 99

10. Mike Davis, *Late Victorian Holocausts: Elnino Famines and the Making of the Third World*, London: Verso, 2001.
11. C. M. Agarwal (1983), *Natural Calamities and the Great Mughals*, Gaya, Patna: Kanchan Publications, p. 42.
12. Agarwal, *Natural Calamities*, p. 44.
13. John Marshall, *Notes and Observations in Bengal 1668–72*, p. 226, quoted in Agarwal, *Natural Calamities*, p. 131.
14. Marshall, *Notes*, p. 131.
15. John R. Mclane (1993), *Land and Local Kingship in Eighteenth-Century Bengal*, Cambridge: Cambridge University Press.
16. See Irfan Habib (1997), 'The eighteenth century in Indian economic history', in P. J. Marshall (ed.), *The Eighteenth Century in Indian History*, Cambridge: Cambridge University Press, p. 111.
17. Nicholas Dirks (2006), *The Scandal of Empire: India and the Creation of Imperial Britain*, Cambridge, MA: Belknap Press of Harvard University Press, p. xiii.
18. Dirks, *The Scandal of Empire*, p. 15.
19. D. Salmon (1913), *Macaulay's Essay on Warren Hastings*, London: Longmans, p. 9.
20. P. Marshall (2006), *Bengal the British Bridgehead*, Cambridge: Cambridge Univesity Press, p. 3.
21. Chitta Panda (1996), *The Decline of the Bengal Zamindars, Midnapore, 1870–1920*, Delhi and New York: Oxford University Press, p. 11. See also B. B. Chaudhuri (1976), 'Agricultural growth in Bengal and Bihar, 1770–1860', *Bengal Past and Present*, 95(1): 290–340.
22. Marshall, *Bengal the British Bridgehead*, p. 10.
23. Panda, *The Decline of the Bengal Zamindars*, p. 12.
24. Habib, 'The eighteenth century in Indian economic history', p. 112.
25. Mclane, *Land and Local Kingship in Eighteenth-Century Bengal*, p. 195.
26. Letter from Select Committee to Court, 30 September 1765 quoted in Nandalal Chatterjee (1956), *Bengal under the Diwani Administration*, Allahabad: Indian Press.
27. Chatterjee, *Bengal*, p. 8.
28. Chatterjee, *Bengal*, p. 9.
29. Chatterjee, *Bengal*, p. 17.
30. Chatterjee, *Bengal*, p. 21.
31. Chatterjee, *Bengal*, p. 23.
32. According to Grove, the failure of the monsoon and the subsequent droughts were caused by the El Niño. For South and South East Asia we are able to rely much more heavily on documentary evidence for the effect of El Niño at a time when little such evidence was available for either Africa or South America. Monsoon failures in South Asia according to him are the best and most direct archival benchmark for calibrating historical responses to El Niño. On the El Niño causes of this famine see R. Grove, 'El Niño associated droughts, floods, famines and other natural disasters: South Asia and South East Asia in global context 1500–1800', paper presented at the German Historical Institute, 2003.
33. George Cambell's memoir cited in 'Memoir by George Campbell on the famines which affected Bengal in the last century', in J. C. Geddes (1874),

Administrative Experience Recorded in Former Famines, Calcutta: Bengal Secretariat Press.
34. C. V. Hill (1997), *Rivers of Sorrow: Environment and Social Control in Riparian North India, 1770–1994*, Ann Arbor, MI: Association for Asian Studies.
35. Nani Gopal Chaudhuri (1970), *Cartier, Governor of Bengal, 1769–1772*, Calcutta: Firma K. L. Mukhopadhyay, p. 31.
36. W. W. Hunter (1872), *Annals of Rural Bengal*, London: Smith, Elder, p. 20.
37. Hunter, *Annals of Rural Bengal*, p. 21.
38. Hunter, *Annals of Rural Bengal*, p. 21.
39. Chaudhuri, *Cartier, Governor of Bengal*, p. 39.
40. Quoted in David Arnold, 'Hunger in the garden of plenty, the Bengal famine of 1770', in Alessa Johns (1999) *Dreadful Visitations Confronting Natural Catastrophe in the Age of Enlightenment*, New York: Routledge, p. 82. See also contemporary report by an anonymous Company official in *Gentleman's Magazine and Historical Chronicle*, vol. 41, sept. 1771, quoted in Mclane, *Land Local Kingship in Eighteenth-Century Bengal*, p. 96.
41. Account of the dreadful famine in India, *Indian Annual Register*, 1771, quoted in Arnold, 'Hunger in the garden of plenty', p. 82.
42. Arnold, 'Hunger in the garden of plenty', p. 82.
43. Letter from the president and council to the court of directors 3 November 1772, see Appendix A, 'Bengal portrayed in 1772', in Hunter, *Annals of Rural Bengal*, p. 381. See also McLane, *Land and Local Kingship in Eighteenth-Century Bengal*, p. 200.
44. Appendix A, 'Bengal portrayed in 1772', in Hunter, *Annals of Rural Bengal*.
45. Chatterjee, *Bengal*, p. 48.
46. Chaudhuri, *Cartier, Governor of Bengal*, p. 50.
47. Adam Smith (1930), *An Inquiry into the Nature and Causes of the Wealth of Nations*, London: Strahan and Cadell.
48. Amartya Sen (1992), *Poverty and Famines: An Essay on Entitlement and Deprivation*, Oxford: Oxford University Press. See also Mike Davies (2002), *Late Victorian Holocausts, El Niño Famines and the Making of the Third World*, London: Verso, p. 19.
49. Alexander De Waal (1989), *Famine that Kills: Dafur, Sudan 1984-85*, Oxford: Oxford University Press, pp. 32–3.
50. Nirmal Sen Gupta (1980), 'The indigenous irrigation system in south Bihar', *Indian Economic and Social History Review*, 17: 157–90.
51. Rangarajan and Sivaramakrishnan, *India's Environmental History*, p. 21.
52. Rangarajan and Sivara,makrishnan, *India's Environmental History*, p. 22.
53. V. Damodaran (1992), *Broken Promises: Popular Protest, Indian Nationalism and the Congress Party in Bihar*, Oxford: Oxford University Press, p. 76.
54. Francis Buchanan and William Van Schendel, *Journey through South East Bengal, 1798*, Dhaka: University Press, p. 112.
55. Agarwal, *Natural Calamities and the Great Mughals*, p. 111.
56. Damodaran, *Broken Promises*, pp. 85–9.
57. Hunter, *Annals of Rural Bengal*, p. 53.
58. Quoted in Mclane, *Land and Local Kingship in Eighteenth-Century Bengal*, pp. 202–3.
59. Minute by Francis, Revenue Consultations of 5 November, 1776 quoted in Hunter, *Annals of Rural Bengal*, p. 38.

60. Selections from the letters, despatches and other state papers preserved in the foreign department of the Government of India, 1772–85, citing memoirs of Warren Hastings, Calcutta, 1890, p. x.
61. Selections from state papers preserved in the foreign department, 1772–85, p. 35.
62. Quoted in Richard Grove (1995) *Green Imperialism*, Cambridge: Cambridge University Press, p. 424.
63. See Arnold, 'Hunger in the garden of plenty', and Paul Greenhough (1982), *Prosperity and Misery in Rural Bengal*, Oxford: Oxford University Press, pp. 267–70.
64. Mclane, *Land and Local Kingship in Eighteenth-Century Bengal*, p. 199.
65. Chaudhuri, *Cartier, Governor of Bengal*, p. 71.
66. Chaudhuri, *Cartier, Governor of Bengal*, p. 69.
67. Chaudhuri, *Cartier, Governor of Bengal*, p. 69, See also Mclane, *Land and Local Kingship in Eighteenth-Century Bengal*, pp. 200–207 for a revision of these estimates.
68. Hunter, *Annals of Rural Bengal*, p. 77.
69. Quoted in Hunter, *Annals of Rural Bengal*, p. 77. See also Ranjit Sen (1988), *Social Banditry in Bengal, 1757–1793*, Calcutta: Ratna Prakashan, for a detailed study of social banditry in the period.
70. Sen, *Social Banditry*, p. 35.
71. Sen, *Social Banditry*, p. 37.
72. Sen, *Social Banditry*, p. 38.
73. Vansittart to Verelst, 20 Dec. 1769, *Midnapur District Records*, Vol. 11, quoted in Sen, *Social Banditry*, p. 61.
74. Rajat Datta (1989), *Some Notes on the Causation of Dearth and Famine in Late Eighteenth Century Bengal*. London: SOAS workshop, p. 10.
75. Rangarajan and Sivaramakrishnan, *India's Environmental History*, p. 22.

5
Colonial Private Diaries and their Potential for Reconstructing Historical Climate in Bombay, 1799–1828

George Adamson

Introduction

As Richard Grove and others have shown, the servants of the East India Company carried a preoccupation with the recording and classification of natural environments.[1] This is particularly true of weather and climate. During the early-mid nineteenth century the East India Company established the first systematic meteorological observatories in several territories under their control, including (in chronological order of opening) Madras, Calcutta, St Helena, Bombay and Singapore. However, the tradition of recording meteorological observations extended back significantly further than this, with weather chronologies of a shorter duration available in numerous archives around the world. These derive from medical observations, travel writings, military records, ships' logs and a variety of personal diaries and correspondences. New territories were assessed for their suitability for European habitation. Likewise, travel 'tours' to new trading regions incorporated meteorological readings to assess the likely crop yields and their responses to droughts and floods.[2] East India Company naturalists corresponding about a series of global droughts in the 1790s arguably discovered El Niño teleconnections some 130 years before Gilbert Walker first defined the Southern Oscillation.[3]

Several interlinking narratives governed this passion for the recording of climate. By the late eighteenth century, the high disease incidence and low life expectancy experienced by colonists in India and elsewhere had transformed early optimism regarding the 'salubriousness' of the subcontinent into fear and trepidation.[4] Hippocratic medical beliefs equating ill health with 'miasmas' were resurgent with the spread of scientific enquiry during the Enlightenment.[5] The migration of the East India Company from a trading company to a territorial organisation resulted in the exploration of new localities (and hence new climates) and raised the possibility of permanent settlement of Europeans in India. This was thought to be perilous to the health of colonists, and it was also feared that the new climate would threaten their racial superiority by limiting their energy levels, intellectual ability and moral character.[6] Sites were therefore sought with climates that were as similar as possible to those of northern Europe, resulting in substantial monitoring and recording of meteorological data, much of which still survives.[7]

At the same time as the official recording, Europeans in the employment of the East India Company undertook substantial recording of climate on an ad hoc basis within private diaries and correspondence. Jan Golinski has previously drawn attention to the importance of weather monitoring amongst the intellectual elite of the eighteenth century, and this was still true in the early decades of the nineteenth.[8] Scientific endeavour raised the middle and upper classes above the 'vulgar superstitions' of the proletariat.[9] This created a fashion for the keeping of weather diaries; the incorporation of instrumental observations elevating the endeavour even further.[10] The recording of meteorological conditions was particularly prevalent amongst the largely educated colonial elite within tropical regions, where the general British fascination with the weather was accentuated by the novelty of the climates in which colonists lived.[11] After the turn of the nineteenth century, medical writings also started to recommend intellectual activity as a way to combat the detrimental influence of tropical climates.[12] The study and recording of extremes of heat and humidity therefore offered a method to counter their supposedly destructive effects.

Although some work has been undertaken to analyse meteorological information within colonial diaries for the history of meteorology[13] and colonial climatic discourse,[14] the significance of these observations for the study of climatology has been generally overlooked.[15] This chapter concerns the meteorological information contained within private diaries kept by four British colonists resident in Bombay (Mumbai) between 1799 and 1828. Two were direct employees of the East India Company: Lieutenant General Sir Jasper Nicolls (then Lieutenant/Captain) who served in the Bombay Army during the Second Anglo-Maratha War of 1803–1805, and the Hon. Mountstuart Elphinstone, Governor of Bombay from 1819 to 1827. A third, Sir James McGrigor, was a military surgeon serving with the 88th Regiment of Foot, stationed in Bombay periodically between 1799 and 1803. The final diary was kept by Lady Lucretia West, wife of Sir Edward West, the Chief Justice of Bombay from 1823 to 1828. Apart from McGrigor's, all are personal diaries, and McGrigor's volumes are casebooks rather than systematic weather diaries. Nevertheless, all contain a large amount of meteorological information.

The early nineteenth century is an important period for meteorological re-analysis. The national instrumental meteorological network in India was established in 1871. Before this date data are sparse, particularly before 1850. In western India, the first regular long record of precipitation began in Bombay in 1817 with the publication of monthly totals of rainfall during the monsoon months (June to October) in the English-language periodicals the *Bombay Courier* and *Bombay Gazette*. However, these are non-standardised and potentially unreliable. Standardised meteorological readings did not begin until 1847 at the Colaba Observatory, with the exception of a brief period from 1816 to 1822, during which daily temperature and pressure observations were published in the *Bombay Courier*. Information from personal weather diaries can therefore be used both to extend the published meteorological record and assess early instrumental records for reliability and homogeneity.[16]

The generation of long records is vital for the study of climatology today. The climatology of South Asia is affected by a number of territorial, oceanic and atmospheric factors, particularly sea surface temperature.[17] Changes in the relative location of warm- and cold-water regions in the major oceans can affect the areas where evaporation occurs, and hence the location of low- and high-pressure systems. In South Asia, where rainfall is seasonal and reliant on pressure systems that prevail for several weeks at a time, a change in their position can have severe consequences. The central Pacific is the location for one particularly important sea-surface temperature phenomenon, the El Niño Southern Oscillation (ENSO). This is the movement of a warm water pool from the east to the central Pacific, which has implications for weather across the globe, including South Asia. An El Niño event, in which warm water moves to the central Pacific, is associated with cooler summer temperatures in India and, importantly, reduced summer monsoon rainfall.[18] A similar system is situated in the Indian Ocean, known as the Indian Ocean Dipole (IOD). In this system the warm water pool moves from the eastern to the western Indian Ocean, with an easterly warm pool associated with deficient monsoon rainfall.[19] The Indian Ocean also affects monsoon rainfall at a shorter timescale. Rainfall is generally more intense when the seas are warmer as this creates heavier evaporation; heavy monsoon rainfall will cool the Indian Ocean and cause weaker rainfall the following season. This results in a two-year cycle of heavier and weaker monsoons, referred to as the Tropospheric Biennial Oscillation.[20]

These large-scale dipoles and oscillations themselves exhibit variability over the timescale of several years. ENSO, for example, has been show to oscillate in intensity with a wavelength of approximately 55–60 years. The relationship between monsoon rainfall and ENSO also appears to oscillate in intensity with a periodicity of approximately 70 years.[21] Quantifying these long-term variations is clearly important for long-term forecasting of both temperature and rainfall over the subcontinent, both of which can profoundly impact upon livelihoods. However, accurately diagnosing climatic variation on the timescale of several decades is problematic when the available data spans only a century and a half.

This chapter adds to existing work by the author to extend the climatic record for western India using documentary sources. In doing so, it will not only benefit the modern study of climatology, but will also illustrate the value of the scientific observations collected by the East India Company. The chapter focuses on the potential of individual diaries for reconstructing temperature and precipitation variability with a high temporal density. This includes monthly temperature maxima, precipitation variability and the occurrence of notable or extreme climatic events.[22] The sources analysed are described below.

Diaries analysed

The case books of James McGrigor

James McGrigor was a Scottish surgeon serving in the British Army with the 88th Regiment of Foot. The Regiment were stationed in Bombay from 3 September 1799 to 28 February 1803, during which time McGrigor and his deputies maintained detailed medical records. The nine 'casebooks' relating to Bombay catalogued in the archives of the Aberdeen Medico-Chirurgical Society date from 3 September 1799 to 28 February 1803.[23] McGrigor was absent from Bombay from December 1800 serving with the 88th in Alexandria[24]; no records are therefore available from 9 December 1800. However, a casebook was kept by a deputy from July 1801, which was continued by McGrigor on his return in June 1802. Later correspondence by McGrigor suggests that deputies also occasionally kept the casebooks at other times. From September 1799 to

October 1800 the books refer to a barracks on Colaba (then an island). After this date McGrigor transferred to a hospital in Bombay Fort, and from August 1801 to an unspecified location in Bombay 'bazaar'.

The entries within the casebooks predominantly comprise of daily notes on the progress of patients within the hospitals, interspersed with detailed weekly summaries of patients' progress. A total of 117 of these weekly summaries include meteorological observations, amounting to 78% of the total weekly records in the casebooks. The observations comprise descriptions of general meteorological conditions through the week, including remarks on temperature, rainfall and prevailing wind direction. A total of 81 of the weekly summaries contain maximum temperature observations for the week; 71 also include minima, although the time of day recorded is not specified.

The following two quotations exemplify the meteorological summaries contained within the casebooks:

> The Monsoon draws near a very little rain has fallen there has been much lightning the sun is hot & sultry, thermometer for some days 93 & the Wind variable tho generally S and SW.[25]

> We had a remarkable change in the weather during the past week after a clouded & hazy sky & a very sultry day, in the afternoon of the 24th, we had much loud Thunder with frequent flashes of lightning, & in the night a very considerable quantity of rain fell. On the two following days we had a little distant thunder & some lightning The extreme range of the thermometer has been from 73° to 82°.[26]

The diaries of Jasper Nicolls

Jasper Nicolls arrived in Bombay in September 1802 and left in February 1805. Like James McGrigor, he spent some of this period away on a military posting, fighting in the Deccan in the Second Anglo-Maratha War from September 1803 to April 1804. From his arrival, Nicolls' diaries display a strong preoccupation with climate, including detailed observations both on meteorological conditions and on the responses of the Indian and European populations to climatic variability. Nicolls' diaries are a particularly strong source of information regarding the famine of 1803–1804 and measures to combat its effects. However, the diary was not kept daily and meteorological information within it is sparser than that contained in McGrigor's casebooks. A total of 63 entries contain meteorological information out of 16 months that Nicolls spent in Bombay, averaging approximately one entry every

10 days. Meteorological observations mainly describe rainfall during the monsoon and storm events during the remainder of the year, with less information on temperature.

Nicolls' diaries also contain summaries of meteorological observations for monthly, and later seasonal and yearly periods. The first of these was written on 30 September 1802. This includes only general descriptions of the weather during the past month:

> This month has been showery; in the morning there has been but very little wind it springs up about 10, and blows refreshingly in general for the remainder, between 5 and 6 in the evening it is a very pleasant air.[27]

By November, however, the summary had been extended to include average temperature readings for 'Morning', 'Noon' and 'Night', maximum and minimum temperatures recorded during the month, and fairly detailed descriptions of wind conditions and rainfall.[28]

> I have this month noted down daily the changes of the wind, which comes alternately from the land and sea; About 12 or near 1 OClock p.m. the sea breeze sets in, and blows between W.N.W. and N.N.W., about 8 or 9 pm – The land breeze succeeds and continues until the following noon to blow from N by E, to E.N.E.: but upon average to the N of the latter point.[29]

Regular monthly observations are more sporadic during the first half of 1803, ascribed by Nicolls to the warmth of the morning preventing observations and 'the time for an evenings walk exactly interfering with our dinner hour'.[30] However, in July 1803, Nicolls included a detailed summary of conditions during the last 6 months. This included thrice-daily average monthly temperatures, maxima and minima of temperature, 'general' averages for each third of the month and qualitative descriptions of wind and rainfall. A similar meteorological abstract was included in an entry of 20 July 1804, covering the period 1 July 1803 to 30 June 1804 and including all of the aforementioned observations with the exception of the thrice-monthly temperature averages. These, Nicolls stated, were taking from the 'General's daily account', with the thermometer placed somewhere in the interior of a house in Bombay 'where it could not be very materially affected by either the cooling sea breezes, or the violence of the sun's heat, which would have been the case, had it been hung in any verandah, or other exposed place'.[31]

It can be reasonably assumed that the General in this case refers to Major General Arthur Wellesley, although some observations must have been collected by a deputy as Wellesley and Nicolls were absent from Bombay from September 1803 to April 1804.

In January 1805 Nicolls' diary includes a summary of monthly temperature variations for the whole of 1804, which included days of 'heavy' and 'slight' rain, although no notes on wind direction. Significantly, on 22 January, Nicolls also included a facsimile of a paper he presented that day to the first meeting of the Bombay Literary Society. This was eventually published in the first edition of the *Transactions of the Literary Society of Bombay*.[32] The paper comprises a synthesis of the temperature observations recorded in Nicolls' diaries for 1803 and 1804, together with days of 'heavy rain' and 'showers' in each month. The paper also contains further information on the temperature readings. Morning observations were made between 6:00 and 8:00 a.m., afternoon from 12:00 to 4:00 p.m., and evening between 9:30 p.m. and midnight. The house in which the thermometer was contained was exposed to the west, but surrounded by buildings to the east and south. From 24 March 1803 readings were taken from several thermometers so as to ensure continuity:

> The thermometers were suspended against a wall, two feet in thickness, within a few inches of the angel formed by the junction of another wall of nearly equal thickness: the room itself spacious and lofty ... On three sides also they have not been exposed to any improper influence, or current of the air, on one being sheltered by a door, which, being kept open, forms a channel for the air from the other. The height at which the instruments were suspended is about 23 feet above the level of the high water mark.[33]

The diaries of Mountstuart Elphinstone

The Hon. Mountstuart Elphinstone arrived in India in 1796 and held several posts within the East India Company, including Envoy to Kabul and Resident at Poona (Pune). He served under General Wellesley in the Second Anglo-Maratha War and was briefly resident in Bombay in 1802–1803 (thus likely having made the acquaintance of Jasper Nicolls). However, his principal posting in Bombay occurred when he was awarded the Governorship of Bombay in late October 1819, a position that he retained until he left India on 15 November 1827. Elphinstone's diary entries display a preoccupation with climate, particularly the influence of climate on his health.[34] He was a reader of academic papers for pleasure, particularly those relating to meteorology.[35] He was also President of the Literary Society of Bombay when the first issue of the *Transactions* was released, and he quotes Nicolls' paper in his diary: 'To day the glass has been at 88°, 3° higher than it has been since I came to Parell & as high as it was at any time during the whole year 1804 as appears by the Trans'c Liti Soci.'[36]

Elphinstone's diary was not kept daily. However, between 1819 and 1827, 315 entries mentioned meteorological conditions, with approximately one entry every nine days. These were ad hoc observations; however, they were regular and are relatively detailed. Heat was noted regularly, generally connected to a complaint Elphinstone referred to as the 'languor of the hot weather'. Rainfall ('the weariness & nervousness of the rains'[37]) and wind direction ('the southerly winds famous among Bombay people for bringing drowsiness & prickly heat'[38]) were also noted frequently. From 7 December 1821, 115 entries include thermometer observations, although not all of these were collected in Bombay. Elphinstone spent the late monsoons of 1822 and 1826 in Pune, and 1823 and 1824 at the Hill Station of Khandala. The winters of 1820 and 1821 were also spent visiting territories in Gujarat. However, the majority of entries referred to Bombay, either at the Governor's main residence on Parel Island or at Elphinstone's summer residence at Malabar Point, where he generally resided from April to June. For example:

> The weather has been hot for three days, today the wind is hot & the thermometer 88° but there is yet no languor. On the contrary I still enjoy the effects of our fortnight of cold weather & scarcely recollect the depression & lassitude of the rains.[39]

The diaries of Lucretia West

Lady Lucretia West was resident in Bombay from February 1823 until July 1828, dying shortly afterwards in Poona. She arrived in Bombay as the wife of the Chief Justice, Sir Edward West. Sir West was not a direct employee of the East India Company; the position of Chief Justice was created by the British Government to investigate supposed abuses of power by the Company at a time when the British Government were becoming increasingly concerned about its position as a trader and administrator. This role brought Edward West into conflict with Mountstuart Elphinstone, with West eventually accusing Elphinstone of having drunkenly challenged him to a duel, an accusation that Elphinstone denied.[40]

Lady West's diaries are generally concerned with the social life of Bombay. However, 653 of her diary entries in Bombay include meteorological observations, representing approximately one entry every two days.[41] These are generally brief, announcing the weather to be 'hot' or 'quite cool', or detailing rainfall events:

> It rains so violently it is almost dark.[42] I have been to the school meeting and found it very hot; yesterday & today are a little warm in the middle of the day – but quite cool Morng and Eveg Ther. at 2 O'clock 84.[43]

Thermometer readings are present throughout the diary, including in earlier entries that West wrote whilst at sea before arriving in Bombay. A total of 212 daily observations were made in Bombay, generally recording the daily maximum temperature. Both West and Elphinstone also recorded unusual or extreme events, particularly storms and periods of unusual cold or warmth. The contemporaneity of the two diaries allows these extreme events to be verified, meaning that detailed reconstruction of climatic conditions from the diaries is possible.

Meteorological analysis

Precipitation

Precipitation information included within the diaries analysed here is fragmentary and in variable forms. Nicolls' diaries contain the most readily quantifiable information in the form of the paper presented to the Literary Society of Bombay. This includes days with 'light' and 'heavy' rainfall throughout 1803 and 1804. However, in the absence of any instrumental comparison it is not possible to determine the exact quantities of rain associated with these terms. The discovery of other contemporaneous records may allow this in the future, particularly if the original 'General's daily account' can be uncovered.

One technique commonly adopted in historical climatology that can allow quantification of qualitative and anecdotal information is content analysis. This is a process whereby key terms (e.g. 'pleasant temperature', 'heavy rain', 'showers', 'quite cool') and meteorological phenomena (such as the occurrence of droughts, floods, snowfall, etc.) are used to derive semi-quantitative reconstructions of climatic conditions. This commonly consists of a five- or seven-point climatic index, running from extreme heat/drought through to extreme cold/floods.[44]

This technique requires a complete or near-complete temporal dataset, and ideally a crossover instrumental period to allow terminology to be compared with instrumental observations. The four diaries analysed here would therefore require supplemental archival materials to extend the precipitation record into a continuous time series.

Such a technique has been previously adopted by this author together with David Nash, using these four diaries combined with contemporary newspapers and government reports. These combined materials were used to generate a 5-point semi-quantitative reconstruction of monsoon rainfall from 1781 to 1860, calibrated against instrumental rainfall observations from the Colaba Observatory (Figure 5.1). The monsoon rainfall index generated spans -2 (scanty monsoon rainfall) to +2 (excess monsoon), with 0 (normal monsoon) corresponding to the 1847–1950 instrumental rainfall average.[45] The exact methodology adopted will not be repeated here, but can be found within the references detailed. However, it is significant to note that the reconstructed index indicates a sustained drought period from 1799 to 1805, with the exception of 1800 which experienced a heavy monsoon. The period 1819–1828 was conversely associated with generally heavy rainfall, with 'excess' monsoon rainfall (the highest rainfall category) experienced in most years, excepting 1821 (average rainfall) and 1823–1824, which experienced severe drought.[46]

Extreme events

Several categories of extreme events are recorded within the diaries, including droughts, extreme heat and cold and periods of rainfall at unusual periods (Table 5.1). For example, on 10 February 1825, during a month that usually experiences rainfall once every ten years,[48] Lucretia West recorded 'a cold gloomy blowing Morning and rather a heavy shower of rain an extraordinary appearance & events at this Season of the year'.[49] Likewise on 23 December 1826 West noted:

> Quite a phenomenon last night we had a deluge of rain & to day has been as cold & gloomy as days usually are in England in November & so damp, the Ther. 72, yesterday it was 86 that one really finds it wretchedly cold and longs for a fire... We have had rain again to day.[50]

Periods of extreme cold were also recorded in February 1820, February 1823, November 1825, May 1826 and January 1827. 'An unusually long & pleasant cold season'[51] was reported by both Mountstuart Elphinstone

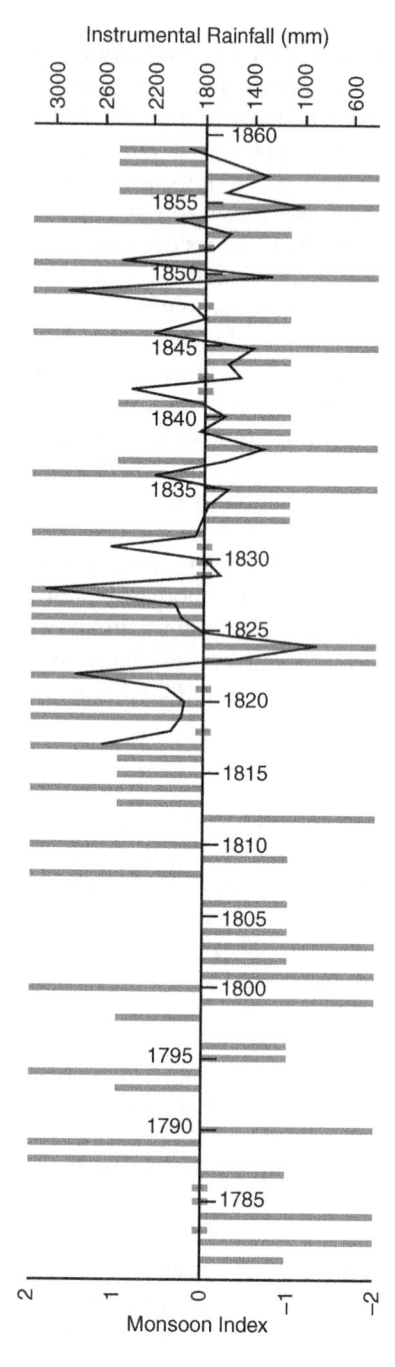

Figure 5.1 Semi-quantitative monsoon rainfall reconstruction for Bombay from East India Company diaries, government reports and contemporary newspapers. Continuous lines represent instrumental observations from the Colaba Observatory (1847–1859) and Bombay newspapers (1817–1846). See Adamson and Nash (2014).[47]

Table 5.1 Chronology of extreme or unusual climatic events. ● heavy rainfall; ≡ flooding; ☐ drought; ◊ storm/cyclone; ✚ thunderstorm; ↑ unusual heat; ↓ unusual cold

	Jan	Feb	Mar	Apr	May	Jun	Jul	Aug	Sep	Oct	Nov	Dec
1799						[●	●(◊)	●]			◊	
1800										◊		
1801											◊	
1802												
1803			◊			[☐	☐	☐	☐]			
1804						✚●	[☐	☐	●≡		↑	
1805		◊										
1820		◊↓										
1821												
1822	↑											
1823		↓								↑		
1824				↑✚●		[☐	☐	☐	☐]			
1825	●[↓	↓]				✚●≡					↓	
1826	◊				↓							✚●↓
1827				◊[↑	↑]						◊●	

and Lucretia West during the winter of 1825. Conversely, extreme heat was recorded in January 1822, October 1823 and during the hot season (April–May) of 1827, noted to be the hottest since 1780.[52] On 2 April 1824, there was recorded a temperature of 94°F (34.4°C), documented by Elphinstone as 'the highest I ever saw in Bombay'.[53] This was superseded on 8 April 1827 with Elphinstone recording 96°F (35.5°C),[54] which was exceeded elsewhere:

> The heat of Sunday has been a general theme At Colonel Scott's at Colaba it was 100° & at Mr Tanqueray's on the esplanade 105° in the sun it was 135.[55]
>
> Ther. 89 on the Esplanade on Sunday 98 & 100 at Malabar Point[56]

The year 1800 was described by James McGrigor as having an 'unusually rainy and severe monsoon'.[57] On 9 June 1825, West described a flooding event, with 'the Esplanade under water'.[58] Droughts were also mentioned regularly; on 6 April 1804 Jasper Nicolls noted a 'famine occasioned by the failure of the rains of last year, and the insufficiency of the fall in 1802'. On 10 August 1804 he commented that 'we have had the most uncommonly mild monsoon hitherto',[59] although this was terminated in September with heavy rainfall and water '2 feet high in the streets'.[60] During the monsoon of 1824 Lucretia West's diary entries contain regular reports of 'no regular Monsoon'[61] or 'no rain'.[62] On 12 August she recorded:

> The weather is very cool and pleasant & rain of a night, but not enough to be of any essential use, the Governor begins to be alarmed & consulted Edward as to what government could do in the event of a famine, which we now begin to dread.[63]

The reports in Elphinstone's diaries are even starker:

> The weather is itself agreeable but as we have had only one shower near once a day of mild rain we are threatened with famine, the most horrible of evils even pestilence is not so dreadful as it falls on all souls & is so evidently beyond human power In famine you blame yourself for not affording sufficient relief & feel your own exemption from the general calamity a fool of reproach.[64]

All four diarists reported particularly violent thunderstorms, and the occurrence of windstorms or cyclones. Windstorms were described as 'hurricanes' (McGrigor), 'gales' (Nicolls, Elphinstone) or 'storms' (Nicolls, Elphinstone, West) and were generally associated with pre-monsoon cyclonic disturbances[65] or with the post-monsoon northerly 'Elephanta' wind. One further 'hurricane' was described by Jame McGrigor in July 1800, likely to be associated with monsoonal cyclonic systems. Thunderstorms were generally reported during the onset of the monsoon, although some were associated with pre-monsoonal or post-monsoonal systems. The details of windstorms reported are provided in Table 5.2.

With a few exceptions, little information is provided in the diaries on the effects of the storms. However, if combined with information on societal impacts the reports may facilitate reconstruction of cyclone pathway and impacts, as has happened elsewhere in the world.[77] This would allow further analysis of the path and strength of cyclones through history, improving both forecasting and disaster management. Newspaper reports would be suitable for this purpose, as would pre-colonial records such as the court records of the Maratha *Paishwas*.[78]

Temperature

Each of the diaries analysed contain regular instrumental temperature observations. These therefore provide potentially very accurate

Table 5.2 Details of windstorm/cyclone events listed within the diaries consulted

Date	Description	Diary entry
4 November 1799	'Destructive wind'	The wind has been stronger – an uncommon phenomenon at this season, in its appearance, on the 4th November we had a considerable fall of rain not less than [blank] inches with a high & destructive Wind.[66]
30–31 October 1800	'Hurricane'	The Wind has been rather variable. There has been 3 days of rain – on the night of 30 and morning of 31st it blew a hurricane and the rain was very heavy.[67]
23–24 March 1804	'Equinorial gale'	Blew very hard last night, an equinorial gale.[68]
10–11 February 1804	'Storm'	This morning there was some slight rain, to the Northward it was much heavier, during the night there was much thunder and lightning, today a little; about 3 P.M. the breeze was very fresh indeed, and the clouds of dust very frequently raised to such a degree, as to be extremely disagreeable ... the coachman stopped the carriage for a minute or two to allow one of these clouds to pass, a proper precaution in a crowded street.[69]
		It continues to blow pretty fresh still, the wind is variable blowing sometimes from the Southward with much violence; it is now known that this is the tail of a storm which has done much injury at Ceylon; the Shurness 44 has been destroyed by it in the inner road of Tuncomalee, two country vessels are on shore, and the barracks and houses of all Kinds in that neighbourhood have been blown down.[70]
2 February 1820	'Gale'	Last night it blew a gale Walter & I sat up late talking ... & could not sleep afterwards for the noise of the sea this morning is really cold at 10.[71]

(*continued*)

Table 5.2 Continued

Date	Description	Diary entry
1 February 1826	'Storm'	The weather quite cold it blows a storm.[72]
19 April 1827	'Storm'	This evening a storm of wind and threatening of rain.[73]
27–28 November 1828	'Violent storm'	We have had a complete Monsoon, night, such a violent Storm of wind & rain & so unexpected every thing was knocking about.[74]
		The loss of lives, in the Storm have been dreadful, Bunder Boats, Patna's going to Surat, one especially laden with People going to the Marriage of a High Priest it is said 100's have perished.[75]
		We have just heard the most deplorable a story as I think I ever heard, the death of Mrs Lewis her Infant and Ayah – She was coming to Bombay for the marriage of Miss Bouchain and her husband put her into a Boat at Rhatnagherry & in a few hour's she hope to be here, they were overtaken by the Storm & her & her child & Servant have all been picked up & no one hardly knows anything more there was I fear no other European & it is said 7 Natives were saved, what must have been her agony and her sufferings of mind as well as body, with her helpless infant & no one near her but common Natives – she was young & healthy & death in so horrible a way is quite lamentable.[76]

measures of climate during the period. However, the only diary within which these observations are systematic is that of Jasper Nicolls, which includes observations collected at 'morning' (6:00 am to 8:00 am), 'noon' (12:00 pm to 4:00 pm) and 'night' (9:00 pm to 12:00 am). However, even these relatively systematic observations do not reach the rigorous levels of standardisation required for modern instrumental meteorological observations, which Nicolls himself recognised:

> The daily observations of the height of the thermometer, from which the following remarks and accompanying Charts have been framed, were not originally intended to form the basis of a very minute enquiry into the variations of the climate; but they have been continued with so much care and punctuality that they may possibly afford a result, which tho' not scrupulously accurate, may not be uninteresting.[79]

The predominant issue with temperature observations within the diaries concerns the location of the thermometers and time of observations. Most thermometers were located indoors; Nicolls' within a 'spacious and lofty room' with a constantly open door, Elphinstone's within his 'tiffen room'[80] and West's in her 'drawing room'.[81] These indoor locations followed the advice of the period, as specified in the *Philosophical Transactions of the Royal Society* by James Jurin in 1723.[82] However, such readings may be affected by microclimatic conditions within the buildings, and may differ from those collected outside. The only thermometer located outside was that used by James McGrigor. This was located 'in the shade' 'near the barrack' while he was in Colaba,[83] and after moving to Bombay bazaar 'suspended about 8 1/2 feet from the ground and in a slight shelter'.[84] Nicolls' thermometer in Bombay is therefore that which is in the most similar situation to the Stevenson Screens used today. Some kind of measurement verification can, however, be attempted between McGrigor's and Nicolls' temperature observations, as they were both recording observations from November 1802 to February 1803. McGrigor's thermometer was in a similar situation to those of today, and Nicolls' observations can be verified for accuracy due to the use of multiple thermometers (although only after March 1803). The most suitable measurement for analysis is the daily maxima. These were recorded at periods that the observers deemed to be the hottest part of the day (usually between 12:00 and 16:00) so should be comparable. Recorded minima are also available in both diaries, although these suffer from variations in the time in the morning in which they were recorded.

In order to facilitate comparison between the two sets of observations, those recorded by Nicolls have been transferred to monthly maxima. The comparable observations are listed in Table 5.3.

Table 5.3 Monthly temperature maxima recorded by James McGrigor and Jasper Nicolls from October 1802 to February 1803. All observations have been converted from the Fahrenheit to Celsius scale

Month	James McGrigor	Jasper Nicolls
October 1802	31.1	29.4
November 1802	29.4	30.7
December 1802	27.8	28.9
January 1803	28.3	27.8
February 1803	26.1	27.8

McGrigor's observations display a mean of 28.5°, which is slightly smaller than the mean of 28.9° displayed in Nicolls' observations. This may be a result of the heat island effect caused by neighbouring buildings around that in which Nicolls' thermometer was placed. Nicolls recognised this limitation:

> The part of the house runs nearly North & South, opening to the West towards the sea, and distant 375 yards from high water mark: It is wholly exposed to the Westward, partly so to the Northward, but to the E. and S. the neighbouring buildings either obstruct the free passage of air, or, from their low roofs, reflect a considerable portion of heat.[85]

The differences between the two averages are minimal, however, and a student's t-test finds no significant difference. Furthermore, the greatest temperature (31.1° in October 1802) was recorded by McGrigor, and McGrigor's observations display a greater standard deviation, 1.86 to Nicolls' 1.22. However, the Fisher f-test suggests no difference in variance between the two samples. These statistics suggest that McGrigor's and Nicolls' observations come from the same population, and can be considered concurrent, with the exception of small microclimatic variations that would be expected with all temperature observations. They are therefore likely to accurately represent 'average' conditions in Bombay.

The data collected by Elphinstone and West (1822–1828) is more difficult to verify as the observations were collected *ad hoc*. However, other contemporary data is available for comparison. From December 1816 to August 1822 the *Bombay Courier* printed monthly meteorological tables, collected in the rooms of the Bombay Literary Society.[86] These comprised of daily temperature observations throughout the year, collected

Historical Climate in Bombay, 1799–1828   119

at 11:00 am, 1:00 pm and 4:00 pm, together with pressure readings collected at 11:00 am and 4:00 pm. These were also apparently collected indoors, and no information is available regarding the location or make of the instruments used. However, as they were collected systematically, they allow for comparison with the data collected by Elphinstone and West in order to determine whether or not the ad hoc observations recorded in the diaries record the true extremes in temperature. The annual average monthly maxima recorded within Elphinstone and West's diaries is 30.4°. In comparison, the average 1816–1822 temperature recorded in the *Bombay Courier* is 29.8°. The values are similar enough to be attributed to variations between years rather than any systematic bias in observations. Moreover, a student's t-test finds no significant difference between the values. Significantly, the f-test finds no difference between variances, suggesting that the spread of monthly maxima is the same between the newspaper observations and the diary observations. This strongly suggests that Elphinstone and West's diaries did record the highest temperatures for the month.

The full dataset of monthly temperature maxima recorded in the diaries of McGrigor, Nicolls, Elphinstone, and West are presented in Table 5.4. To account for gaps in daily observations between observers, where monthly data are replicated the highest value has been chosen.

Comparison with recent records

Detailed daily and monthly temperature observations, collected at the Satacruz Observatory in Mumbai, are available for 1973 to 2013. This allows for comparison between recent temperature observations and the temperature readings collected from the East India Company diaries analysed in this chapter. This is presented in Table 5.5. The average monthly maximum collected from the four diaries analysed is 30.1°C. This decreases to 30.0°C when the temperature data from 1816 to 1822 printed in the *Bombay Courier* are included. In contrast, the average monthly maximum recorded between 1973 and 2013 is 35.0°, representing a difference of 5°C. The reason for this variation is likely to be a heat-island effect caused by the rapid urbanisation that occurred in the city during the nineteenth and twentieth centuries. This finding that is consistent with other studies looking at twentieth-century warming in Mumbai/Bombay.[87] Global warming caused by anthropogenic releases of CO_2 is also likely to have a role in this warming.[88] However, it is also possible that there is a systematic under-recording of temperature in *all* thermometers used in Bombay in the early nineteenth century. This will require experimental verification.

Table 5.4 Monthly temperature maxima within observations recorded by James McGrigor, Jasper Nicolls, Mountstuart Elphinstone and Lucretia West. All observations have been converted to Celsius scale

	1799	1800	1801	1802	1803	1804	1822	1823	1824	1825	1826	1827	1828	Avg.
Jan				29.4	29.4	27.5	31.1		28.9		31.1		27.2	29.2
Feb				27.8	27.8	27.8		27.8	28.9	27.8	30.0	30.6	26.7	28.3
Mar				31.7	31.7	29.4	31.7	31.7	31.1	32.2	30.0	31.1	33.3	31.4
Apr				32.2	32.2	31.7	32.2	33.3	34.4	31.7	31.1	35.6		32.7
May		33.9		32.3	32.8	31.1	31.7	31.1	31.1	33.9	30.6	30.6	33.3	32.0
Jun		33.3		29.0	31.4	31.1		31.1	31.7	33.3	27.8		31.7	31.2
Jul		28.6	29.4	28.9	29.3	30.0		28.3	26.7	30.0	25.6			28.5
Aug		29.4	28.6		28.1	28.8		27.8	26.7	30.0	27.8			28.4
Sep	28.3	30.0	29.4	30.0	29.3	28.2		27.8	31.7	30.0	32.2			29.7
Oct	30.8	32.2	31.7	31.1	31.1	29.7		32.2	31.7	31.7	31.7			31.4
Nov	30.0		28.9	30.6	30.6	28.9		26.7	31.1		32.8			29.9
Dec	27.8		25.6	29.0	29.0						31.1			28.5

Table 5.5 Monthly temperature maxima from East India Company diaries, compared with the 1973–2013 average. Column 3 uses diaries only; column 4 incorporates observations presented in the *Bombay Courier*, collected in the rooms of the Literary Society of Bombay. All temperatures in °C

Month	1973–2013	1799–1828 from East India Company diaries	1799–1828 including 1816–1821 from *Bombay Courier*
January	34.8	29.2	28.6
February	36.1	28.3	28.8
March	37.9	31.4	31.0
April	37.0	32.7	32.4
May	36.0	32.0	31.8
June	34.8	31.2	31.2
July	32.4	28.5	28.7
August	31.5	28.4	28.4
September	33.1	29.7	29.6
October	36.1	31.4	31.1
November	35.8	29.9	30.0
December	34.8	28.5	28.5
Average	**35.0**	**30.1**	**30.0**

Discussion

> It is not necessary to inform our readers at the Presidency that early on Tuesday morning the rain fell pretty freely, accompanied with some lightning and thunder; and that there has been some severe showers since: we mention, however, the circumstances of this early commencement of the South West Monsoon, by way of record.[89]

The above quotation is a short item presented in the *Bombay Courier* on 1 June 1822.[90] That these 'records' are continuing to inform the study of climatology is testament to the East India Company and its associates in India in recording, measuring and cataloguing natural phenomena. Other chapters in this volume have highlighted the Company's role in botany and plant transfer, natural history medicine and resource management. This chapter has focused on meteorological recording. It highlights not only the Company's contemporary scientific endeavours, but also their continuing importance for the study of climatology. Whilst the original reasons for data collection may not have been philanthropic (having as much to do with racial and class superiority as with scientific exploration),[91] the measurements can now inform the global issue of climate change, regularly referred to as the greatest challenge facing humanity.

In terms of the contribution to climate science, this chapter has demonstrated that temperature in Bombay around the turn of the nineteenth century was around 5°C cooler than today. This is likely to be predominantly the result of huge urbanisation in the region, the population of Bombay in 1800 being around 150,000,[92] compared to around 20 million in 2013. Anthropogenic global warming also likely has a role to play, although further research is needed to determine whether any bias existed in the thermometers used during the period. The precipitation reconstructions over western India described earlier in this chapter are also shedding further light on the relationship between the Indian monsoon and ENSO, suggesting that the strength of the relationship may be affected by Indonesian volcanic eruptions.[93] This has potentially significant implications for forecasting. Previous research using East India Company materials to reconstruct monsoon onset date has demonstrated a delay in monsoon onset over Mumbai in the last 50 years, relative to the previous 170 years.[94]

This chapter has demonstrated the viability of temperature observations within diaries that were not intended as systematic weather journals in assessing historical climatic conditions. Although thermometer readings analysed from these diaries were collected in a largely ad hoc manner, they show no significant difference to methodical temperature observations also collected during the period. This is significant as it opens up new, previously unused observations into historical climatology, which may be particularly useful elsewhere in India. It should be noted, however, that these personal ad hoc observations may only be a viable representation of daily temperature maxima in regions such as Mumbai where the temperature has a small variation, and where a hot climate means the temperature maxima are likely to be a significant event for individuals. In temperature regions where the diurnal variation is higher and where climatic conditions can change markedly through a day there is a far greater chance that the daily maximum temperature will be missed. However, personal observations of temperature minima may be a viable source for colder regions. It is unlikely that personal diaries will prove a viable source for average temperatures, although this will be worth exploring.

This study has also highlighted the viability of personal diaries in cataloguing meteorological extremes. This approach has benefits for the incorporation of natural disasters into the study of history.[95] It also allows for the identification climatic events such as cyclones, which may be studied in greater detail in the future. This approach of cataloguing extreme events from personal diaries has only been attempted once before in India, using Danish missionary records for the eighteenth-century Coromandel Coast.[96] There is great potential for extending this, using both European- and Indian-language records. The extensive East India Company archives of the Bengal Presidency have, for example, not been explored for this purpose. Neither have English-language observations for South India, despite knowledge of the existence of detailed weather diaries such as that kept by William Roxburgh.[97] Furthermore, the significance of pre-colonial documents cannot be stressed strongly enough.

It is hoped that this study will spark further exploration of Indian-language records to extend the climatic record in India back further, potentially including Maratha, Tamil, Persian and Sanskrit materials.[98]

Notes

1. R. H. Grove (1997), *Ecology, Climate and Empire*. Cambridge: White Horse Press, pp. 124–146; R. H. Grove (1998), 'The East India Company, the Raj and the El Niño: The Critical Role Played by Colonial Scientists in Establishing the Mechanisms of Global Climate Teleconnections 1779–1930' in R. H. Grove, V. Damodaran and S. Sangwan (eds.), *Nature and the Orient: The Environmental History of South and Southeast Asia*. Oxford and New York: Oxford University Press, pp. 301–323; S. Sangwan (1998), 'From Gentlemen Amateurs to Professionals: Reassessing the Natural Science Tradition in Colonial India 1780–1840' in Grove et al., *Nature and the Orient*, pp. 301–323; M. Harrison (1999), *Climates and Constitutions: Health, Race, Environment and British Imperialism in India 1600–1850*. Oxford: Oxford University Press; J. Golinski (2007), *British Weather and the Climate of the Enlightenment*, Chicago and London: University of Chicago Press; R. H. Grove (2007), 'The Great El Niño of 1789–93 and its Global Consequences: Reconstructing an Extreme Climate Event in World Environmental History', *The Medieval History Journal* 10: 75–98; G. C. D. Adamson (2012), '"The languor of the hot weather": everyday perspectives on weather and climate in colonial Bombay, 1819–1827', *Journal of Historical Geography*, 38: 143–154.
2. See, for example, A. P. Hove (1855), *Tours for scientific and economical research, made in Guzerat-Kattiawar, and the Conkuns, in 1787–1788*. Bombay: Government of Bombay.
3. G. T. Walker (1924), 'Correlation in seasonal variations of weather, IX. A further study of world weather', *Memoirs of the India Meteorological Department* 24: 275–333; Grove, 'The East India Company, the Raj and El Niño'.
4. Harrison, *Climates and Constitutions*.
5. Harrison, *Climates and Constitutions*.
6. D. N. Livingstone (2002), 'Race, Space and Moral Climatology: Notes Towards a Geneology', *Journal of Historical Geography*, 28: 159–180.
7. The predominant archives are those of the India Office at the British Library, St Pancras, and the archives of the Bombay, Bengal and Madras Presidencies at Mumbai, Kolkata and Chennai. Other materials are known to exist in the National Archives of India and the National Library of Scotland, as well, potentially, as several other archives worldwide.

8. J. Golinski (2003), 'Time, Talk and the Weather in Eighteenth-Century Britain' in S. Strauss and B.S. Orlove (eds.), *Weather, Climate, Culture*. Oxford and New York: Berg, pp. 17–38; Golinksi, *British Weather and the Climate of the Enlightenment*.
9. Golinski, 'Time, Talk and the Weather'.
10. Golinski, 'Time, Talk and the Weather'.
11. T. Harley (2003), 'Nice Weather for the Time of Year: The British Obsession with the Weather', in Strauss and Orlove (eds.), *Weather, Climate, Culture*, pp. 103–120; Golinski, 'Time, Talk and the Weather'.
12. J. Johnson (1818), *The Influence of Tropical Climates on European Constitutions*, 2nd edn. London: Mottley and Harrison.
13. Grove, *Ecology, Climate and Empire*; Grove, 'The East India Company, the Raj and the El Niño'; Grove, 'The Great El Niño of 1789–93 and its Global Consequences'.
14. Grove, *Ecology, Climate and Empire*; G. H. Endfield and D. J. Nash (2002), 'Missionaries and Morals: Climatic Discourse in Nineteenth-Century Southern Africa', *Annals of the Association of American Geographers*, 94: 727–742; Adamson, 'The languor of the hot weather'.
15. Notable exceptions to this are: G. C. D. Adamson and D. J. Nash (2013), 'Long-Term Variability in the Date of Monsoon Onset Over Western India', *Climate Dynamics*, 40: 2589–1603; and G. C. D. Adamson and D. J. Nash (2014), 'Documentary Reconstruction of Monsoon Rainfall Variability Over Western India, 1781–1860', *Climate Dynamics*, 42: 749–769. These will be discussed further later. A few other studies have been attempted using colonial missionary records, see: R. Glaser, S. Militzer and R. P. D. Walsh (1991), 'Weather and Climate at Madras, India, in the Years 1732–1737 Based Upon an Analysis of the Weather Diary of the German Missionary Geisler', *Würzburger Geographische Arbeiten*, 70: 45–86; R. P. D. Walsh, R. Glaser and S. Militzer (1999), 'The Climate of Madras During the Eighteenth Century', *International Journal of Climatology*, 19: 1025–104; D. J. Nash and G. H. Endfield (2002), 'A 19th Century Climate Chronology for the Kalahari Region of Central Southern Africa Derived From Missionary Correspondence', *International Journal of Climatology*, 22: 821–841; D. J. Nash and G. H. Endfield (2008), '"Splendid Rains Have Fallen": Links Between El Niño and Rainfall Variability in the Kalahari, 1840–1900', *Climatic Change*, 76: 257–290; D. J. Nash and S. W. Grab (2010), '"A Sky of Brass and Burning Winds": Documentary Evidence of Rainfall Variability in the Kingdom of Lesotho, Southern Africa, 1824–1900', *Climatic Change*, 101: 617–653; S. Grab and D. Nash (2010), 'Documentary Evidence of Climate Variability During Cold Seasons in Lesotho, Southern Africa, 1833–1900', *Climate Dynamics*, 34: 473–499.
16. Adamson and Nash, 'Documentary Reconstruction'.
17. For a review of Indian monsoon dynamics, see: S. Gadgil (2003), 'The Indian Monsoon and its Variability', *Annual Review of Earth and Planetary Science*, 31: 429–467; Y. Ding (2007), 'The Variability of the Asian Summer Monsoon', *Journal of the Meteorological Society of Japan*, 85: 21–54.
18. V. Krishnamurthy and B. N. Goswami (2000), 'Indian Monsoon-ENSO Relationship on Interdecadal Timescales', *Journal of Climate*, 13: 579–595; Gadgil, 'The Indian Monsoon and its Variability'; Ding, 'The Variability of the Asian Summer Monsoon'.

19. N. H. Saji, B. N. Goswami, P. H. Vinayachandran and T. Yamagata (1999), 'A Dipole Mode in the Tropical Indian Ocean', *Nature*, 151: 360–363; K. Ashok and N. H. Saji (2007), 'Impacts of ENSO and Indian Ocean Dipole Events on the Sub-Regional Indian Summer Monsoon Rainfall', *Journal of Natural Hazards*, 42: 273–285. For the role of ENSO in the Indian Ocean Dipole system see also R. Allan, D. Chambers, W. Drosdowsky, H. Hendon, M. Latif, N. Nicholls, I. Smith, R. Stone and Y. Tourre (2001), 'Is There an Indian Ocean Dipole, and is it Independent of the El Niño – Southern Oscillation?', *CLIVAR Exchanges*, 6: 18–22.
20. G. A. Meehl (1994), 'Coupled Land-Ocean-Atmosphere Processes and South Asian Monsoon Variability', *Science*, 271: 263–267; Ding, 'The Variability of the Asian Summer Monsoon'.
21. Adamson and Nash, 'Documentary Reconstruction'.
22. The cataloguing of notable climatic events is a technique adapted from a study of climatic information contained within eighteenth-century Danish missionary records pertaining to the Coromandel Coast. See Walsh et al., 'The Climate of Madras During the Eighteenth Century'.
23. Available online at digitool.abdn.ac.uk
24. J. McGrigor (1804), *Medical Sketches of the Expedition to Egypt from India*. London: John Murray; Edinburgh: Bell and Bradfute; Dublin: Gilbert and Hodges.
25. University of Aberdeen Library (UAL) GB0817 AMCS 4/1/4/17 Casebook of James McGrigor 1 June 1800 (available online).
26. UAL GB0817 AMCS 4/1/4/23 27 November 1802.
27. British Library (BL) MSS Eur F175/2 Diary of Jasper Nicolls 30 September 1802.
28. BL MSS Eur F175/2 30 November 1802.
29. BL MSS Eur F175/2 30 November 1802.
30. BL MSS Eur F175/3 31 May 1803.
31. BL MSS Eur F175/4 20 July 1804.
32. J. Nicolls (1819), 'Remarks on the Temperature of the Island of Bombay During the Years 1803 and 1804', *Transactions of the Literary Society of Bombay*, 1: 6–11.
33. Nicolls, 'Remarks of the Temperature of the Island of Bombay'; BL MSS Eur F175/9 22 January 1805.
34. Adamson, 'The Languor of the Hot Weather', pp. 146–147.
35. Adamson, 'The Languor of the Hot Weather', p. 147.
36. BL MSS Eur F88/425 Diary of Mountstuart Elphinstone 15 January 1822, British Library.
37. BL MSS Eur F88/425 26 March 1822.
38. BL MSS Eur F88/426 10 June 1823.
39. BL MSS Eur F88/425 1 March 1822.
40. S. Banks (2010), *A Polite Exchange of Bullets: The Duel and the English Gentleman*. Woodbridge: Boydell Press, pp. 104–105.
41. The monsoon of 1827 and 1828 were spent in Pune and December 1823, 1824 and 1825 spent travelling, in the Deccan, Goa and at the Hill Station of 'Lanowlie' (Lonavala) respectively.
42. BL MSS Eur D888/1 24 June 1823.
43. BL MSS Eur D888/1 5 May 1826.

44. D. W. Moodie and A. J. W. Catchpole (1976), 'Valid Climatological Data from Historical Sources by Content Analysis', *Science*, 193: 52–53; C. Pfister (1992), 'Monthly Temperature and Precipitation in Central Europe from 1525–1979: Quantifying Documentary Evidence on Weather and its Effects', in R. S. Bradley and P. D. Jones (1992), *Climate Since A.D. 1500*. London and New York: Routledge, pp. 118–142; R. Brázdil, C. Pfister, H. Wanner, H. von Storch and J. Luterbacher (2005), 'Historical Climatology in Europe – The State of the Art, *Climatic Change*, 70: 363–430.
45. Adamson and Nash, 'Documentary Reconstruction'.
46. Adamson and Nash, 'Documentary Reconstruction', p. 14.
47. Adamson and Nash, 'Documentary Reconstruction', p. 14.
48. National Oceanic and Atmospheric Administration (2012), Global Historical Climatology Network, http://www.ncdc.noaa.gov/ghcnm/ (home page), accessed January 2012.
49. BL MSS Eur D888/1 10 February 1825.
50. BL MSS Eur D888/1 23 December 1826.
51. BL MSS Eur F88/426 25 March 1825.
52. 'A fine wind to day but Ther. 90, the Natives say there has not been so hot a Season since 1780.' BL MSS Eur D888/1 19 May 1827.
53. BL MSS Eur F88/426 2 April 1824.
54. BL MSS Eur F88/426 8 April 1827.
55. BL MSS Eur F88/426 11 April 1827.
56. BL MSS Eur D888/1 11 April 1827.
57. UAL GB0817 AMCS 4/1/4/17 19 July 1800.
58. BL MSS Eur D888/1 9 June 1825.
59. BL MSS Eur F175/8 10 August 1804.
60. BL MSS Eur F175/8 6 September 1824.
61. BL MSS Eur D888/1 22 June 1824.
62. BL MSS Eur D888/1 9 July 1824, 11 July 1824, 18 July 1824, 20 July 1824, 26 September 1824.
63. BL MSS Eur D888/1 12 August 1824.
64. BL MSS Eur F88/426 15 August 1824.
65. T. N. Krishnamurti, P. Ardanuy, Y. Ramanthan and R. Pasch (1981), 'On the Onset Vortex of the Summer Monsoon', *Monthly Weather Review*, 109: 344–362.
66. UAL GB0817 AMCS 4/1/4/16 9 November 1799.
67. UAL GB0817 AMCS 4/1/4/18 1 November 1800.
68. BL MSS Eur F175/3 24 March 1803.
69. BL MSS Eur F175/9 10 February 1805.
70. BL MSS Eur F175/9 11 February 1805.
71. BL MSS Eur F88/363 3 February 1820.
72. BL MSS Eur D888/1 1 February 1826.
73. BL MSS Eur F88/426 19 April 1820.
74. BL MSS Eur D888/1 28 November 1827.
75. BL MSS Eur D888/1 2 December 1827.
76. BL MSS Eur D888/1 3 December 1827.
77. R. J. Murnane and R. J. K. B. Liu (eds.) (2004), *Hurricanes and Typhoons: Past, Present and Future*. New York: Columbia University Press; L.-A. Dupigny-Giroux and C. J. Mock (eds.) (2009), *Historical Climate Variability and Impacts in North America*. New York: Springer.

78. Rulers of much of the Deccan during the eighteenth and early-nineteenth centuries, based at Poona (Pune).
79. BL MSS Eur F175/9 22 January 1805; Nicolls, Remarks upon the temperature of the island of Bombay, p. 6.
80. BL MSS Eur F88/425 7 December 1821.
81. BL MSS Eur D888/1 16 April 1823.
82. J. Jurin (1720), 'Invitatio ad Observationes Meteorologicas Communi Consilio Instituendas', *Philosophical Transactions*, 32: 422–427.
83. UAL GB0817 AMCS 4/1/4/18 4 October 1800.
84. UAL GB0817 AMCS 4/1/4/21 12 December 1801.
85. BL MSS Eur F175/9 22 January 1805.
86. BLNC MC1112 *Bombay Courier*, issues January 1817 to September 1822, British Library Newspaper Collections. The originals of these observations have not been located.
87. K. Rupa Kumar and L. S. Hingane (1988), 'Long-Term Variations of Surface Air Temperature at Major Industrial Cities of India', *Climatic Change*, 13: 287–307; A. Dhorde, A. Dhorde and A. S. Gadgil (2009), 'Long-Term Temperature Trends at Four Largest Cities of India During the Twentieth Century', *Journal of the Indian Geophysical Union*, 13: 85–97.
88. D. R. Kothawale and K. Rupa Kumar (2005), 'On the Recent Changes in Surface Temperature Trends Over India', *Geophysical Research Letters*, 32: XIII; G. Alory, S. Wijffels and G. Meyers (2007), 'Observed Temperature Trends in the Indian Ocean Over 1960–1999 and Associated Mechanisms', *Geophysical Research Letters*, 34: II.
89. BLNC MC1112 *Bombay Courier*, 1 June 1822.
90. Mountstuart Elphinstone also recorded the monsoon onset at this date in 1822, writing on 3 June 'we still have rains no doubt the monsoon', BL MSS Eur F88/425 3 June 1822.
91. See Harrison, *Climates and Constitutions*; Golinski, *British Weather and the Climate of the Enlightenment*. For a fuller discussion of wider colonial climatic discourse within the diaries of Elphinstone and West see Adamson, 'The languor of the hot weather'.
92. S. M. Edwardes and J. Campbell (1909), *The Gazetter of Bombay City and Island*. Government of the Bombay Presidency: Bombay.
93. Adamson and Nash, 'Documentary Reconstruction'.
94. Adamson and Nash, 'Long-term Variability in the Date of Monsoon Onset Over Mumbai'.
95. For a fuller discussion of the importance of natural disasters in Indian history see T. Roy (2012), *Oxford Short Introductions: Natural Disasters in Indian History*. New Delhi: Oxford University Press.
96. Walsh et al., 'The Climate of Madras During the Eighteenth Century'.
97. Grove, 'The East India Company, the Raj and the El Niño'.
98. A brief overview of Indian climate variability over the last millennium has been attempted, although this used secondary sources only and did not generate a chronology. See G. B. Pant, K. Rupa Kumar, N. A. Sontakke and H. P. Borgaonkar (1993), 'Climate Variability Over India on Century and Longer Time Scales', in R. N. Keshavamurty and P. C. Joshi (eds.), *Advances in Tropical Meteorology*. New Delhi: Tata McGraw-Hill Publishing Company, pp. 71–84.

6
Mischievous Rivers and Evil Shoals: The English East India Company and the Colonial Resource Regime

Rohan D'Souza

Increasingly, in the twilight years of Empire, Bengal's rivers were declared to be an indisputable 'water problem'.[1] For the official colonial imagination, the delta's fluvial arms were too temperamental and snaked their way across the capacious flood plains only to wastefully empty 'millions of tons' of their watery burden into the Bay of Bengal. Usually a swollen rage during the monsoon and an irrelevant trickle by the winter, such hydrographic quirks, it was authoritatively held, regularly depressed and enfeebled the Bengal peasant.

In a radio broadcast around December 1945, R. G. Casey, then governor of Bengal, argued for a definitive response to this perplexing hydrology:

> the water problem of Bengal necessitate[s] our so handling [of] the great rivers that their flow is equalised and controlled as between summer and winter in order that they may provide an adequate and balanced output ... . This would avoid the disastrous flooding in the monsoon and would cure the dry or stagnant state of many of our rivers in the winter.[2]

The governor's declarations seemingly held much technological seduction and a potentially grand solution. By 'equalising' the rivers and moderating its discharges, the Bengal delta's fluvial tapestry, it appeared, could be rationalised and its troubling variability finally rendered consistent, becalmed and tractable. The broadcast, however, was not restricted to simply announcing a quest for engineering elegance. The governor's emphatic suggestions for 'balancing' the Bengal rivers, in the remaining portion of the radio address, was most profoundly dramatised in terms of a productivist cornucopia: controlled rivers, he claimed, through a slew of large dams and barrages across the Teesta, Ganges, Damodar and the mighty Brahmaputra rivers could be harnessed for the simultaneous realisation of irrigation, electricity, flood control and navigation. In effect, 'rationalised' rivers could lubricate an intense economic moment that could rescue Bengal's starving millions from their dismal fate; so clearly caused, it appeared, by a fickle and hostile fluvial environment.

Governor Casey's remarkably self-assured clarity on how the water problem of Bengal could be solved was not exceptional for its times. The 1940s witnessed the emergence of a new era in river control: the promotion of multi-purpose river valley development, the national quest to replicate the 'triumph' of the Tennessee Valley Authority (TVA) and that science and technology could be neutral drivers of the economy.[3] These robust tropes were made to rapidly combine, in this period, to energise and substantiate the soon to be formulated Truman doctrine of 1949 – the grand master text, according to Arturo Escobar, that laid out and announced the rearrangement of the world along a new hierarchy based on 'development'.[4] Nonetheless, it would be inadequate, if not entirely flawed, to reveal this hydraulic utopia of Governor Casey as being a simple, unequivocal effect of the post-Second World War development paradigm.

The framing thus of the Bengal delta's river as a particular kind of water problem, as this chapter will argue, was made possible and drew upon roughly a century and a half of hydraulic practices in the region. This was a period in which a set of conceptions about river behaviour and a series of hydraulic interventions were repeatedly, as I will argue, aimed at harnessing the Bengal rivers as a specific type of economic resource. And central to initiating this 'great transition', as it were, lay the overwhelming role and imperatives of the English East India Company (1600–1858), which actively sought to forge the delta into what David Gilmartin has so felicitously termed as 'the colonial productive regime'.[5]

In making this argument, this chapter will try to temper and tweak certain claims that have become central to several contemporary writings on the globalised 'diffusion', 'exchange,' 'transmission', 'movement', imposition', 'making' or 'circulation' of scientific ideas, knowledge, techniques and technological practices between the seventeenth and nineteenth centuries.[6] According to A. G. Hopkins, as part of the historical periodization of globalization, these centuries can be categorised as heralding the proto-modern phase.[7] A period, more so for the Western world, that witnessed not only the dramatic emergence and intensification of commercial expansion through mercantile trading companies but critically initiated the inauguration of a knowledge revolution that involved the mapping, surveying and classification of Europe's 'other'.[8]

In the great empirical sweeps of *Green Imperialism*, Richard Grove, in fact, admirably and brilliantly reassess the nature of this dense traffic in ideas and forms of knowledge which were circulated in the proto-modern period. Instead of the staid structural determinism of the imperial metropole simply radiating its notions on science and ecological conceptions to the colony, Grove's account reveals a kaleidoscopic picture of complex threads, overlapping networks, feed-back loops and vast assemblages of links that excited innumerable polycentric patterns of correspondence and communication. *Green Imperialism*, in several ways, appears to have meaningfully fleshed out and described the English East India Company very much in the striking terms of 'new imperial history': a significant turn in British imperial historiography in which the empire is revealed not as a fixed spatial core emanating imperatives for profit and rule but instead as a collection of nodes, in turn entangled in layers of crisscrossing networks, circuits and webs. New imperial history, as pointed out by Alan Lester, in dissolving the metropole as a fixed spatial core argues for the colonial project to be understood as a site laden with contradictory tensions, polyvalent discourses and riven by multiple trajectories and often articulated by conflicting material and cultural practices.[9]

Whilst such an angle of vision has undoubtedly opened an immense set of possibilities for dramatically rewriting the script on empire and its impacts, new imperial history may tend, in its extreme interpretations, to arguably leave open-ended the quest to understand the nature and defining features of the colonial project itself. That is, the British empire is not marked as being a specific form of political economy nor determined as a historically particular and coherent political moment, but largely as a collection of unstable shifting sites, each unique and relative and thereby unable to explain conditions that reproduce rule as being peculiarly colonial in character.

This chapter will be a modest attempt at tweaking some of the open-endedness in new imperial history writings by throwing a searching light on the English East India Company, which in its time, as an unprecedented commercial corporate body, was not only amongst the first truly modern modules for globalisation but, as has been widely observed, acted to craft many a material and cultural foundation for the British colonial empire. Instead of recovering or illuminating unstable networks and circuits, therefore, this chapter will look to recover *formats* that enabled and followed the shift from merchant body to colonial empire. In employing the term 'format', I refer to a cogent rubric or sets of logics that helped order the peculiar requirements for colonial rule and domination.

Philip Stern has insightfully attempted to redraft the sequence of the standard narrative on the Company and the emergence of the sovereign moment for the British empire. Stern, in his study of the early East India Company in St Helena (1673–1709), credibly argues for acknowledging that the Company had already, before its acquisitions in eighteenth-century India, become 'a polity in itself: a self sustaining global system built upon sound civic institutions and informed by a coherent if composite political ideology'.[10] That is, some of its defining features as a potential company state had already been tested and forged in the island of St Helena. Stern followed this article with his longer work on the 'Company state', which argues that the EEIC should be contextualised within wider processes of the making and interaction of early modern polities.[11] This chapter, partly in step with Stern's template, argues that one of the early environmental formats that the Company officials had sought to organise in its possessions in the Bengal delta was aimed at trying to transform the delta's rivers into an economic resource, which alongside private property in land, became integral to the presence of the EEIC in the region.

For the EEIC, the delta's rivers appeared in two opposed moods; they either burst their banks and injured cultivation or were so weakened by poor flows that crops in surrounding lands withered from lack of water. In short, understood only from some distant higher ground on land, the river appeared as an unpredictable, volatile and unstable element; a fluid phenomena that was temperamental and inured to regularly reworking its boundaries with powerful, yet yielding, qualities. This was a conception, in effect, in which the rivers were premised as the unstable opposite to the permanence of soil.

In terms of hydraulic practice, for the EEIC, the delta's rivers thus had to be disclosed only through the language of control. Rivers needed to be 'equalised', 'balanced' or 'tamed', with their flows harnessed through engineering skills and technical structures. In this official imagination, the Bengal delta lost its appearance as a composite of land and water and instead was treated as a terrain marked by discrete disconnected domains of soils and flows.

Through a series of snapshot debates, this chapter will attempt to outline how the EEIC initiated the separation of land and water and how the congealing of such an environmental format became critical to making the Bengal delta legible and calculable for rule. And once thus transformed from its natural cogency as an organic geomorphologic process to instead becoming a collage of disconnected fluvial events, that were regulated principally as practices of political economy. Such

Shifting heads, shoals and river improvement

Our first snapshot concerns the East India Company's encounters with rivers in the district of Nadia (in modern West Bengal). What came to be treated as the administrative district of Nadia in the colonial period was observed to be crisscrossed by several flailing fluvial arms which erupted from the main stem of the Ganges (notably the Bhagirathi, Jalangi and Mathabanga).[12]

In one of the first references in 1813, it was recorded that the Company administration had entrusted the 'improvement' of the Mathabanga to the offices of the Collectorate and the local police department. And by way of improvement, the tasks listed were the regular clearing of the bed of the river channel from sunken boat wrecks, loose timber and large trees.[13] Such clearances, it was reasoned, would make the river safe for navigation. In 1818, however, the 'obstructions' were deemed to have become so dangerous that innumerable boats were wrecked and costs, on account of demurrage paid for detention of cargo-laden ships, spiralled. The merchants of Calcutta, in that year, also urgently petitioned Government, that steps immediately needed to be taken to remedy the 'evil from which commercial interests suffered so severely'.[14] Subsequent to these developments, one Mr C. K. Robinson was appointed Superintendent and Collector of the Mathabhanga and commenced his duties in the winter season of 1819–20. In January 1820, a toll office was established at Kissenganj, aimed primarily at recovering the now rapidly mounting expenses for river improvement.

The pursuit of river improvement, however, increasingly pushed the navigation establishment into more troubled and muddied depths. From initially simply clearing obstructive logs and capsized boats from the channel, the EEIC officials began to debate the need for making the often-times moody and capricious currents more stable and predictable. Driven thus, Mr Robinson, sometime in 1820 itself, sought to divert a part of the current of the Como (*katcheekatta*) river into the Mathabhanga by erecting an embankment across the former and running its waters down a canal and into a cut made into the latter.[15] The embankment, unfortunately, immediately gave way and was followed soon enough by Mr Robinson being ejected from the responsibility, with the position of Superintendent now being given to one Mr May in June 1820.[16] Mr May, in time, became the longest-serving Superintendent for the Nadia rivers (1820–1840). And in the course of his turbulent twenty-odd years of service, Mr May grimly wrestled with the recurring challenges that were thrown to the EEIC administration by the truculent rivers of the delta.

In particular, there was a growing realisation that the flows of the Nadia rivers would regularly wax or wane in either extremes rather than maintain a steady volume. Such fickleness was complicated further by the fact that the entrances or 'heads' from which these rivers respectively drew their waters from the Ganges regularly shifted. Thus, in virtually every season the very character or nature of the river's channel could be substantially altered, often in fundamental ways. In 1823, for example, at the head of the Mathabhanga, a series of shoals[17] rapidly emerged and threatened to disrupt navigation. Mr May in an attempt to keep the river open for shipping, spent £1,040 to remove the shoals by employing dredging machines worked by oxen. Amidst these onerous efforts, however, the Ganges suddenly flexed and deposited 'masses of sand' onto the Mathabhanga's head and thereby forcibly brought the dredging machines to a complete halt. Having thus suffered a complete rout, Mr May was caused to wearily remark 'that the constant changes in the course of the Ganges rendered it almost impossible to keep the heads of the Mathabhanga and Jalangi fixed'.[18] In fact, it strikingly appeared as well to him that in no two seasons had he seen the heads of these rivers in the same position.

Besides dredging operations that aimed to flush out shoals by physically stirring the muddy waters, the navigation establishment had also advocated 'bandalling'. As a device, the bandal was ingenious; it comprised a set of fixed vertical screens mounted on a frame. Typically, the screens were made of bamboo mats and the frames consisted of bamboos driven into the riverbed. These bandals were placed at an angle to the flowing current so that the water near the surface got deflected on hitting the screens, whilst the heavier sediment-laden water that was ponderously moving near the depths of the channel passed more or less perpendicularly under the screens.[19] The result of the bandal was at first to increase the velocity of the current within the channel before being guided elsewhere.[20]

The Nadia river's navigation establishment also constructed minor dams and carried out cuts into the banks of rivers in order to move waters between channels; all efforts intended in the final scheme of things to enable the river bed to carry enough draught for shipping. Many of these efforts, however, often came to grief. The Bhagirathi river, despite many such interventions, it was observed, had upwards of 23 shoals developing in 1830 near its entrance and between 1826–27 to 1830–31 could not be navigable in the dry season.[21] But paralleling the perplexing concern with maintaining the river's depth and volume for navigation was the equally troubling consequences when these fluvial forces began to 'encroach' upon land. In particular, noted Mr May, the 'mischief' arising when trees were allowed to stand near the edge of the rivers banks. When the rivers ate into their banks, these trees were simply dragged into the river's raging torrents. Much of these obstructions, in the opinion of Mr May, in fact, could have been stopped by the cutting down and disposal of the trees in advance. Given, however the 'aversion of the Hindoos to cut the Peepul and Bur (Banyan)', he irately declaimed, these large trees were simply left standing perilously at the edges of the fast-eroding banks until they were ultimately gulped up by the dreary current and lodged dangerously in the river's bed, much unsurprisingly to the detriment of shipping.[22]

The trying nature of the routines and the relentless ratcheting upwards in the requirements for keeping the Nadia rivers navigable was made vividly visible by Mr May in a statement of accounts submitted to the Military Board in early 1833. In it, Mr May furnished a list of the works that had aimed, for the past three years, at improving the rivers:

> Bandhals constructed 359
> Sunken Boast removed 118
> Ditto trees and timbers ditto 219
> Pucca buildings pulled down 12
> Trees cut down on the banks 1,731

Mr May, nevertheless, besides flatly revealing what was clearly a formidable list of interventions and expenses involved, also felt it pertinent to acknowledge in the very same account that 'it was impossible to lay down any fixed rules of guidance or plan of operations; by which the navigation of the Nuddea rivers could be permanently maintained'. This claim that was followed a somewhat glum conclusion that, after almost 13 years of experience of handling the unpredictable inundations, 'no assurance that the measures adopted for mitigating or repairing the evils of one season would be of the least avail in the ensuing one'.[23]

In the dying years of the EEIC presence in the Bengal delta, Mr May's prescience seemed to have been redoubled in the pronunciations of one Major J. Lang who had summed up on similar lines in a comprehensive report submitted in 1854 entitled *Memorandum on the Ganges and the Nadia Rivers*.[24] In the report, Major Lang observed, in a forceful tone, 'that the deepening or shoaling of a channel, in many cases, indicates nothing more than a change in the distribution of the water, and are, of themselves, no criterion of the improvement or deterioration of a river'.[25] And, as if in anticipation of Governor Casey's remarks that I mentioned earlier, Major Lang concluded somewhat with seeming clarity that the real problem of the delta's rivers lay with the fact that it was 'the vast disproportion between the supply of the inundation and that of the dry season that the real evil lies'.[26]

Revenue and the 'craze' for embankments

The second snapshot reviews the Company's various administrative strategies and technical interventions that were aimed at enabling it to collect its revenue claim in the Bengal delta. The Company administrators swiftly realised that preventing seasonal inundations were inextricably tied to the quest for revenue maximisation alongside the other, equally perplexing, problem of organising private property in land. Unlike perhaps the relatively stable landscapes that Company officials had been used to in England, lands surrounded by active deltaic rivers produced unusual challenges for administration and rule. Deltaic rivers possessed propensities such as seasonal overflow, unpredictability, wild oscillations, avulsions, dramatic channel alteration and, often times, onrushing currents that swept vast swathes of adjoining cultivated tracts into their watery depths. It was a dynamic environment, in other words, part water and part land, involving a geography that was relentlessly rearranged. Not, unsurprisingly, the Company's 'rigid' economic practices for revenue assessment and collection were regularly undermined in the delta.[27]

In the course of formulating the revenue demand for Bengal, as part of the exercise for the permanent settlement elaborated in 1793, the incipient Company administration declared that certain estates were to be granted allowances on the revenue demand (*Jama*) as compensation for maintaining their bunds (flood control embankments).[28] In 1796, the Board of Revenue received a report that the neglect of the bunds by the zamindars or landlords of Kasijorah pargana in the district of Midnapore had resulted in 'serious inundation'. After another report of allegedly similar zamindari laxity and indifference in the pargana of Mynachour, the Company administration realised that embankment repair and maintenance had become a source of considerable contention and dispute and required a far more forceful administrative approach.

In March 1798, the Board of Revenue authorised the Collector of Midnapore to undertake embankment repairs in the parganas of

Kasjijorah and Shahpore, and recover the expenses from the zamindars in 'proportion to the interest which they respectively possess[ed] in the bunds'. The decision immediately drew the ire of several zamindars, who insisted that rather than pay potentially higher costs to the Company for repairs that the latter might carry out, the estate owners should be allowed to do it themselves. Some zamindars, however, even chose to refuse to undertake any repairs altogether. This caused the Board of Revenue to extend an order passed earlier in January 1798 to the parganas, specifying that if the zamindars failed to repair their bunds the Company administration would then carry them out on its own initiative and forcibly recover the expenses from the intractable landlords.[29]

In the adjoining district of Murshidabad, as well, the Company found itself 'habitually compelled' to carry out repairs because of what was perceived to be zamindari recalcitrance. In 1800, for example, the Collector of Mushidabad was directed by the Board of Revenue to spend Rs. 32,788 on the bunds in the district and was authorised to put up for sale the lands of the 'defaulting' zamindars to recover the costs of the repairs.[30] The Company's sale laws brought into effect in the permanent settlement territories, however, further frustrated the administration as frequent changes in estate ownership and regular dismemberment of large holdings into smaller plots defeated attempts to stabilise procedures that clearly fixed responsibilities for bund maintenance.[31]

Thus, throughout the early and tumultuous years of their rule, Company officials found themselves increasingly, on the one hand, arrogating to themselves the right to determine the need for and to carry out embankment repair, while, on the other, they were being entangled in the fairly sordid task of ascertaining and recovering from the concerned zamindars the costs for restoring the 'protective' works. Not unexpectedly, in the subsequent enactment of Embankment Regulation VI of 1806, the Company's first directives on the subject of flood control in Bengal, the administration sought to officially endorse their then ongoing efforts to enforce private responsibility in the maintenance of the bunds.[32] Through Regulation VI of 1806, Embankment Committees were set up and empowered to act:

> if the zemindars neglected their duty, [the Embankment Committees had] to call upon them to make the repairs, and, if they still persisted in their neglect, to submit an estimate to Government, and after approval to carry out the repairs, and recover the amounts from the zemindars (*sic*) or farmer bound to keep the embankments in a proper state of repair.[33]

But in attempting to compel the zamindars to bear the financial costs for protecting their estates, the Company inadvertently also devolved onto itself the task for monitoring and ascertaining the nature of the supposed threat posed by the deltaic rivers. In effect, the incipient Company bureaucracy through the Embankment Committees and armed with Regulation VI of 1806 ended up singularly acquiring the onerous responsibility of defining, maintaining and interminably perpetuating the separation of land and water. Thus, urged by the need to secure property and the recovery of revenue, the colonial authorities increasingly felt compelled to encourage the construction of permanent protective embankments – structures designed to insulate lands comprehensively from inundation. Inevitably, to the official colonial mind, the plan for running protective embankments, as some sort of barrier separating cultivated tracts from the inundating channel, began to assume an overwhelming administrative imperative in which the interests on land were categorically viewed as being dependent on restraining the rivers.

The earliest colonial observations on structures that were presumed to be flood control embankments were made as references to the term 'pool bundy'. These obstructions or small dams that were thrown across the beds of rivers or alongside (at various angles) of the flowing channel were interpreted as being structures 'for the protection of the tract of country, against the irruption of waters'.[34] To the Company's consternation, however, the native embankments turned out to be not only constructed in several shapes and sizes but appeared to have been deployed for functions other than that for exclusively insulating lands from seasonal river inundation.

In an 1838 report on the status of the embankments in the adjoining district of Cuttack, an enquiry Committee chose to classify the innumerable types of structures under eight broad groups, based largely on the latter's location and presumed functions.[35] According to the Committee, the embankments or bunds served a number of purposes such as: (a) excluding salt water during spring tides, (b) damming mouths of hollows (*khalls*) in order to retain fresh water, (c) diverting water for irrigation (d) leading excess water into drainage channels and (e) protecting lands that adjoined river channels from flood spill. Many of these structures, they further concluded, were intended to perform different functions in different seasons or situations; a protective structure for excluding the salt water of spring tides, for example, was often also used to retain fresh water for irrigation. Cultivators, furthermore, often made 'cuts' into the bunds to allow or quicken the passage of water for drainage or irrigation and in certain circumstances they were not averse to either abandoning some embankments altogether or constructing a bund or two for a single season only. Lastly, the colonial authorities noticed that the 'native' bunds were more like a patchwork of haphazard constructions that often ran perpendicular to the river rather than parallel to it and did not comprise a 'uniform' or 'continuous' system.[36] And yet, the virtual kaleidoscope of bund types and their innumerable functional possibilities, nevertheless, appeared to have also been harmonised by the cultivators to complement an intricate system for irrigation and drainage.[37]

Clearly, the colonial view that bunds were exclusively part of a system of permanent structures for insulating lands from floods was not necessarily shared on the ground.[38] Rather, the need to treat land and water as two discrete and separate domains of the colonial resource regime required that embankments be treated as exclusive flood control structures.

Plugging leaks and shoring up the land: the drainage conundrum

The third snapshot refers to the many dilemmas caused by drainage. As pointed out earlier, the delta is riven by innumerable drainage lines that leak waters into surrounding basins, rivers and ultimately into the Bay of Bengal: a kind of encompassing fluvial tapestry of crisscrossing rivulets, lean streams and circuitous flows that are vital to calibrating the overall hydraulic momentum in the delta. Traditionally, it appears, that 'natural drainage' in the deltaic tracts was a valued element in the calculus of both habitation and agrarian production. Some of this orientation is indicated in an account of the 'general system' of village drainage in Bengal in the *Bengal Drainage Committee Report* of 1907 (quoted in turn from the *Epidemic Commission Report of 1864*):

> The drainage of all villages ... in Lower Bengal is effected by the water first running into the nearest paddy-fields lying in the direction of their slope, thence it collects in the beels from which it rushes through khals into larger streams, which again communicate with navigable rivers.[39]

The above description suggests that, historically perhaps, villages and their production contexts in the delta were strategically situated with regard to drainage. Water, in effect, was kept circulating between different types of depressions and basins and finally led unhindered to a flowing stream or river. Such an equilibrium, however, was fragile or tenuous, as a single disturbance or obstruction could upset an entire network of carefully maintained circulation. Something, perhaps, akin to the 'butterfly effect' in Chaos theory. Despite the delicate nature of the drainage pattern, colonial rule had, during the course of the nineteenth century, inaugurated a number of projects for road, railway and embankment construction in the region. These modes of transport with their emphasis on permanent all-weather structures and mostly built in unrelentingly straight lines marked a sharp break from movement in the earlier era, which was predominantly based on circuitous rough paths and 'crooked' routes.[40] The colonial transport network in Bengal, in fact, radiated along the East–West axis, while the region's natural drainage lines, in contrast, dropped from North to South.

By the second half of the nineteenth century, official concern built up over what was rapidly discussed as the problems caused by the obstruction to drainage. Several enquiry committees were commissioned to deliberate on issues of water-logging, the impacts of stagnant water bodies on malaria and the question over the railways and roads in interrupting natural drainage. One of the first of these Commissions, which debated the impacts of drainage congestion on the spread of malaria, was the Epidemic Commission of 1864. In the course of its enquiry, the Commission had to contend with a somewhat comprehensive response on the issue of drainage from one Raja Digamber Mitter (more about him later). In the years 1867 and 1868 another set of elaborate enquiries were held on the subject and their conclusions were summed up by Colonel Nicolls, then Chief Engineer of Bengal. The Colonel, stated in a Note of 4 March 1869:

> [R]oads and railways in Bengal have not obstructed the drainage of the country so far as to cause or to aggravate sickness. But some obstruction is inevitable and should be remedied as soon as possible.[41]

Colonel Nicoll's mixed assessment, which dismissed claims about the impacts of roads in causing malaria while nevertheless recognising that waterlogging did occur, marked the general tenor of the findings and conclusions by a succession of similar investigations. It appears, for the authorities, there was an inability to conclude that a straightforward correspondence existed between malaria and the construction of roads and railways. On the other hand, there could be no doubt that all-weather transport structures would logically interrupt and cause several scales of drainage impacts. In fact, it was precisely over this contradictory colonial assessment that two sharply opposed ideas on the issue of drainage began to coalesce. On one hand, formulated chiefly by Raja Digamber Mitter, it was argued that Bengal's drainage problems were entirely man-made, in that the 'natural drainage system' had been systematically interrupted by obstructions. The solution, according to this view, was for restoring the 'natural' pattern by reconnecting the circuits for water circulation. In effect, drainage should flow from 'villages to the arable lands, from paddy fields to beels and from the beels through khals and water-courses to the navigable rivers'.[42]

In contrast, the other proponents argued that drainage congestion was characteristic and intrinsic to the Gangetic delta, and that only man-made interventions through artificial drainage schemes could cure the delta from its stagnant malarial swamps. Thus, in this latter assessment, the deltaic tract was not perceived as a single organic bloc made up of intricate patterns of drainage but instead appeared as a disconnected aggregation of marshes and waterlogged sites. This divide over the question of drainage, between those arguing for the restoration of natural circuits against those insisting that the delta had to be cured of its naturalness, was most dramatically played out during intense discussions over the Bengal Sanitary Drainage Act, that had been introduced at the meeting of the Governor's Council on 9 February 1894.

In a subsequent debate by the Council on 24 February, the members broke out into various kinds of dissenting voices over the Bill. One of the members, Mr L. Ghosh, averred that the solution to drainage congestion in the delta lay in carrying out schemes that facilitated 'surface drainage' in the villages. Ghosh, however, contrasted his advocacy of village-level surface drainage schemes as being in sharp opposition to those who were arguing for 'subsoil drainage', which would mean the draining of maidans, paddy-fields and beels.[43] In fact, the differences between the proponents of surface and sub-soil drainage respectively, mirrored the larger disagreements over the question whether the delta's unsanitary conditions could be relieved through the restoration of the natural drainage pattern (surface schemes) or, on the reverse, removing its naturalness (subsoil schemes). Along the same curve of differences was the other fear that the Bill had evolved a string of procedures for addressing the issue of drainage only through the narrow optic of propertied interests. According to the format specified in the Bill, the government would act on a drainage 'complaint' only if it was moved, at the local level, through a Drainage Commissioner, who had been qualified by his 'interests in the land'. The Drainage Commissioner was then expected to conduct a survey of the afflicted locale and submit a report based not only on the physical nature of the undertaking but, more specifically, with an eye towards the 'particulars as to the estate and tenure holders and cultivating raiyats of the local area with the annual value of the estates, tenures and holdings...'.[44]

This procedure for addressing both how drainage was to be assessed and solved was clearly weighted with an obvious bias towards landed elements in the delta. That is, drainage was to be perceived only as an adjunct to the land question, with the reasoning for relieving congestion based entirely on its 'value' in terms of meeting the revenue demand. Thus drainage was treated as a localised affair; that too, though not obviously stated, preferably in only remunerative zones. In effect, the Drainage Bill, in terms of its operative part, was slanted clearly in favour of those who had suggested that the delta had to be delivered from its naturalness and the government should, in the main, push for sub-soil drainage, while only carrying out financially remunerative surface schemes.

The Bengal Sanitary Drainage Act (BSDA) was finally passed in late 1895. The much debated and disputed section 3, which had urged for the draining of marshy lands and even rice fields, however, was entirely deleted in the new version of the BSDA . The new BSDA was instead concentrated on stating that drainage measures were to be taken only when obstructions deteriorated sanitary conditions in the locale. Nevertheless, the BSDA was a little too late and not enough in terms of reversing the congestion that almost a century of colonial rule had brought about in the delta. More specifically, to highlight just one example, in the extreme fringes of the delta, in the districts of the 24 parganas and in areas abutting the Sunderbans, a rabid period of land reclamation had been ongoing from the earliest decades of the nineteenth century.

In the normal course of tidal action, lands were continuously raised with the deposition of silt by slack ebb currents from the Bay of Bengal. After a point these raised lands became high enough to encourage the growth of jungles, which after some years could be cleared for settled agriculture after an embankment was thrown around it. This strategy for reclamation of land from the sea, however, if prematurely carried out – without the lands being sufficiently raised – could result in drainage complications such as water-logging or the silting-up of the rivers' beds that were trapped behind the embankments. This was especially so as the deltaic rivers when approaching the sea are extremely sluggish and prone to rapidly dissipate into marshes, creeks or just stagnant lakes.

To explain the consequences of such premature reclamation efforts, I quote C. Addams Williams, then Executive Engineer in the Public Works Department, who details a telling example:

> On the south-east of Calcutta are situated what are called the salt lakes. On the flow side the water finds its way from the Bidyadhari river through side branch khals into the lakes and deposits its silt; on the ebb tide the water flows back into the river and the flow and ebb keep the river open. A part of the northern portion of the lake called the Panchannagram basin was some years ago cut off from tidal spill into the lakes by an embankment and brought under cultivation. In the meantime the tides have continued to spill into the lakes to the south of the embankment; the land has continued to rise in consequence... We have therefore a low depression ... from which it is almost impossible to drain the rain water ... it is quite possible that these low lands will become entirely waterlogged before long and cultivation will entirely cease....[45]

The pursuit of premature reclamation was, in fact, the dominant response amongst the colonial authorities to drainage in the region, keen as they were to extend the arable frontier, which was backed with equal earnestness to realise revenue from settled cultivation. The conundrum over drainage in the Bengal delta and its often times baffling consequences, nevertheless, haunted British engineering expertise. By the latter decades of the nineteenth century, as I have all to briefly alluded to above, colonial officialdom found itself sharply divided over the issue of drainage. The split essentially occurred over the question of whether to restore the 'natural regime' of the delta or, in contrast, command the flow of the waters through a spectrum of drainage schemes. For various reasons of political economy the colonial dispensation overwhelmingly chose the latter path by taking up often costly works such as the Magra Hat Drainage Scheme, the Dankuni Drainage works, the Rajapur Drainage scheme and so on and so forth.[46] But over-shadowing these elaborate undertakings was a fairly consistent critique by both local opposition and members within the administration and engineering branches as well, who argued that the delta's hydraulic regime would only be further complicated and aggravated by such initiatives. The congealing of these two opposed views on the question of drainage, in fact mirrored similarly intense opinions on the issue of river navigation and flood control in the delta.

Conclusions

Through these three snapshot debates (navigation, flood control and drainage), this chapter has sought to not only provide a context for Governor Casey's hydraulic utopia but sought to flesh out the notion of the environmental format. As argued earlier, new imperial history has tended to leave open-ended the possibility for arriving at a consistent understanding of the nature and character of British colonialism. Whilst this historiographic turn has been insightful in revealing the colonial project as an intensely conflictual and contradictory process, by drawing upon information technology theory and recent intellectual shifts in the discipline of geography, there, nevertheless, appears to be the danger of conceptual relativism. Colonialism, as an assemblage of networks, webs, circuits, hubs, bridgeheads and multiple trajectories, might lose the ability to convey explanations for the persistence of certain kinds of structures of political economy or even features that were integral to realising and reproducing colonial rule.

Through the environmental format, this chapter argues, certain specific aspects of the colonial project can be revealed as a particular political and economic moment. Towards this, exploring the role of the English East India Company and the actions and experiences of its many and varied layers of officials acquires considerable salience. The EEIC was undoubtedly one of the earliest modern modules, as it were, that pursued the global ordering of the world through routines and particular configurations of knowledge/power.

In the case of the Bengal delta, as the above snapshot debates have tried to show, the sustained and often times trying attempts to separate land and water in order to be harness these entities as discrete economic resources defined the Company's presence in the region, which, in turn can be linked to attempts to calculate soils and flows as elements of the colonial productive regime.

Notes

1. This chapter was initially presented as a paper at a workshop entitled 'East India Company and the Natural World' at the University of Sussex, 18 June 2008.
2. The British Library, London. Oriental and India Office Collection (henceforth OIOC), R. G. Casey, 'Poverty or Plenty', Broadcast Speech by the Right Honourable R. G. Casey, Governor of Bengal — On All-India Radio, Calcutta, On Saturday, December 8th, 1945 in *Personal Diary R. G. Casey*, MSS.EUR. F48/4, May 1945–February 1946.

3. Rohan D'Souza (2006), *Drowned and Dammed: Colonial Capitalism and Flood Control in Eastern India*, Delhi: Oxford University Press.
4. See A. Escobar (1995), *Encountering Development: The Making and Unmaking of the Third World*, Princeton, NJ: Princeton University Press.
5. According to David Gilmartin, the colonial productive regime refers to the attempted admixture of irrigation science, routines of land revenue and the intended colonial control of society and nature. D. Gilmartin (2003), 'Water and Waste: Nature, Productivity and Colonialism in the Indus Basin', *Economic and Political Weekly*, 38(48): 5057–65.
6. This is now a large and voluminous debate. For a flavour of the different sides and shades of how the question of the constitution of imperial/colonial science has been framed see D. Kumar (1995), *Science and the Raj*, Delhi: Oxford University Press; R. Grove (1995), *Green Imperialism: Colonial Expansion, Tropical Island Edens and the Origins of Environmentalism, 1600–1860*, Cambridge: Cambridge University Press; R. Drayton (2000), *Nature's Government: Science, Imperial Britain, and the 'Improvement' of the World*, New Haven: Yale University Press; K. Raj (2006), ,*Relocating Modern Science: Circulation and the Construction of Scientific Knowledge in South Asia and Europe*, Delhi: Permanent Black; and M. Harrison (2005), 'Science and the British Empire', *Isis*, 96: 56–63.
7. A. G. Hopkins (ed.) (2002), *Globalization in World History*, Sydney: Pimlico, pp. 1–10 & 11–46.
8. T. Ballantyne, 'Empire, Knowledge and Culture: from Proto-Globalization to Modern Globalization', in Hopkins (ed.), *Globalization in World History*, pp. 115–40.
9. A. Lester (2006) 'Imperial Circuits and Networks: Geographies of the British Empire', *History Compass*, 4(1): 124–41.
10. P. J. Stern (2007), 'Politics and Ideology in the Early East India Company-State: the Case of St Helena, 1673–1709, *Journal of Imperial and Commonwealth History*, 35: 1–23.
11. Philip J. Stern (2011), *Company State: Corporate Sovereignty and the Early Modern Foundations of the British Empire in India.* New York: Oxford University Press.
12. *Selections from the Records of the Government of Bengal Relating to the Nadia Rivers (From 1848 to1926)*, Calcutta: Bengal Secretariat Press, 1931.
13. 'Notes on the changes of the heads of the Mathabanga river since 1825 compiled by Mr. S. C. Sur, Executive Engineer, Nadia Rivers Division', in *Nadia Rivers (From 1848 to 1926)*, p. 35.
14. 'Report on the Nuddea Rivers and the advantages derived from the measures annually adopted for facilitating their navigation. No. 89, dated Kishnaghur, the 14th July 1848. From Captain John Lang, 36th Regiment, Bengal N.I., Officiating Superintendent, Nuddea Rivers. To The Officiating Superintending Engineer, Lower Provinces', in *Nadia Rivers (From 1848 to 1926)*, pp. 72–89.
15. 'Report on the Nuddea Rivers', p. 73.
16. 'Notes on the changes of the heads of the Mathabanga river since 1825', pp. 34–8.
17. Shoals: A sandy elevation at the bottom of a body of water constituting a hazard for navigation.

Mischievous Rivers and Evil Shoals 145

18. 'Notes on the changes of the heads of the Mathabanga river since 1825', p. 35.
19. P. P. Jansen, L. van Bendegom, J. van den Berg, M. de Vries and A. Zanen (1979), *Principles of River Engineering: The Non-Tidal Alluvial River*, London: Pitman. See also C. V. J. Varma, K. R. Saxena and M. K. Rao (eds.) (1989), *River Behaviour, Management and Training*, Delhi: Central Board of Irrigation and Power, Publ. No. 204, Vol. I.
20. 'Report on the state of the Bhaugirutty and Jellinghee Rivers between the Ganges and Nuddea, with the result of the means used to improve Navigation during the dry season of 1847–48', in *Nadia Rivers (From 1848 to 1926)*, p. 90.
21. 'History of the Bhagirathi river compiled by B.R. Haldar, Executive Engineer, Nadia Rivers Division' [6 September 1925], in *Nadia Rivers (From 1848 to 1926)*, p. 2.
22. 'Report on the Nuddea Rivers', p. 72.
23. 'Report on the Nuddea Rivers', pp. 75–80.
24. 'Notes on Changes of the Jalangi and Jalangi-Bhairab rivers', Compiled by Mr. S. C. Sur, Executive Engineer, Nadia Rivers Division, *Nadia Rivers (From 1848 to1926)*, p. 28.
25. 'Notes on Changes of the Jalangi and Jalangi-Bhairab rivers', p. 29.
26. 'Notes on Changes of the Jalangi and Jalangi-Bhairab rivers', p. 28.
27. R. D'Souza (2004), 'Rigidity and the Affliction of Capitalist Property: Colonial Land Revenue and the Recasting of Nature', *Studies in History*, 20(2): 237–72.
28. H. L. Harrison, Collector Midnapore, to the Officiating Commissioner of the Burdwan Division, 3rd December 1877, *Cossye and Seyle Floods, May 1860 to September1893, vol. I* (Calcutta, 1928), p. 331.
29. Harrison, *Cossye and Seyle Floods*, p. 331.
30. Government of Bengal, 'Embankments in Murshidabad', *Nadia Rivers (From 1848 to 1926)* p. 53.
31. The Company administration in a bid to maximize its income and enforce its new proprietary laws initiated the sale of any estate whose owner had defaulted on the revenue instalments. In both Orissa and Bengal an innumerable number of such defaulting zamindaris were sold in the first two decades of colonial rule. See B. B. Chaudhuri (1982), 'Agrarian Relations: Eastern India', in Dharma Kumar (ed.), *Cambridge Economic History of India 1757–1970*, vol. II, Delhi: Cambridge University Press, pp. 91–8.
32. Regulation XXXII of 1793 was the first directive on the embankments, followed by the appointment of local Committees in 1801 to supervise the embankments. Regulation VI of 1806, in fact, superseded the previous two rulings. See *Embankments in Bengal: Note on their Origin, Development and Utility (1772–1850)*, pp. 131–2, National Archive of India, Land Revenue Records (28 March 1851), 20–21, in Index to Land Revenue Records (1838–59), vol. II (Henceforth *Embankments in Bengal*).
33. Harrison, *Cossye and Seyle Floods*, p. 331.
34. OIOC, *Report on the Embankments of the Rivers of Bengal*, Calcutta: Bengal Military Orphan Press, 1846. V/27/732/36, p. 2.
35. *Gungoareah Bundee, Bahar Bundee, Hussea Bundee, Khall Bundee, Khall Kundee, Falni Kassie, Bheera Bundee* and *Bheree Bundee*. See *Embankments in Bengal*, p. 33.
36. *Embankments in Bengal*, pp. 33–8.
37. OIOC, *Embankment Committees Reports* (Calcutta, 1901), V/27/730/7, pp. 36–40.
38. *Embankments in Bengal*.

39. Government of Bengal (1907), *Report of the Drainage Committee, Bengal (Presidency Division)*, Calcutta: Bengal Secretariat Press, pp. 20–21.
40. See J. Deloche (1993/1994), *Transport and Communication in India: Prior to Steam Locomotion*, vols. I & II, Oxford: Oxford University Press.
41. *Report of the Drainage Committee, Bengal*, p. 33.
42. W. A. Inglis (1911), *A Review of the Legislation in Bengal*, Calcutta: Bengal Secretariat Press, p. 69.
43. Inglis, *A Review of the Legislation in Bengal*, p. 68.
44. Inglis, *A Review of the Legislation in Bengal*, p. 67.
45. C. Addams-Williams, Executive Engineers, Public Works Department (1913), *Drainage Problems in the Ganges Delta: A Series of Six Letures Delivered At the Sibpur Engineering College*, March 1913, Calcutta: Bengal Secretariat Book Depot, p. 6.
46. Some of the debates around the issue of drainage are illustrated by the following sources: W. A. Inglis (1909), *The Canals and Flood Banks of Bengal*, Calcutta: Bengal Secretariat Press, pp. 465–561; *Papers from 16th March 1901 to 14th April 1914 Relating to the Magra Hate Drainage Scheme in the 24 Parganna District*, Selections from the Records of the Bengal Government, Calcutta; Bengal Secretariat Press, 1915; G. C. Machnonchy, Superintending Engineer, Public Works Department, *Problems Regarding Flood Drainage*, Calcutta: Bengal Secretariat Book Depot, 1905; C. Addams-Williams, Executive Engineers, Public Works Department, Bengal (1919), *History of the Rivers in the Gangetic Delta 1750–1918*, Calcutta: Bengal Secretariat Press.

7
The *Rafflesia* in the Natural and Imperial Imagination of the East India Company in Southeast Asia

Timothy P. Barnard

Rafflesia is a genus of plants that is among the largest parasitic flowers in the world; the number of species of the plant is disputed but most likely is between fifteen and twenty. They are only found in Sumatra, Java, the Malay Peninsula and southern Philippines. The plant is not only unique due to its size, but also its parasitic nature and appearance. The only visible part of the plant is the flower; there are no stems, roots or leaves. The *Rafflesia* is connected to its host, the *Tetrastigma* (a genus of the grape family) vine, via fine microscopic threads. In addition, it is a slow growing plant. Tissue threads of the *Rafflesia* will spread in the vine for up to eighteen months before a bud appears. This bud then takes up to nine months to bloom.[1] Since coming to the attention of European scholars/explorers in the late eighteenth century, the collection – or even sighting – of the flower has come to be the goal of a number of scientific expeditions, which is reflected in it depiction in local literature, botanical gardens, natural history museums and scientific classification pamphlets. The origin of much of this fascination contains many interconnecting threads, much like the microscopic ones that connect the *Rafflesia* to its host. It involves the network of ideas and understandings that the English East India Company (EIC) promoted throughout the world through it personnel, trade and related scientific societies that were related to the natural world and its classification.

Knowledge of the natural world, particularly plants, was vital for European trading companies to remain viable. For the various East India Companies plants were one of the main motivations for their push into Asia. The holy trinity of spices – cloves, nutmeg and mace – were among the most valuable items in early modern European markets, and combined with other plants such as black pepper, cinnamon and tea, formed a key component of their profits and motivations.[2] This made knowledge of the natural world a component of profit as well as curiosity, and results in comments, descriptions and analysis of botanical wonders a presence in almost all documents associated with these trade organizations. An example can be found in the letters of John Adolphus Pope, a young merchant who gathered information in the Bay of Bengal in the 1780s. The letters are wide ranging, but a common thread that runs through all of the correspondence he sent back to London was information on the natural world. An example of the knowledge Pope gathered is his account of the betel palm, one of the most important trade items in the Indian Ocean world, and its life cycle as well as how it was processed. As Barbara Andaya emphasizes in a recent paper on Pope, such information was necessary to plan trips so that they could access the product when it was at its maximum profitability.[3]

Over the two centuries that the English East India Company traded, and ruled, in Asia a complex network of information gathering developed that influenced their understanding of the natural world. The pursuit of this knowledge extended to exotica of Asian forests. Many of the early expeditions that identified the *Rafflesia* used its gigantism as an important trope to represent the strange nature of the Southeast Asian jungle to Western audiences. This large botanic parasite became a symbol of not only the alterity of this vast tropic region, but also a justification for such expeditions and their role in the collection and development of knowledge, which was also interconnected to the spread of empire.

The discovery, collection and identification of the *Rafflesia* was the culmination of the interaction of knowledge, trade and the natural world for the English East India Company in Southeast Asia. This chapter will provide insight into this process through a discussion of some of the early natural scientists who influenced the collection of knowledge, particularly about flora, of Southeast Asia, as well as the process in which this plant was discovered, identified and named during a period in which the Company was reaching the apex of its influence in not only politics and economics but also science. The *Rafflesia*, therefore, will be placed within the discourse of imperial control and classification originating in the laboratories and botanical gardens of Europe. In the process, it has come to reflect larger Western imperial desires and understandings of Southeast Asia and its forests. Only when the importance of controlling a plant, naming it after an iconic European in Southeast Asia, and the unique nature of the plant, is made, can the 'strange virtues' of the *Rafflesia* be exposed.[4]

Classifying and controlling flora, fauna and lands

Despite its name, a Frenchman, Louis Auguste Deschamps, first recorded and described the existence of the *Rafflesia*. Deschamps examined a specimen in 1797, leaving a legacy of disputed findings which represents the desire that discovery lends itself to the claim, control and description of a new species. The plant Deschamps documented was found on Java, thus most likely making it a flower known as a *Rafflesia patma*, a smaller version of the large plant found in Sumatra and Borneo.[5] Although Deschamps first described the flower in the late eighteenth century, it did not enter the public imagination until it was publicized as part of British scientific and colonial expansion into Southeast Asia that was the result of developments in Europe in the eighteenth century in which the various East India Companies were involved, and often were related to the natural world.

Southeast Asia had long been an area of fascination for European scientists. In the seventeenth century, the pioneering work of Georg Everard Rumpf, better known as Rumphius, brought considerable attention to the region, particularly with his descriptions of the 'poison tree'.[6] A United East India Company (*Vereenigde Oost-Indische Compagnie*, VOC) employee posted to Maluku (commonly known as the Moluccas, or Spice Islands), Rumphius spent his spare time in the collection and identification of new species. Decades of research resulted in *The Ambonese Herbal*, an early book on the botany of the region, and the *Thesarus Amboiniensis*, which is better known as the 'Ambonese Cabinet of Curiosities', with its descriptions of shells, shellfish, minerals and stones. Written in the vein of a pre-Linnaean classification system, these works combined the aesthetic and scientific to open the exotic world of Southeast Asia to scientific classification, pushing it beyond the exaggerated tale of previous adventurers.[7] Rumphuis' work, however, was only published after 1740, some forty years after his death, reflecting how information about the natural world was considered to be of highly classified importance among the East India Companies. After all, the natural trade products of Southeast Asia were the cornerstones of profitability for European explorers and enterprise in the region. The period between the writing and publishing of his influential work was one in which vast changes in science and empire had taken place.

While Rumphius played an important role in the development of classification systems, and focused attention on Southeast Asia for its unique natural resources, the importance of classification emerged following the flood of overwhelming information that arose with the discovery and exploration of 'new worlds' during the early modern period that would influence the understanding of everything that was considered acceptable knowledge. These changing understandings influenced how Europeans approached all aspects of their lives, ranging from politics to religion to science. Key to these developments was the maintenance, classification and control over many of these new discoveries, and the support of governmental institutions in this process. An important part of this process was the development of public areas of research and interaction, of which botanical gardens were vital.

Botanical gardens had existed in Europe as part of the institutionalization of science since the Renaissance. They were first associated with medical faculties, and the rise of anatomy (public operation) theatres, as the plants would have a medicinal purpose. During this period, such 'private' facilities acted as pleasure gardens for the nobility and elite. Following the exponential growth of the natural world following the discovery of the New World, however, it became apparent that very little was known about plants. Botanical gardens thus became more public, as they became associated with the entire university. By the mid sixteenth century most universities with medical faculties that embraced the new era of learning had botanical gardens filled with plants from the New World and Asia.[8]

A problem arose, however, and it was related to classification of these new plants. Initially the curators of these new botanical gardens would use *De materia medica*, a standard botanical book written by the first-century Greek physician Discorides, which designated plants on an Aristotelian system of trees, shrubs and herbs. As new flora continually arrived, and the *De materia medica* method became outdated, some curators began to classify plants geographically, although this system also soon became overwhelmed as newly discovered species continued to arrive in Europe. This also corresponded with the development of the herbarium, a collection of dried plants that could be transported for study, which was an attempt to take 'nature home' beyond the confines of its foreign – and often climatically different – origin.[9] The herbarium also provided botanists with a convenient tool to organize specimens, which began to reflect the difficulty of classification.

By the eighteenth century the issue of classification became more perturbing as it was clear that a new system needed to be developed. Although previous systems had used either an Aristotelian or geographical system, it was not until a Swedish physician, Carolus Linnaeus, developed a new approach to nomenclature that brought some order to the natural world. The Linnaean system was based on observable sexual characteristics and the use of binomial nomenclature. Combined with the publication of pamphlets explaining how to develop a herbarium, plant a garden and organize an excursion or voyage of discovery, Linnaeus promoted the spread of botanical collection beyond a few elite collectors.[10]

While Linnaeus developed the system of classification, it was the blending of state policy and science that pushed England to the forefront of developments in the eighteenth century. The two key figures in these developments were Francis Bacon and Joseph Banks. In the sixteenth century Bacon pushed for science to move beyond the control of an elite few magicians to an ethical and effective collaboration between well-trained individuals, all for the public good. Although France under Louis XIV and other monarchies embraced this idea earlier, the Royal Society in England, founded in 1660, was at the forefront of calling for state support of scientists. The Royal Society eventually developed into a source of advice for the government. As its rivals expanded overseas, the English government began a more active programme of exploration, as well as a growth of scientists and the government mutually supporting each other. Key to these developments was Joseph Banks, who promoted a vision of science serving national interests.[11]

Joseph Banks came from a well-to-do landowning family that afforded him the ability to pursue his scientific interests as a collector. Beyond his wealth and status, Banks' reputation was sealed when he served as the natural historian on James Cook's first voyage to the Pacific. Upon his return to England in 1771, he controlled the vast store of specimens collected on this voyage, as well as other specimens collected on voyages to Newfoundland and Iceland, thus making him the curator of the most diverse collection in England, all held at his own home, which also served as a research institute. The power that this collection gave Banks led to his appointment as the director of the Royal Gardens at Kew, which he developed into the premier botanical garden of his time, and led to him becoming a key figure in both the Royal Society and the Linnaean Society, an organization founded in 1788. In this regard, he developed one of the largest private collections of the time, which after his death became the nucleus of the British Museum of Natural History. Banks was also one of the first to fully adopt the Linnaean system of classification, believing that it instilled discipline and focus onto a seemingly chaotic natural world. In the process, it took the exotic out of the discoveries of distant lands, and placed them on a level at which all educated people could discuss and debate.[12]

Banks' control over both private and royal institutions of science also led to promotion of the idea that botany was a vital component of the imperial state and for the good of society. Supported by the development of the Linnaean Society – a society for those interested in documenting the natural world – and the Botanical Gardens at Kew, as well as private collections held by organizations such as the East India Company, understanding and documenting distant regions had become part and parcel in understanding the expanding empire. The interest in the natural world that the EIC and its quasi-governmental representatives such as Banks stood for meant that naturalists coming from the distant lands in Asia would have an audience upon their arrival in England.

As few naturalists actually made the trip to Southeast Asia, Banks would meet with interested amateurs prior to their journey for organizations such as the East India Company, providing them with instructions on proper collection. In the process Banks developed, in the words of David McKay, 'the most extensive scientific network in the world at that time'.[13] This was also true outside of England. For example, Carolus Clusius, the founder of the Leiden botanical gardens, gave physicians and apothecaries instructions on what to collect during their journeys on VOC ships.[14] Under Banks, however, this was to be done in the service of England and empire. In the process these amateur naturalists took part in an effort to rationalize and systematize the non-Western world so that it could be exploited in a more efficient manner.[15] With regard to Southeast Asia, the attempt of members of the Royal Society to reach out to distant scholars and explorers led to the inclusion of William Marsden in their ranks.

In his tenure as an EIC official in Southeast Asia Marsden was an early model for these natural historians. Born the son of a Dublin merchant in 1754, Marsden began working for the East India Company when he was 16 years old. His first posting was in Bengkulu, a small, isolated pepper port in southwestern Sumatra. It is during this period that he turned his attention to the natural world. As Marsden describes in his memoir, 'my curiosity being ever awake to the novelty of objects around me, I omitted no opportunities of making remarks on, and enquiries concerning, whatever was striking in the productions of the country'.[16] Knowing that Banks and the Royal Society were interested in meeting those who 'visited distant countries and communicated their observations', Marsden made it a goal to interact 'with such men, and to become a participator in their liberal pursuits'.[17] Soon after his return to London, he seized this opportunity following an invitation to a breakfast meeting with Banks and other members of the Royal Society during which 'much discussion took place on the subject of the vegetable productions of the eastern islands'.[18] Following this introduction, Marsden proceeded to write *The History of Sumatra*, a key work that first appeared in 1783, and was quickly translated into French and German, leading to his election as a Fellow of the Royal Society. The book documented a range of topics from languages and geography to natural products on the large island, and became a model for enterprising young colonial officials in Southeast Asia hoping to document their surroundings.[19] Following this entrée to polite society, Marsden took on various posts in the East India Company, and ultimately the Admiralty, which he came to head in 1805. At this time the efforts the influence of Banks in the linking of science with governmental expeditions came to fruition as Marsden began to subsidize the inclusion of a natural historian on naval vessels, making it common for those with a scientific bent by the early nineteenth century to find work as naturalists, collecting the unique, to be employed upon almost any ship leaving England.[20]

Many of these rationalizations in scientific collection occurred as the English East India Company was expanding into Southeast Asia. Although the EIC had been present in the region for over a century, it only began to establish permanent bases in 1781 with the founding of Penang in the northern Melaka Straits. The English presence was further boosted during the Napoleonic Wars, as the EIC took control over Dutch-controlled territories for fear that they would fall into the hands of Napoleon's expanding armies as they took over the Netherlands. In these new territories, EIC employees actively collected for Banks and institutions such as the Linnaean Society. Often armed with Marsden's *History of Sumatra*, using it as a guide when entering new and exotic ports in Southeast Asia, these naturalists collected and preserved plants, sketched them and arranged for their transport to London.

A key figure in many of these developments was Thomas Stamford Raffles, who had become an EIC employee at the age of 15 and risen through the ranks. Raffles developed into an important, energetic and vocal proponent of English expansion in the region. By 1811 he advocated the invasion of Java, which he saw as an opportunity to enact a more enlightened rule over a land that had suffered due to Dutch monopolistic practices as well as a variety of other hindrances, and also an opportunity to counter the continuing fear of Napoleonic influences in Europe. Related to his understandings of economics and politics, which were steeped in Enlightenment principles, Raffles also was a key proponent of the Banksian expansion of the sciences to the

Figure 7.1 Rafflesia Arnoldii, in S. Raffles (1835) *Memoir of the Life and Public Services of Sir Thomas Stamford Raffles*, Vol. 1 (London: James Duncan), p. 343 (Image in the public domain).

far corners of the world. It was this obsession with the natural sciences, and the corresponding collection and classification of plants, animals and minerals as well as peoples and cultures, which led to the discovery of a large parasitic plant in the jungles of Sumatra.

A discovery

Upon his arrival in Java, and influenced by a deep respect he felt for Marsden, Raffles began a concerted effort to collect and classify elements of the natural world. Important in these developments was Raffles' acquaintance with Thomas Horsfield, who would come to play a key role in the development of natural history museums and descriptions of Southeast Asia in England between the 1820s and 1840s. An American naturalist, Horsfield worked in the East Indies between 1801 and 1819, during which he was an avid collector of geological, botanical and zoological specimens.[21] Horsfield was first introduced to Asian botany when he wrote his dissertation on experimental pharmacology at the University of Pennsylvania, where he graduated in 1798. His dissertation focused on poisonous plants, which drew him to many of the early fantastic descriptions of the Indies, particular the *Upas* tree of Java, to which Rumphius had first drawn attention in his pioneering accounts of classifying plants in the region.[22] This tree had become a sensation in the European imagination after the publication of an account in *The London Magazine* in 1783 and it being mentioned in Erasmus Darwin's poem, *The Botanic Garden*.[23]

Upon arriving in Batavia in 1801, Horsfield worked as a physician while also helping the government with the classification of 'useful products of the vegetable kingdom' with a particular focus on finding medicinal applications.[24] For the next decade and a half, Horsfield busied himself with expeditions in search of medicinal herbs, often with the support of the Bataviaasch Genootschap van Kunsten en Wetenschappen (Batavian Society of Arts and Sciences), which hired him in 1803 as a salaried employee tasked with conducting botanical investigations, carrying out experiments and determining the medical uses of his discoveries. This new position allowed Horsfield to expand his research interests into the areas of geology and zoology. As he conducted research in these fields in Java, Horsfield's worth to the government grew. In 1811 he was commissioned to continue his research with the goal of producing a comprehensive guide to the flora of Java.[25]

The British invasion of Java in the second half of 1811 barely interrupted Horsfield's plans. In December of that year, Horsfield met Thomas Stamford Raffles, who was the head of the new administration. Raffles, who shared a keen interest in natural history, supported Horsfield in the continuation of his research, particularly when they bonded over their mutual fascination with the *Upas* tree. Raffles eventually supported Horsfield's proposal to include these specimens in a natural history collection for the East India Company Museum in London, which Joseph Banks managed. This began a period in which Horsfield would supply Banks with numerous plants, as well as descriptions, drawings and inscriptions, which found a receptive audience in Banks' Herbarium and Library. When the English transferred control of Java back to the Dutch in 1816, Horsfield continued to work with his patron Raffles, seemingly due to the recognition he was receiving from Banks and his growing fame among those interested in natural history in England.[26]

Following the terms of the Treaty of Vienna, the English were to transfer the territories they had 'maintained' for the Dutch back to their previous owner. This relegated Raffles from Lieutenant Governor of Java to the overseer of Bengkulu, the small outpost on the lightly travelled southwestern coast of Sumatra where Marsden had begun his career. Despite the diminishment of power, Raffles continued enthusiastically to embrace expeditions into areas that were little-known in England, as he had little to do beyond overseeing the loading of one or two ships a year with pepper.[27] It is during this period that he first came across the flower that would eventually carry his name.

From April to June 1818 Raffles led an expedition to the hinterlands of Bengkulu. On 19 May 1818 at Pulau Lebar on the Manna River, a member of the expedition saw a large flower (Figure 7.1). As Raffles later described in a letter:

> The most important discovery throughout our journey was made as this place. This was a gigantic flower, of which I can hardly attempt to give anything like a just description. It is perhaps the largest and most magnificent flower in the world, and is so distinct from every other flower, that I know not to what I can compare it – its dimensions will astonish you – it measured across from the extremity of the petals rather more than a yard, the nectarium was nine inches wide, and as deep; estimated to contain a gallon and a half of water, and the weight of the whole flower fifteen pounds.
>
> The Sumatran name of this extraordinary production is Petimun Sikinlili, or Devil's Siri (beetle) box. It is a native of the forest, particularly those of Passumah Ulu Manna.
>
> This gigantic flower is parasite on the lower stems and roots of the Cissus Angustifolia of Box. It appears at first in the form of a small round knob, which gradually increases in size. The flower-bud is invested by numerous membranaceous sheaths, which surround it in successive layers and expand as the bud enlarges, until at length they form a cup round its base. These sheaths or bracts are large, round, concave, of a firm membranaceous consistence, and of a brown colour. The bud before expansion is depressive, round with five obtuse angles, nearly a foot in diameter, and of a deep dusky red. The flower, when fully expanded, is, in point of size, the wonder of the vegetable kingdom....[28]

In his letter, Raffles then went on to explain that, since the plant was a fungus, it was not possible to preserve a specimen, and hopefully the sketches and drawings would do it some justice. Raffles then rasped euphoric on the wonders of the Southeast Asian natural world: 'There is nothing more striking in the Malayan forests than the grandeur of the vegetation. The magnitude of the flowers, creepers, and trees, contrasts strikingly with the stunted and, I had almost said, pigmy vegetation of England.'[29]

Despite his powerful descriptions of the plants, and the vegetation of the region, it was not Raffles who first sighted the plant on the expedition. This honour fell to Joseph Arnold, a surgeon who had joined the Royal Navy to pursue his interest in botany abroad. Arnold arrived in Java in 1815 to conduct natural history research as a member of the Linnaean Society. After several collecting expeditions he planned to deliver the specimen boxes back to Joseph Banks on his return journey in 1816. This return journey, however, became a tale of misfortune. Arnold was the victim of a ship sinking. His troubles were compounded when local English officials refused to assist him in finding alternative transportation. The destruction of the boxes of specimens he was to present to Banks on behalf of Raffles further exacerbated his problems.[30] Despite these setbacks, the scientific community continued to support the newly returned Arnold, who spent several months in 1817 in Banks' library familiarizing himself with the various publications on Asian flora. After two years in England, Arnold was ready to return to collecting specimens overseas, and found the opportunity when he became both Raffles' personal physician and naturalist upon the latter's return to Bengkulu.[31]

Shortly after their arrival in the Sumatran port in 1818, Raffles organized an expedition to the Passemah highlands, which had been experiencing migration due to internal conflicts and corvée requirements concerning pepper plantations. In a letter dated 9 July 1818 to Dawson Turner, a banker and natural historian who was close to Banks, Arnold wrote a long description of many of the peoples and places that he had encountered on the trip, as well as a new flower he had encountered near the village of Manna. As Arnold wrote:

> But here I rejoice to tell you I happened with what I consider as the greatest prodigy of the vegetable world; I had ventured some way from the party, picking specimens of plants, when one of the Malay servants came running to me with wonderment in his eyes, and said... 'come with me, Sir, come!, a flower very large, beautiful, wonderful!'. I immediately went with the man about an hundred yards in the Jungle, and he pointed to a flower growing close to the ground under the bushes, which was truly astonishing. My first impulse was to cut it up and carry it to our hut, I therefore seized the Malay's

prang ... and began to chop away. I then found that it sprang from a small root (perhaps as large as two fingers or a little more) which ran horizontally. I therefore soon detached it and removed it to our hut .... It had precisely the smell of tainted beef .... Now for the dimensions, which are the most astonishing part of the flower. It measured a full yard across; the petals (which were sub-rotund being twelve inches from the base to the apex, and it being about a foot from the insertion of the one petal to the opposite one. Sir Stamford, Lady Raffles and myself taking immediate measures to be accurate in this respect, by pinning four large sheets of paper together, and cutting them the precise size of the flower.[32]

Despite efforts to preserve the specimen, by transporting it in alcohol back to Manna, the giant flower rotted in its box, 'wasted, full of Maggots and like a rotten mushroom'.[33]

Realizing that he had found something unique, Arnold proceeded to instruct Turner to pay special attention to this new find and to bring it to the attention of the members of the Linnaean Society:

I think that the drawings and description with every thing attached to this flower out not to be shoved aside among Sir Joseph's collection. I should be glad to see it properly described, named, delineated, and published in the Linnaean transactions, but as I am so far removed from Botanical intelligence, after all, the flower may have been described before ... but if it really is new, and Mr Brown should be ill, or unable to attend to it, may I beg of you to trouble yourself with describing and naming it and dissecting the buds .... At any rate when you receive this letter ... will you write to Sir Joseph mentioning that I have described such a flower to you, and if possible will you prevent its being thrown on the shelf.[34]

The concern that Arnold showed for this specimen was prescient. Arnold, however, would never learn of the journey it was about to take. He died in late July 1818, most likely from malaria, while in Padang, the largest settlement on the western coast of Sumatra. Although Arnold believed he was the first to document the existence of large parasitic flower in jungles of Sumatra, the flower would now return to England, where it was to be classified, named and controlled in the imperial establishment that was vital in making its 'discovery' an example of the wonders of the expanding science of botany in the service of empire.

Claiming the flower

Horsfield learned of Arnold's discovery of the gigantic flower when he arrived in Bengkulu to meet with Raffles in June 1818. Horsfield recognized the plant as being similar to one he had seen in Java 'several years earlier'. Horsfield's earlier discovery is mentioned in Arnold's letter of 9 July 1818, in which he initially wrote of the discovery. In this letter he explains the basic difference in the two plants. As Arnold wrote, 'in looking over Dr Horsfield's immense collections of the Plants of Java I find something which perhaps may approach to it, ... the main difference of the two plants appears from this that his full blown flower is about three inches across, whereas mine is three feet'.[35]

This led to a contentious period, in which various naturalists laid claim to the right to name the flower, which was highly reflective of the powerful politics that surrounded the imperial expansion of science. Horsfield's 'discovery' – ultimately identified as *Rafflesia horsfieldii* or *Rafflesia patma* – was at first trumpeted as being the first time someone had seen the flower.[36] On this same journey, Horsfield interacted with Arnold, collected geological specimens and arranged for the entire collection to be transported to London, where it became part of the collection of the Natural History Museum. In 1819, following Arnold's death, Horsfield sailed to England on the *Lady Raffles*, accompanied by many of the collections that would form a vital part of the Library and Museum of the East India Company.[37] In addition, there was a small fragment, as well as descriptions and drawings, of the large flower Arnold had seen outside of Manna.

Upon arrival in London Horsfield introduced himself to Joseph Banks, through a letter of introduction from Raffles. Among the items Horsfield presented to Banks were books of Javanese flora, zoological essays, as well as outlines and essays on the mineralogy and geology of Java and descriptions of the various expeditions that had taken place over the past few years of British control of the island. The volume of material collected, as well as a supporting letter from Raffles, resulted in Horsfield being hired by the East India Company, which housed his collection at the East India Company Museum on Leadenhall Street. From here Horsfield began his prolific second career as the overseer of a growing natural history collection. Over the next fifteen years Horsfield became a conspicuous member of a variety of societies and organizations that were related to natural history and zoology, such as the Zoological Club of the Linnaean Society of London and the Royal Society, and cemented his reputation with the publication of *Zoological Researches in Java, and the Neighbouring Islands*, which was originally published in eight parts between 1821 and 1824. In the role he played in scientific circles at the time Horsfield is perhaps best known as the Keeper of the Museum of the East India Company in the 1830s and 1840s.[38]

The volume of the collection Horsfield brought back from Sumatra in 1819 meant that there was a considerable amount of material to sift through and catalogue. The fragment of the large flower and its description ended up under the control of Robert Brown, who was at the center of the system that Linnaeus had developed and Banks had reinforced. In 1805 Brown had been the first botanist that Banks and Marsden – as Secretary of the Admiralty – had arranged to be paid for his efforts as part of a naval voyage to the Pacific and Australia. Although Brown was to become a prominent professional botanist, as well as discoverer of the cell nucleus and 'Brownian motion', he owed his entire career to Banks, who continually arranged for Brown to take up various positions. His close relationship with Banks gave him great power, as he had control over access to the impressive collection, eventually becoming the overseer of the Banks Library and Herbarium upon Banks' death in 1820. Brown's control over such a valuable collection eventually led to its integration into the British Museum in 1827, where it became the core botanical collection, a process that Brown oversaw.[39]

In 1819 Robert Brown was Secretary of the Linnaean Society, and it was his task to identify the flower, and he faced a conundrum. Should he name the flower for Raffles, who oversaw the expedition and was well known in scientific circles in London, or Arnold, who had been the chief naturalist, and the first white man to see the flower on the expedition? Brown spent the next eighteen months confirming whether or not it was a botanical novelty and contemplating its official classification. He eventually decided that the proper name should be *Rafflesia arnoldii*. By designating the genus name to Raffles, Brown was following the convention of the day, providing credit to the sponsor of the expedition while also reinforcing the status Raffles was achieving amongst the scientific establishment in England. As Brown stated in the announcement, it was 'the name I am persuaded that Dr Arnold himself would have chosen had he lived to publish an account of it'.[40]

The newly designated plant carried the name of both Raffles and Arnold, and represented the convention of the time. Brown, however, had considered alternatives. Among these alternatives was *Arnoldia grandiflora*, which is how he initially designated the flower in the slip catalogue at the British Museum of Natural History.[41] Raffles would have supported this decision to a limited extent. As John Bastin has pointed out, Raffles gave credit to Arnold in a number of private letters written during this period to prominent individuals such as Joseph Banks. In almost every public forum, however, Raffles failed to mention Arnold's role in its discovery. The two most glaring examples of this omission come from an 1822 review – most likely written by Raffles – of John Crawfurd's *History of the Indian Archipelago* in which 'the discovery' of this 'extraordinary gigantic flower' was 'communicated by Sir S. Raffles to Sir Joseph Banks in 1818', and that it was 'appropriately named *"Rafflesia"*'.[42]

The various alternatives for naming the flower, as well as the ultimate solution, represents the hierarchical structure of both science and the East India Company at the time. Raffles was man of growing reputation – much of it self-induced – in England, particularly among the upper class that controlled institutions such as the Linnaean Society.[43] His contemporaries, such as Arnold, had little trust in Brown, who was seen as selfish, as he would monopolize access to any specimens that were returned to England, restricting the ability to compare and contrast – the key to classification – and thus limiting the ability to announce new discoveries.[44] The naming of a plant, first pointed out by a Malay guide to a frequently unfortunate naval surgeon, had now passed into the imperial realm. It was now a symbol of England's expansion overseas and growing power, reflective of a man who represented these ambitions in Southeast Asia as well as a reinforcement of the rigid English class system.

Conclusion

Now that the gigantic flower had been properly classified and named, it became a sensation, the largest plant in the world, in the early 1820s. It was a metaphor for the English East India Company and its ability to bring products of wonder from distant Asia. As the fame of the plant grew, along with the reputation of Raffles, Brown and the Company, representatives of governments and botanical gardens throughout Europe requested samples, or even just descriptions. While popular periodicals reprinted versions of his descriptions of the plant, the rewards for being connected to the plant were impressive. For example, the Empress Mother of Russia sent a ring to Brown in 1820 in gratitude after he passed along an account of the plant and its discovery.[45] The fascination with the *Rafflesia* has continued long after the dissolution of the Company that employed and influenced all of the main participants in its discovery, identification and naming. It now was to become a 'precious rarity', in the words of Henry O. Forbes, a traveller in western Sumatra in the late nineteenth century.[46]

As science and empire continued to expand, the rarity of sighting a *Rafflesia* became something special that must be recorded as a description of the largest plant in the world made any travel account seem more authentic, particularly due to its ephemeral nature. Once it blooms the *Rafflesia* only survives for a few days before it begins to decompose. Thus, a sighting is often a matter of serendipity. Beyond the dimensions of the flower, however, travellers began to focus on the freakish nature of its size, as well as its smell, thus further exoticizing the plant and the jungles from which it came, an event that was distant from the original goals of explaining and normalizing the plant world under Linnaeus and Banks. For example, in his description of the flower, Forbes mentions that it 'looks like a diseased growth that is sapping the strength of the body'.[47]

While such descriptions became an important marker of a trip to the jungles of Southeast Asia, little scientific research on the plant was done until the twentieth century. S. H. Koorders conducted the first extensive account of the plant when he classified into twelve different species, although it is believed that at least four of those he documented are now extinct.[48] Among the leading contemporary scientists who have focused on the *Rafflesia* since World War Two have been Willem Meijer, Todd Barkman and John Beaman.[49] Among the most important developments in the study of the plant has been an understanding of its relationship to others in the scheme of classification. Key in this development has been genome research. Since the *Rafflesia* has no leaves, stems or flowers, it is not capable of photosynthesis, or at least the ability has been curtailed to the point that it is non-existent. This means that the plant does not belong in the family in which Brown had originally placed it. Recently, these scientists have placed it in the *Malpighiales* order, alongside violets, poinsettias and willows.[50]

Whether the *Rafflesia* is desired as a unique product of the forest, a remnant of British imperial rule in the region or as symbol of the role that the EIC played in the natural world, its gigantism and unique nature have entered the historical and social imagination of the region, making it iconic on a number of levels. Its discovery – or at least the attention it achieved in the West – and its naming for one of the key imperial figures in Southeast Asia reflects the level at which European nations sought to control the environment, and understand it for their own profit.

The conclusion of this tangled tale of imperial desire, botany, science and Southeast Asia, however, does not end with the *Rafflesia*, as many of the characters interacted and influenced each other as they gathered in the learned societies and institutions that were housed in London. In 1836 Horsfield was appointed as the Librarian of the East India Company Museum, which also involved overseeing the Museum. Up to this point the Museum received few visitors, thus placing little burden upon the employees. In the 1840s, however, there began a boom in the use and acceptance of such institutions by the public. By 1845 the museum received 20,000 visitors. Key to our story, however, is a visitor who stopped by in 1848. Prior to his departure on an expedition to the Amazon with Henry Walter Bates, Alfred Russel Wallace called upon Horsfield. The Museum curator took Wallace over to some large boxes in which Horsfield kept his butterfly collection from Java. This was to spur Wallace to Southeast Asia in the 1850s, leading to his role in the concept of the theory of evolution through natural selection. This meeting – in the words of Wallace and to paraphrase John Bastin – led to the passing of the torch from the 'stagnant' world of eighteenth-century science, based simply on claiming and classifying, to the wonders of enquiry and theory that Wallace would play a vital role in promoting.[51]

Notes

1. K. M. Salleh (1991), *Rafflesia: Magnificent Flower of Sabah*. Kota Kinabalu: Borneo Publishing Company, pp. 6–7, 22.
2. L. Y. Andaya (1993), *The World of Maluku: Eastern Indonesia in the Early Modern Period*. Honolulu: University of Hawaii Press.
3. B. W. Andaya (2011), 'Gathering "Knowledge" in the Bay of Bengal: The Letters of John Adolphus Pope, 1785–1788', Paper presented at Penang and the Indian Ocean Conference, p. 7. The letter Pope wrote about betel can be found in A. Bulley (1992), *Free Mariner: John Adolphus Pope in the East Indies, 1786–1821*. Putney: British Association of Cemeteries in South Asia, p. 105.
4. Isaac Henry Burkill – one of the most influential botanists of twentieth-century Southeast Asia – described the unique characteristics of the *Rafflesia*, and its ability to impress observers, as 'an object so strange, fancy attributes strange virtues'. I. H. Burkill (1966), *A Dictionary of Economic Products of the Malay Peninsula*, Vol. II. Kuala Lumpur: Ministry of Agriculture and Cooperatives, p. 1894.
5. C. G. G. J. van Steenis et al. (1954), 'Louise Auguste Deschamps: A Prominent but Ill-Fated Early Explorer of the Flora of Java, 1793–1798', *Bulletin of the British Museum (N. H.), Historical Series* I: 51–68.
6. M. R. Dove and C. Carpenter (2005), 'The "Poison Tree" and the Changing Vision of the Indo-Malay Realm: Seventeenth to Twentieth Centuries', in R. Wadley (ed.), *Histories of the Borneo Environment: Economic, Political and Social Dimensions of Change and Continuity*. Leiden: KITLV, pp. 183–210.
7. E. M. Beekman (1993), *The Poison Tree: Selected Writings of Rumphius on the Natural History of the Indies*. Kuala Lumpur: Oxford University Press, pp. 1–40.

8. P. Findlen (2005), 'Sites of Anatomy, Botany, and Natural History', in K. Park and L. Daston (eds.), *The Cambridge History of Science, Volume 3: Early Modern Science*. Cambridge: Cambridge University Press, pp. 280–2.
9. Findlen, 'Sites of Anatomy', p. 282; P. Findlen (2005), 'Natural History', in Park and Daston, *The Cambridge History of Science*, p. 447.
10. L. Koerner (1999), *Linnaeus: Nature and Nation*. Cambridge, MA: Harvard University Press, pp. 33–55; A. B. Shteir (1996), *Cultivating Women, Cultivating Science: Flora's Daughters and Botany in England, 1760 to 1860*. Baltimore: Johns Hopkins University Press, pp. 11–32.
11. J. Gascione (1998), *Science in the Service of Empire: Joseph Banks, the British State and the Uses of Science in the Age of Revolution*. Cambridge: Cambridge University Press, pp. 16–23.
12. J. Gascoigne (1995), *Joseph Banks and the English Enlightenment: Useful Knowledge and Polite Culture*. Cambridge: Cambridge University Press. I would like to thank Robert Cribb for discussing these ideas with me.
13. D. McKay (1996), 'Agents of Empire: The Banksian Collectors and Evaluation of New Lands', in D. P. Miller and P. H. Reill (eds.), *Visions of Empire: Voyages, Botany and Representations of Nature*. Cambridge: Cambridge University Press, p. 39. These developments were mirrored in the Netherlands Indies with the founding of the Bataviaasch Genootschap van Kunsten van Wetenschappen (Batavian Society of Arts and Sciences); P. Boomgaard (2006), 'The Making and Unmaking of Tropical Science: Dutch Research on Indonesia, 1600–2000', *Bijdragen Tot De Taal-, Land- En Volkenkunde*, 162(2–3): 195–6.
14. Findlen, 'Natural History', pp. 453–4.
15. R. Drayton (2000), *Nature's Government: Science, Imperial Britain and the 'Improvement' of the World*. New Haven: Yale University Press, pp. 126–7; Findlen, 'Natural History', pp. 444–6.
16. W. Marsden (1838), *A Brief Memoir of the Life and Writings of the Late William Marsden*. London: J. L. Cox, p. 15.
17. Marsden, *A Brief Memoir*, pp. 25–6.
18. Marsden, *A Brief Memoir*, p. 45.
19. W. Marsden (1986), *The History of Sumatra, with an Introduction by John Bastin*. Singapore: Oxford University Press, 1986; Marsden, *A Brief Memoir*, pp. 53–4, 139.
20. Drayton, *Nature's Government*, pp. 126–7; Findlen, 'Natural History', pp. 444–6.
21. T. Horsfield (1990), *The Natural History Researches of Dr Thomas Horsfield (1773–1859): First American Naturalist of Indonesia, with a Memoir by John Bastin*. Singapore: Oxford University Press, p. 3.
22. The original description of the tree claimed it was from Makassar, and can be found in Rumphius' *Cabinet of Curiosities*. A more accessible account can be found in Beekman's *The Poison Tree*. Throughout his career in the East Indies, Horsfield's fascination with the tree continued. He eventually published an account of his findings several times; T. Horsfield (1814), 'An Essay on the Oopas or Poison Tree of Java, Addressed to the Honorable Thomas Stamford Raffles Lieutenant Governor', *Verhandelingen van de Bataviaasch Genootschap van Kunsten en Wetenschappen*, 7: 1–59; These findings, however, had been superseded by the findings of Leschenault de la Tour, a French naturalist who published a series of ground-breaking articles on the subject in 1810; J. B. L. C. Th. Leschenault de la Tour (1810), 'Mémoire sur le *Strychnos Tieute*

et l'*Antiaris Toxicaria*, Plantes Vénénueses de l'Ile de Java', *Annales du Museum D'Histoire Naturelle*, 16: 459–82.
23. Horsfield, *The Natural History Researches*, p. 7; J. H. Foersch (1783), 'Description of the Poison Tree, in the Island of Java', *The London Magazine: or Gentleman's Monthly Intelligencer*, 52: 512–17; E. Darwin (1781), *The Botanic Garden: A Poem, in Two Parts. Part I. Containing the Economy of Vegetation. Part II. The Loves of the Plants, with Philosophical Notes*. London: Jones and Co.
24. Horsfield, *The Natural History Researches*, p. 8.
25. Horsfield, *The Natural History Researches*, pp. 8–10, 32.
26. Horsfield, *The Natural History Researches*, pp. 34–42; 52–7; 63–5; McKay, 'Agents of Empire'.
27. J. Bastin (1973), 'Dr Joseph Arnold and the Discovery of the Rafflesia Arnoldi in West Sumatra in 1818', *Journal of the Society for the Bibliography of Natural History*, 6: 325.
28. S. Raffles (1835), *Memoir of the Life and Public Services of Sir Thomas Stamford Raffles, Vol. 1*. London: James Duncan, pp. 344–5.
29. Raffles, *Memoir of the Life and Public Services*, p. 345.
30. Bastin, 'Dr Joseph Arnold', pp. 309–13.
31. D. J. Mabberley (1985), *Jupiter Botanicus: Robert Brown of the British Museum*. Braunschweig: J. Cramer, p. 219; Bastin, 'Dr Joseph Arnold', p. 310.
32. Mabberley, *Jupiter Botanicus*, p. 221; Bastin, 'Dr Joseph Arnold', p. 329.
33. Bastin, 'Dr Joseph Arnold', p. 329.
34. Bastin, 'Dr Joseph Arnold', p. 330.
35. Bastin, 'Dr Joseph Arnold', p. 330.
36. R. Brown (1820), 'An Account of a New Genus of Plants, Named Rafflesia', *Transactions of the Linnean Society*, 13: 224–5.
37. Bastin, 'Dr Joseph Arnold', pp. 66–7.
38. Bastin, 'Dr Joseph Arnold', pp. 66–7.
39. Mabberley, *Jupiter Botanicus*; Drayton, *Nature's Government*, pp. 126–8, 143–4; D. P. Miller, 'Joseph Banks, Empire, and "Centers of Calculation" in Late Hanoverian London', in Miller and Reill, *Visions of Empire*, p. 32.
40. Brown, 'An Account of a New Genus of Plants, Named Rafflesia', p. 206.
41. Due to naming conventions of the time, *Arnoldia* was a synonym of *Weinmannia* (Cunoniaceae), and thus could not be used. Mabberley, *Jupiter Botanicus*, pp. 222–3.
42. Bastin, 'Dr Joseph Arnold', pp. 309, 343. The review appeared in *The Quarterly Review* 28(55) (Oct. 1822): 118; the quotes come from a footnote on p. 138. The review was written anonymously, but John Bastin attributes it to Raffles.
43. T. Hannigan (2012), *Raffles and the British Invasion of Java*. Singapore: Monsoon.
44. Drayton, *Nature's Government*, pp. 126–8, 143–4; Miller, 'Joseph Banks', p. 32.
45. Mabberley, *Jupiter Botanicus*, p. 225.
46. H. O. Forbes (1885), *A Naturalist's Wanderings in the Eastern Archipelago. A Narrative of Travel and Explorations from 1878 to 1883*. New York: Harper and Brothers, p. 28.
47. Forbes, *A Naturalist's Wanderings*, p. 28.
48. S. H. Koorders (1918), *Botanisch Overzicht der Rafflesiaceae van Nederlandsch-Indië*. Batavia: G. Kolff.

49. The main focus of Meijer's work is on the classification of the plant, although his most famous work is related to conservation; W. Meijer (1985), 'Saving the World's Largest Flower', *National Geographic* (July), 136–40.
50. Brown had originally placed it in the Aristolochiaceae family. The *Rafflesia* is so unique it is also the name of its own family, Rafflesiceae. T. J. Barkman, S. H. Lim, Kamarudin Mat Salleh and J. Nais (2004), 'Mitochondrial DNA Sequences Reveal Photosynthetic Relatives of Rafflesia, the World's Largest Flower', *Proceedings of the National Academy of Sciences of the United States of America* 103(3): 787–92.
51. Horsfield, *The Natural History Researches*, p. 77.

8
'A proper set of views': The British East India Company and the Eighteenth-Century Visualization of South-East Asia

Geoff Quilley

In the churchyard of St Mary's, Rotherhithe, stands the substantial tomb of Lee Boo, the first Palauan Islander to visit Britain, who died of smallpox at the home of Captain Henry Wilson in Paradise Row, Rotherhithe, on 27 December 1784. The tomb and its inscription, composed by no less a figure than Brook Watson, the merchant and celebrated subject of John Singleton Copley's recent (1778) painting *Watson and the Shark*, were erected at the expense of 'the Honourable United East India Company', as the inscription states:

> as a Testimony of Esteem for the humane and kind Treatment
> afforded by his Father to the Crew of their Ship
> the *Antelope*, Captain Wilson,
> which was wrecked off that Island
> in the Night of the 9th of August 1783.

Then Watson's epitaph concludes on a note of sentimental pathos:

> Stop, Reader, stop! – let Nature claim a Tear –
> A Prince of Mine, Lee Boo, lies bury'd here.[1]

That a Pacific Islander should be accorded celebrity status in late-eighteenth-century London is not necessarily surprising, given the acclaim and publicity surrounding the arrival of Mai on Cook's returning second voyage less than a decade previously.[2] However, that he should be treated with such deference, admiration and compassion as Watson's – admittedly somewhat melodramatic – couplet demonstrates, is indeed extraordinary. It is still more remarkable that he should be buried within a genteel London churchyard, in a tomb more appropriate to the merchant class or gentry, and paid for by the East India Company, which was hardly renowned for its generous treatment of subaltern peoples.

In one sense, Lee Boo may be seen as just one of a growing number of non-Western visitors to Britain in the eighteenth century, a consequence of its rapidly expanding empire and global trade, alongside other significant individuals or groups such as Mai, Olaudah Equiano, Dean Mahomet or the embassies of American Indians.[3] Yet, as his epitaph indicates, his celebrity status, which continued well into the nineteenth century, was associated with a rather different form of cross-cultural exchange than that deriving from exploratory voyaging, colonial expansion, or the iniquities of the African slave trade. It was rather linked to what was taken to be a natural nobility and humanity in the hitherto unknown islanders of Palau, which turned on its head the conventional opposition of colonial encounter between the supposed superiority and power of the civilized West and the 'inferiority' of the primitive savage 'other'. Indeed, the circumstances surrounding Lee Boo's arrival in London offer a remarkable and complex instance of the East India Company's attitudes and responses to cross-cultural encounter, and its awareness of the value and potential of visual culture as a means of interpellation of encounter with 'others', and more particularly of its activities and interests in the expanding market of the Pacific and China Seas. In this chapter I want to consider the events leading up to Lee Boo's passage to England as exemplary of the Company's intent to penetrate and open up Indonesia and the Far East in order to expand its trade eastwards towards China, through the creation of networks of knowledge and cultural interchange, in which visual culture would play a significant part.

Lee Boo was memorialized in printed text as well as stone, most importantly through the publication of his story in George Keate's book of 1788, *An Account of the Pelew Islands*, which was in significant aspects a tribute to the young islander and contained a narrative of his life and death in England as a postscript to the story of the *Antelope*'s shipwreck and the events of the British crew's time in Palau. According to Nicholas Thomas, Keate's *Account* was in all likelihood, 'after Cook's voyages, the most popular Pacific voyage work of the late eighteenth century'.[4] It is therefore worth considering in depth as an account of East India Company voyaging in the region at this period, particularly in terms of the larger ideological and commercial frameworks within which the voyage was both undertaken and subsequently reported. Keate's narrative personalizes these by reference to the story of Lee Boo, with the consequence that this rather tragic figure becomes a paradigm for an idealized form of cross-cultural encounter resulting from commercial voyaging, and thus a paradigm also for East India Company maritime enterprise. I shall begin, then, by examining the voyage of the *Antelope* in some detail, with particular attention to the role of visual records relating to it. Placing this voyage in the wider context of exploratory or speculative Company voyages in the South Asia / Pacific region at the same period, I shall argue that the increasing Company maritime activity in the area marked a shift in commercial interest south and eastwards, both to unsettle the Dutch monopoly in Indonesia and also to open up potential markets in China.[5] Within these voyages, visual culture played a significant and complex role, at once associating them with a wider culture of 'scientific' investigation and global knowledge (and thus moderating any purely commercial motives), and also providing, in Alexander Dalrymple's words, a 'proper set of views' for the benefit of subsequent navigation and trade in hitherto largely unknown seas, as well as providing a means of self-promotion for individual officers seeking to make their fortune through service to the Company.

The *Antelope* in the Palau Islands

Keate's *Account* followed the narratives of Cook's voyages in more than just its popularity. Indeed, Thomas, following Bernard Smith, sees it not only as emulative of these accounts, but as offering a corrective to John Hawkesworth's notorious and widely derided narrative of Cook's first voyage:

> The experience of contact at Palau, and with the Palauan people, can be seen to resolve problems that the Tahitian encounter, and the Tahitians had opened up. Where Hawkesworth had characterized voyaging as a morally uncertain practice, as well as a physically hazardous one, Keate's narrative and encounter are sympathetically reconciled, despite or even because of the tragic death in London of one of his principal characters, the famous Lebuu [sic].[6]

Hawkesworth's account of Cook's first voyage quickly became sensational and infamous in the years following its first publication, due to the detailed attention it paid to the morally questionable and, in the minds of many, licentious sexual exchanges between Europeans and Tahitians, reaffirming – but with distinct overtones of promiscuity – the

Bougainvillean idea of Tahiti as the island of Venus. This depraved image was further reinforced by the book's apparent irreligiosity: in one of the most celebrated incidents in the narrative, recounting Cook's near-shipwreck on the Great Barrier Reef, Hawkesworth conspicuously put the ship's escape down to nothing more than chance, rather than the intervention of divine providence.[7] In spite of the succeeding accounts of Cook's second and third voyages to the Pacific, in which these issues were unambiguously addressed, it was undoubtedly the sorry example of Hawkesworth that prompted Keate to emphasize repeatedly the role of providence throughout his own description of the shipwreck and salvation of the crew of the *Antelope*.

At the outset, therefore, Keate sets up his narrative as one of positive expectation, grounded in reasoned and civilized social morality, which is centred significantly on the treatment of women.

Keate consistently implies throughout the narrative that there was no sexual contact between the *Antelope*'s men and the Palauan women. But such moral propriety was not one-sided; rather, the natural morality of the Palauans was superior to the civilized manners of the Westerners:

> One of our people, endeavouring to make himself agreeable to a lady belonging to one of the rupacks [chiefs], by what we should term a marked assiduity, Arra Kooker [the 'brother' of the 'king'], with the greatest civility, gave him to understand it was not right to do so.[8]

The lessons of civilization, Keate makes clear, in this case are not only in one direction. This is significant not only in overturning the conventionally understood relation of the Western to the non-Western world, insofar as the *Account* is 'not simply an expression of European primitivist discourse', but also in terms of the specific character of the *Antelope*'s voyage: for if the 'scientific' remit of Cook's Admiralty-sponsored voyages, undertaken by his 'experimental gentlemen', conflicted controversially with an actuality of contact that was morally dubious at best, then Keate's *Account* emphasizes, by contrast, that proper and mutually improving cross-cultural exchange takes place under the auspices of a voyage made in the spirit and practice of commerce: 'A benevolent people are made known to the world by the recipients of benevolence, which is to say that a certain representation is fostered by a certain encounter.'[9]

Commerce was perhaps the predominant ideological paradigm for eighteenth-century British society, presented in countless treatises of history and social philosophy, above all by Scottish Enlightenment philosophers such as David Hume, Adam Smith or Henry Home, Lord Kames, as the defining principle of society itself, through which human beings are brought together freely and in mutually supportive interdependence. Thus, commerce for Hume was closely aligned with the emotion of sympathy and the individual capacity to engage with the interests of one's fellow men and women, and humanity at large; while for Smith, commercial society presented the apogee of human social progress thus far.[10] In this sense, Keate's insistent observation of the Palauans's curiosity about their European visitors, and their eagerness to learn the latter's skills and knowledge, which were of such impact as 'to impose on their minds a kind of magic influence', betokens more than just an evocation of an idealized type of 'noble savage', but provides evidence of the Palauans' capacity both for self-improvement and also to engage in sympathetic commercially derived social exchange:

> To describe people in these terms was not only to celebrate their degree of advancement, it was also to present the morality of contact in potentially positive terms. If they were receptive to improvement, then they might be improved, and contact was essentially improving.[11]

Yet, improvement in the charmed islands of Palau, according to Keate, worked both ways: the natural civility and good manners of the islanders positively affected the British, through the latter's contact with a form of georgic paradise found. For the islanders' benevolent treatment of the shipwreck victims must, Keate observes, have been motivated by the pure 'flame of philanthropy':

> Nor was this conduct of theirs an ostentatious civility exercised towards strangers. – Separated as they were from the rest of the world, the character of a stranger had never entered their imagination ... No; it was the pure emotions of native benevolence – It was the love of man to man. – It was a scene that pictured human nature in triumphant colouring – And, whilst that liberality gratified the sense, their virtue struck the heart!

> Our people had also many occasions to observe, that this spirit of urbanity operated in all the intercourse the natives had among themselves. The attention and tenderness shown to the women was remarkable, and the deportment of the men to each other mild and affable ...Their manners were courteous, though they were far from being of loose, or vicious dispositions; – they in general rejected connections with our people, and resented any indelicate, or unbecoming freedom with a proper sense of modesty.[12]

This almost otherworldly benevolence, therefore, is taken to be completely unsophisticated, without any motive other than itself, a spontaneous expression of the innate goodness of humanity when left uninterrupted in a state of nature, which impresses itself upon the British visitors, with the implied potential for the latter's moral improvement. This once again contrasts with the discourse on Cook's voyages, which frequently lamented the deleterious effects upon native Pacific Islanders caused by the irruption upon them of European ships and crews. George Forster in particular regretted that contact had ever been made at all: 'the voyages of Europeans cannot be performed without being fatal to the nations whom they visit'.[13] The voyage and, as it transpired, serendipitous wreck of the *Antelope* provided a stark counter, from the perspective of a commercial endeavour, to such pessimistic assessments of Western global expansion.

It is important, therefore, to note the wider context for this discourse of natural, 'innocent' philanthropy. Not only does it tie into the wider debate at this period about the relation of nature to culture, and the discourse of sensibility, but in its primitivist discourse it has sharper associations. For, at exactly the same time as Keate's publication, the same idea of natural benevolence among 'untutored savages' was being promulgated more widely on behalf of native Africans, as part of the growing campaign for the abolition of the slave trade. George Morland's celebrated pair of paintings and prints, *Execrable Human Traffic* (1788) and *African Hospitality* (1790), presents native African benevolence towards European shipwreck victims in a precisely analogous manner to Keate's relation of the events at Palau.

Whether or not Morland's representation was directly influenced by Keate's *Account* is hardly a major concern (though it is certainly plausible that it was). The larger point is that through such a discourse of natural benevolence, there was an association, at least by implication, of the voyage – and by extension the Company – with progressive moral reform. This is particularly significant in light of the scandal, also increasingly visible at precisely the moment of Keate's publication, over Company corruption in the figure of Warren Hastings, whose impeachment had been unfolding spectacularly at Westminster since 1787, and which hinged – most luridly in Edmund Burke's highly publicized rhetorical denunciations of Company policy and practice – on the supposedly despotic, barbaric and near-genocidal treatment of the Indian peoples under its subjection.[14]

Keate's *Account* is therefore far from being a disinterested text. And it is worth observing that, although not directly sponsored by the

Company, the book was dedicated to the Company Directors 'by their permission, and at the particular desire of Captain Wilson', so Wilson was obviously aware of the book's potential service to Company interests, as well no doubt as his own. Both in its emulation of the natural historical models of Cook's voyage accounts, and in its construction of 'noble savagery' and an ideal paradigm of cross-cultural encounter, it promotes the ends of the East India Company through presenting it in a very favourable light at a time when it was under severe, and potentially fatal, criticism. As Nicholas Thomas notes, the voyage of the *Antelope* was essentially a commercial one

> that had no connection with the patriotic lineage of naval and Royal Society exploration, even if its aims in fact may have been partly strategic. The slender connection with the voyage of discovery stems rather from the 'eager curiosity' they awakened regarding 'the history of mankind'.[15]

Although I would argue that the separation between Company voyaging and the 'patriotic lineage' of Admiralty exploration is not so clear-cut and the connection between them not so slender, this common thread of 'eager curiosity' about the 'history of mankind' does provide an important further context for one of the most extraordinary aspects of the *Antelope*'s venture, in which it departs from the singularly commercial character of most Company voyages, and which was undoubtedly tied to its 'partly strategic' purpose that Thomas observes. For Wilson's voyage in the *Antelope* was 'after Cook' in more than just the way it was subsequently written up.[16] Following Cook's example, and under the influence of Warren Hastings, Alexander Dalrymple and, quite possibly, Sir Joseph Banks, the *Antelope* took on board a professional artist, Arthur William Devis, termed a 'Passenger' by Keate, to make visual records of the places, peoples and cultures encountered en route. Similarly, in the same manner as William Hodges or John Webber, the artists on Cook's second and third voyages respectively, Devis produced both coastal profiles and drawings of individual native people (not the British party), which were subsequently engraved as illustrations for the published account. Furthermore, again similar to Cook's voyages, the professional artist was not the only person on board who produced visual records: three of the midshipmen – John Wedgebrough, Robert White and the Captain's son, Henry Wilson junior – also made drawings that formed the basis for subsequent prints. Indeed, one of Devis' roles, like Cook's artists before him, may have been to instruct junior officers in drawing techniques. The similarity with the art of Cook's voyages was even more pronounced in the formal and generic qualities of the resulting visual material itself. For example, Devis' landscape views present a similar format and a comparable focus on ethnographic content as John Webber's view of Pacific Islands from Cook's third voyage. Equally, his remarkably sensitive portrayals of Palauan islanders closely follow both the format and the ethnographic imperative of Hodges' red chalk drawings of Pacific Islanders. Devis' drawing of Ara Kooker (Figure 8.1), for example, the 'brother' of the so-called 'king' Abba Thulle, who had

Figure 8.1 Arthur William Devis, *Ara Kooger*, 1783, black chalk on paper, 231 × 183mm. British Museum, Department of Prints and Drawings, 1876,0708.2371 © Trustees of the British Museum

politely but firmly intervened at the over-attentiveness of one of the British party towards one of the Palauan women, can be compared to Hodges' portrayal of the Polynesian Islander Tu (Figure 8.2), in emphasizing the alert upward glance, an expression of sympathetic engagement, in a three-quarter profile view that promotes the fully rounded form of the head and shoulders, as well as the bright, almost laughing face of a figure noted for having a 'very particular turn for mimickry

OTOO KING OF O-TAHEITE.

Figure 8.2 William Hodges, engr. John Hall, *Otoo King of O-Taheite*, 1777, engraving, from James Cook, *A voyage towards the South Pole, and round the World: Performed in His Majesty's Ships the Resolution and Adventure, in the Years 1772, 1773, 1774, and 1775* (London, 1777), vol. 1, plate 38. British Museum, Department of Prints and Drawings, Oc2006,Prt.32 © Trustees of the British Museum

and humour'.[17] 'Mimickry' and 'humour' here are again not neutral terms, but betoken the 'unbounded ... curiosity' that characterized another of Abba Thulle's 'brothers', and the Palauans more generally, in wishing 'to have an explanation of everything he saw, to imitate whatever our people did, and to enquire into the principle and causes of all he observed brought about by them'.[18] Thus other images display similar features and characteristics: of Abba Thulle himself and of his son Lee Boo (Figure 8.3), whom he sent back to England on Wilson's rebuilt ship 'that he might have the advantage of improving himself by

Figure 8.3 Arthur William Devis, *Prince Lee Boo*, 1783, black and red chalk on paper, 264 × 194mm. British Museum, Department of Prints and Drawings, 1943,0409.1 © Trustees of the British Museum

accompanying the English, and of learning many things, that might at his return greatly benefit his own country'.[19] Of course, Lee Boo never did return to his own country, dying of that most civilized of diseases, small-pox, two days after Christmas, 1784, his death at just the age of 20 inscribing into Keate's narrative a sense of loss and melancholy ironically appropriate, within an eighteenth-century context, to his evocation of Palau as a form of paradise or Arcadia. Others of Devis' drawings emulate the art of Cook's voyages more pointedly through their translation into engravings for Keate's volume, his drawing of Ludee, one of Abba Thulle's wives, assuming an openly eroticized character in the engraving, that departs from Devis' original portrayal and renders it closer to Webber's portrait of Poedua of 1783–4. The drawings of Devis, therefore, an artist on an East India Company commercial voyage, can be seen as a paradigm for positive cultural interchange, or more bluntly, for benevolent empire at work.

Yet, the comparability of Devis' images and those of Cook's voyages points to another more strategic context for understanding the voyage of the *Antelope* in relation to East India Company policy in south-east Asia, and the function of visual imagery within it. The shared emphasis on ethnographic detail, such as bodily adornment, hairstyle, costume and custom (for example, Devis' careful observation of Abba Thulle's carrying his hatchet over his shoulder), tattooing or scarification, suggests not only a mutual concern between the voyages with a culturally relative, philosophical inquiry into human development, but also a more blunt colonialist or commercial imperative to investigate unknown or little-known regions towards the establishment of future markets or military outposts. In this context the *Antelope*'s expedition, despite its rarity in taking on board a professional artist, may be seen as just one of many similar voyages forming part of a long-term, overarching Company policy of expansion eastwards towards China and south towards Indonesia, which had been ongoing since the early 1770s.

The visualization of the 'Eastern Islands'

In 1769 Alexander Dalrymple, later the official East India Company hydrographer, argued in his *A Plan for Extending the Commerce of this Kingdom and of the East-India-Company* for the establishment of a British settlement or factory at Balambangan, just off the northern tip of Borneo, partly in order to challenge and undermine the monopoly of the Dutch spice trade in the East Indies by creating plantations of spices on British-controlled territory, but most importantly to establish a British presence in the region to support and facilitate the China trade.[20] The following year Captain Thomas Forrest was given command of the East India Company marine on the west coast of Sumatra, no doubt because of his extensive experience of conducting trading voyages in the area, from where he moved on to the newly established settlement at Balambangan. Here he was given orders by the Company to explore the numerous but little-known and largely uncharted islands to the east. This formed one of the first voyages in Dalrymple's ambitious and extensive plan to form an encyclopedic series of charts, both historical and newly commissioned, to assist future navigation from England throughout the entire region of south-east Asia, from the Bay of Bengal to Papua New Guinea. He publicized his scheme in 1783, the very same year as the voyage of the *Antelope*, in his *General Collection of Nautical Publications by Dalrymple*, explaining his proposal

> to publish a *compleat collection*, or *Series* of VIEWS of ALL the LANDS, from ENGLAND to the *most remote* parts of the EAST INDIES; which will not only be very useful to Navigators, but comprehend such a Description of the External Form of the Globe, as can no otherwise be had.[21]

Importantly, Dalrymple emphasizes here the fundamental importance of visual imagery and the practice of drawing to the successful completion of his scheme, contrary to received opinion of the value of visual records:

> Many *mere Seamen*, thinking they are incapable of drawing Views, hold them in disdain as *useless*: common sense is more than a sufficient match for such an absurd notion! Can the *best* mode of *expressing* the *forms* and *appearances* of Land, *which* are *essentially necessary to be known, be useless?* Perhaps no man has in words a competent power to describe the *marks* of *Land*: A man who carries that knowledge in *his* memory *without help*, keeps his knowledge to himself alone ... A *proper Set* of VIEWS should contain, not only *distant prospects* to distinguish the *Land*, from the time it becomes first visible above the Horizon, 'till within a few miles of it; but also VIEWS still *nearer* the Shoar which are useful, to give the most competent Description of the Country.

And he adds in a footnote that, 'Reeves's coloured Pencils will be very convenient for giving explanatory touches to the *Views of Land*.'[22] Dalrymple thus advocates a systematic method for the compilation of commercial and imperial knowledge in which the visual image is given a new and central role. Evidently, this was another reason for the employment of Thomas Forrest to explore the islands east of Balambangan in the mid-1770s – precisely the same time that Cook was employing artists on his much better known voyages to the Pacific. For Forrest was more than a competent draughtsman, and in his subsequent publication of his explorations, *A Voyage to New Guinea, and the Moluccas, from Balambangan ... Performed in the Tartar Galley, belonging to The Honourable East India Company, during the Years 1774, 1775, and 1776*, first published in 1779, he emphasizes that it is illustrated with 'thirty copperplates' based on his own first-hand drawings; and sets himself up as something of a natural historian in the manner of Cook or Johann Reinhold Forster, the German-born naturalist who, with his son George, accompanied Cook's second voyage, and of whose extensive accounts of that voyage published in 1777 and 1778, Forrest would surely have been aware in the preparation of his own publication.

The initial purpose of the voyage was to take up Dalrymple's belief that 'cinnamon, cloves, nutmegs, pepper and clove bark' could be easily introduced into the new settlement of Balambangan, by exploring islands in the East Indies outside Dutch control for specimens of spices and plants that could be brought back and cultivated there under British supervision, thus ending the dependence on the Dutch for the import of these valuable commodities and creating a lucrative rival trade in them.[23] However, the main motive behind the voyage was strategic: 'to undertake a voyage of discovery in seas very little known to the English' and investigate the possibility of further bases for Company business in the seas towards China.[24] So, on his return voyage from New Guinea in 1775 Forrest made a lengthy stopover at Mindanao, where his 'main concern was to find a site where the East India Company could, if it wished, establish a fort and warehouses', towards which end he secured the grant of Bunwoot Island, near the capital of Mindanao, from the Sultan.[25] The role of visual records in this major initiative was significant, and was made explicit in Forrest's instructions, which stipulate:

> If the object in expectation fails of the wished-for success, yet your voyage may have a very good effect towards the improvement of navigation. You must therefore be as accurate as possible, in laying down all shoals, &c. as well as explicit in your remarks and observations. Charts and drawings thereof must be taken, minutely marking every thing that may conduce to the above purpose.[26]

Forrest went far beyond the specific remit of these instructions, producing remarkable drawings of an extensive range of subjects deemed worthy of detailed observation. So he produced the expected charts and coastal profiles, though these were given an extraordinary and inventive treatment in the adoption of a seemingly unprecedented 'circular view' of coastal landscapes, providing a 360° panorama of Ubal Harbour in his newly acquired territory for Company exploitation, Bunwoot Island, no doubt with the aim of providing as much clear and detailed information about the new harbour and anchorage for potential Company use. He also made close studies of spice plants, such as cinnamon leaves, linked to the overall purpose of transplanting spices to Balambangan; a depiction of a wedding ceremony at Mindanao (Figure 8.4), where he engaged in lengthy studies of the native culture, preparing a genealogical table of the rulers of Mindanao as well as a supplementary 'Vocabulary of the Magindano Tongue'. All this was written up, Forrest's drawings and plans engraved, the whole dedicated to the Court of Directors of the East India Company, and published as the monumental *Voyage to New Guinea*, the first book of its kind, as Forrest is quick to point out in the Introduction, in which he gives a brief historical account of European contact with New Guinea, starting with the first contact made by the Portuguese in 1511. This provides a scholarly and 'scientific' platform for his own endeavour, the significance and originality of which he justifies by the claim that, although contact had been made several times since that early encounter, no European had had 'friendly intercourse with New Britain; and since Roggewein, nobody we know of, has had any with New Guinea'.[27] The visual counterpart to this weighty claim for a place in the history of exploration is the published chart of the voyage, which prefaces the textual account in time-honoured fashion (and emulating, again, the more immediate precedent of Cook's voyage accounts, where, for example, his Chart of the Southern Hemisphere has a similar placement and function).[28] Dedicated to Sir William James, Deputy Chairman of the Company, out of 'Esteem and Regard for his great Maritime Abilities', it shows the track of Forrest's voyage from Balambangan, in the top left corner of the chart, to New Guinea at the bottom right, thus offering a clear, focused testimony of the voyage in the form of an authoritative documentary record, as the complement to its historical genealogy already outlined.

There are two other plates that preface the text of Forrest's *Voyage*, and which are significant in the way they amplify the elevated claims made by the book as a work of natural history and scientific discovery. The first is the frontispiece, a portrait of the author, to which I shall return. The

A MAGINDANO MARRIAGE.

Figure 8.4 William Hamilton, engr. James Caldwell, *A Magindano Marriage*, 1779, etching and engraving, from Thomas Forrest, *A Voyage to New Guinea, and the Moluccas, from Balambangan: including an Account of Magindano, Sooloo, and Other Islands; and Illustrated with Thirty Copperplates: Performed in the Tartar Gallery, Belonging to the Honourable East India Company, during the Years 1774, 1775, and 1776, by Thomas Forrest* (London, 1779), plate 23. British Museum, Department of Prints and Drawings,1981,U.498 © Trustees of the British Museum

second is the 'View of Dory Harbour on New Guinea' (Figure 8.5), drawn (presumably after Forrest's own sketch made on the spot) by no less an artist than Thomas Hearne, a leading landscape watercolourist, who had recently returned from the Caribbean where he had been employed in making views of Antigua for the Governor-in-Chief of the Leeward Islands, Sir Ralph Payne. Given the ambitious scale of Forrest's book,

Figure 8.5 Thomas Hearne, engr. James Caldwell, *View of Dory Harbour on New Guinea*, 1779, etching and engraving, from Thomas Forrest, *A Voyage to New Guinea, and the Moluccas, from Balambangan: including an Account of Magindano, Sooloo, and Other Islands; and Illustrated with Thirty Copperplates: Performed in the Tartar Gallery, Belonging to the Honourable East India Company, during the Years 1774, 1775, and 1776, by Thomas Forrest* (London, 1779), frontispiece. British Museum, Department of Prints and Drawings, 1978,U.689.+ © Trustees of the British Museum

it is perhaps unsurprising that the 'View of Dory Harbour' is dedicated effusively:

> In Testimony of Esteem & Regard to Joseph Banks Esq.; President of the Royal Society, who thirsting after Knowledge, left the Enjoyment of Opulence and Ease, to sail round the World.

Forrest surely not only wanted to cultivate patronage from this most influential figure, but also to draw comparisons between Banks' seminal voyage with Cook of 1768–71 and his own endeavour, characterizing it, not as a mission of commercial speculation, but as foregoing 'the enjoyment of opulence and ease' in favour of a 'thirsting after knowledge'. Thus the print corresponds to a lengthy and detailed passage in the voyage account, describing this key location in Forrest's encounter with New Guinea, in a sophisticated mixture of ethnographic observation, topographical documentation, navigational information, and most impressively, specialized comparative cultural anthropology, that does enormous credit to Forrest's own inter-cultural sensibilities, in a way that surely invites comparison with the considered reports of cross-cultural encounter that emerged from Cook's voyages, and was intended to supplement the archive of global scientific knowledge under the aegis of the President of the Royal Society. It is worth quoting this passage at length:

> Off the mouth of the bay before the harbour, but out of the swell, a boat, with two Papua men, came on board, after having conversed a good deal with our linguists at a distance: satisfied we were friends, they hastened ashore, to tell, I suppose, the news. Soon after, many Papua Coffres came on board, and were quite easy and familiar: all of them wore their hair bushed out so much round their heads, that its circumference measured about three feet, and were at least, two and a half. In this they stuck their comb, consisting of four or five long diverging teeth, which they now and then combed their frizzling locks, in a direction perpendicular from the head, as with a design to make it more bulky. They sometimes adorned their hair with feathers. The women had only their left ear pierced, in which they wore small brass rings. The hair of the women was bushed out also; but not quite so much as that of the men [...]

> We anchored about four in the afternoon, close to one of their great houses, which is built upon posts, fixed several yards below low water mark; so that the tenement is always above the water: a long stage, supported by posts, going from it to the land, just at high water mark. The tenement contains many families, who live in cabins on each side of a wide common hall, that goes through the middle of it, and has two doors, one opening to the stage, towards the land; the other on a large stage towards the sea, supported likewise by posts, in rather deeper water than those that support the tenement.

On this stage the canoes are hauled up; and from this the boats are ready for a lanch, [sic] at any time of tide, if the Haraforas attack from the land; if they attack by sea, the Papuas take to the woods. The married people, unmarried women, and children, live in these large tenements, which, as I have said, have two doors; the one to the long narrow stage, that leads to the land; the other to the broad stage, which is over the sea, and on which they keep their boats, having outriggers on each side. A few yards from this sea stage, if I may so call it, are built, in still deeper water, and on stronger posts, houses where the batchelors live. This is like the custom of the Batta people on Sumatra, and the Idaan or Moroots on Borneo, where, I am told, the batchelors are separated from the young women and the married people.

At Dory there were two large tenements of this kind, almost four hundred yards from each other, and each had a house for the batchelors, close by it: in one of the tenements were fourteen cabins, seven on a side; in the other, twelve, or six on a side. In the common hall, I saw the women sometimes making mats, at other times forming pieces of clay into earthen pots; with a pebble in one hand, to put into it, whilst they held in the other hand also a pebble, with which they knocked, to enlarge and smooth it. The pots so formed, they burnt with dry grass, or light brushwood. The men, in general, wore a thin stuff, that comes from the cocoa nut tree, and resembles a coarse kind of cloth, tied forward round the middle, and up behind, between the thighs. The women wore in general, coarse blue Surat baftas, round their middle, not as a petticoat, but tucked up behind, like the men; so that the body and thigh were almost naked; as boys and girls go entirely. I have often observed the women with an ax or chopping knife, fixing posts for the stages, whilst the men were sauntering about idle. Early in the morning I have seen the men setting out in their boats, with two or three fox looking dogs, for certain places to hunt the wild hog, which they call Ben: a dog they call Naf. I have frequently brought them pieces of wild hog; which, however, I avoided carrying on board the galley, but dressed and eat it ashore, unwilling to give offence to the crew.[29]

Through reference to this extraordinary, detailed textual account, we are led to understand the image as a work of complex ethnography and natural history, incorporating references to dress, manufactures, building, food gathering and preparation, gender roles and language. So the principal focus of the view shows the large tenements on stilts, with the bachelor apartments alongside, but also shows us in the left foreground carefully delineated Papuans, showing their mode of dress and singular hairstyle, as well as their weaponry for hunting: for Forrest goes on to tell us that the Papuans at Dory 'are exceeding good archers, and some of their arrows are six foot long; the bow is generally of bamboo, and the string of split ratan'. This he extrapolates into a wider commentary on local trade routes:

> They purchase their iron tools, chopping knives, and axes, blue and red baftaes, china beads, plates, basons, &c. from the Chinese. The Chinese carry back Missoy bark, which they get to the eastward of Dory, at a place called Warmasine, or Warapine; it is worth 30 dollars, a pecul (133lb) on Java. They trade also in slaves, ambergrease, swallow, or sea slug, tortoiseshell, small pearls, black loories, large red loories, birds of Paradise, and many kinds of dead birds, which the Papua men have a particular way of drying.[30]

Forrest then gives a lengthy description of the Papua coast, no doubt for Dalrymple's benefit. There is a wealth of information here, that combines an elevated discourse of natural history and anthropology that bears comparison to the Forsters' published accounts of Cook's second voyage, with strategic data of immediate value to the East India Company, particularly with its growing interests in China: the understanding of Papuans' trading practices with the Chinese proleptically enfolds Papua, and Dory in particular, within a larger local commercial maritime network, of which Balambangan, and the East India Company base there, would also certainly be a part.

This is the work of no simple sea captain, but of a highly ambitious and multi-talented individual, with pretensions to presenting himself as an East India Company equivalent to Cook through transforming his voyage account into a work of natural history and imperial strategy. So his illustration of 'Papua Ovens for baking Bread from the Pith of the Sago (Palm) Tree' is tied to an extravagant project to cultivate sago as a simple and inexpensive means of subsistence throughout the expanding British settlements in the region, whereby 'three trees ... may maintain one man for a year, and an acre ... would maintain 100 men for the same time'.[31] On the back of this pragmatic strategy for facilitating colonial settlement and subsistence (which bears comparison with Banks's scheme for transplanting breadfruit from the Pacific to the Caribbean as food for slaves, the principal purpose – though rapidly eclipsed – of

Captain Bligh's voyage in the *Bounty*) Forrest proffers a philosophical meditation on human progress, of Forsterian proportions:

> So far the inhabitants of the globe, in low latitudes, may be justly considered as happily situated; something like what is said of the golden age, they may live almost without labour. But certain evils, in a great measure, counterbalance this seeming happiness: the faculties of the mind are blunted, and the body is enervated by indolence, that these petty states are subject to be overcome, by what Europeans would call a very despicable enemy, as they know nothing of the polity of great societies.
>
> The inhabitants of the Moluccas in particular, not being able to maintain their independence against Europeans, (whatever they did before history gives an account of them) have had their country continually in a state of war, as the monopoly of the clove and nutmeg has been successively a subject of contention between the Portuguese, Spaniards, and Dutch.
>
> I choose to draw a vail [*sic*] over that part of history, which informs us that our own country ever had any share in that trade.[32]

At one level this is no more than a straightforward and clichéd exercise in exoticizing and orientalizing non-European peoples, echoing longstanding associations between oriental climate and luxury, in combination with a view of Asia-Pacific islanders existing in a state of prelapsarian 'golden age' that, once again, derives from early European encounters with Polynesia (though once more, it might be thought surprising that this is voiced by the captain of an East-Indiaman). Yet it also casts a strategic and canny eye over the broader geopolitics of the region that have come about as a consequence of the European spice trade, in which he chooses discreetly not to include Britain, bearing in mind his employers and the dedicatees of his book, but which might offer potential opportunities for British East India Company initiatives. Likewise at Bali he provides a similar combination of detailed observations on strategic navigational and trading potential, with ethnographic notices of local custom, trade and manufactures, and larger philosophical commentary (in this instance, on the local version of *sati*), though also tells us that, through discretion, 'I did not trust myself ashore'.[33]

The aspirational, elevated claims for the book and its author are confirmed in the other plate that prefaces it: the frontispiece half-length portrait of Forrest, engraved by Sharp after J. K. Sherwin (Figure 8.6). In his seated pose, with his own chart open on the table before him, the image surely emulates Nathaniel Dance's recent, celebrated portrait of Cook, a connection supported by the choice of Sherwin as the artist, who was intimately familiar with Cook's portrait, since he had completed the print after it, published the same year as the portrait of Forrest, 1779.

Figure 8.6 John Keyse Sherwin, engr. William Sharp, *Captn Thos Forrest*, 1779, etching and engraving, from Thomas Forrest, *A Voyage to New Guinea, and the Moluccas, from Balambangan: including an Account of Magindano, Sooloo, and Other Islands; and Illustrated with Thirty Copperplates: Performed in the Tartar Gallery, Belonging to the Honourable East India Company, during the Years 1774, 1775, and 1776, by Thomas Forrest* (London, 1779), frontispiece. British Museum, Department of Prints and Drawings, 1841,0313.139 © Trustees of the British Museum

In all likelihood, Sherwin was working on both images at the same time. He had also engraved many of the plates after Hodges for the publication of Cook's second voyage.

Before a back-drop, visible past his right shoulder, of the open sea, on which are New Guinea vessels, Forrest is shown with his right forefinger resting on the chart and pointing at Indonesia and New Guinea; and with his left hand pointing upwards, although it is not clear at what, except the blank wall behind him, or else in a gesture of commanding address to the viewer, as though to draw attention to the importance of what follows. In a later edition of the print, the blank wall above his shoulder is filled with the representation of a medallion or 'chapp' with Malay characters, which commemorates a visit to Atcheen (Aceh) in 1784 where Forrest was honoured as 'Orancayo of the Golden Sword' and conferred with the medallion, and which visually answers his gesture in the print.[34] However, this later addition to the plate obscures the potential significance and iconographic reference of Forrest's gesture and pose. For it appears to be directly and significantly based on a late-seventeenth-century print by Nicholas de Larmessin, of the sixteenth-century Spanish explorer Hernán Cortés, which was published as an illustration to Isaac Bullart's *Académie des Sciences et des Arts* (1682), a book that surely only Forrest (or Dalrymple), rather than Sherwin, would have known.

The sixteenth-century conquest of Mexico, and the part of Cortés in it, was a contentious subject for eighteenth-century British historians, presenting a model of dubious morality for imperial expansion. Yet it was generally agreed that Cortés himself was an exceptional figure 'whose exploits have placed him with the most illustrious heroes of ancient or modern times'.[35] According to this commentator:

> The character of Cortez is differently represented by historians: but they all agree, that to great strength of body, and the ability of enduring the most excessive fatigue, he united great vigour and perseverance of mind; that he had a graceful person, an engaging aspect, was singular for dexterity in all warlike exercises, and possessed in an eminent degree that address and insinuation necessary to acquire an ascendency over the minds of others. To these high qualities his admirers add, a sagacity that foresaw every thing; a presence of mind not to be disturbed by the most untoward events; calm prudence in concerting his schemes, steady resolution in executing them; animated by that enthusiastic love of glory, which has ever been considered as the leading qualification in a hero, and

which may rather be said to command success, than to earn it. But the moral portrait of this extraordinary man is best delineated in his actions[36]

To the discerning viewer or reader of Forrest's print and book (which would undoubtedly have included his friend, Dalrymple, and Sir Joseph Banks) it was not, therefore, the conquest of Mexico and the wanton expansion of empire with which Forrest was asking to be associated, but the qualities of 'strength', 'sagacity', 'presence of mind', 'calm prudence', 'steady resolution' and 'love of glory'; and above all, perhaps, with the idea that his 'moral portrait ... is best delineated in his actions', of which the book is both the record and the witness. The portrait, therefore, complements the 'View of Dory Harbour' both in terms of echoing the sentiments of the latter's dedication to Banks, and also in its status as a record of Forrest's 'actions' in reaching and charting part of New Guinea. Of added significance here is the fact that the 'View of Dory Harbour' is also a demonstrable confirmation that visual recording, whether in the form of charts, coastal profiles or landscape views, must equally count as an important part of those 'actions' by which his 'moral portrait' is to be delineated.

This fascinating document needs to be placed, like Wilson's voyage in the *Antelope*, as part of an overall Company strategy to compile a 'proper set of views' towards the end of expanding Company interests towards China. This was maintained, following Wilson's return from Palau and the publication of Keate's *Account*, by John McCluer, who sailed back to Palau in 1790, in part to inform Abba Thulle of his son, Lee Boo's death, but more specifically to establish a permanent British foothold there, en route to further exploration and surveying of New Guinea and the neighbouring islands. McCluer had been actively surveying and recording the regional waters for several years, clearly under instructions from Dalrymple, who published his resulting reports with effusive encomia for their standard and accuracy, beginning with McCluer's account of navigation between India and the Gulf of Persia. Dalrymple excuses the '*few obscurities*' and 'any imperfection of stile and language' of this report on the grounds that it 'contains so much important information' and that the 'Young Man, to whom the Publick are indebted for this valuable Work, is *self-taught*', reiterating the potential anomaly of asking relatively ill-educated and untrained seamen to engage in the level of documentary hydrographical and geographical recording required for his project.[37] Nonetheless, McCluer clearly met Dalrymple's expectations, no doubt because of the former's assiduous and systematic commitment to recording, in which visual documentation played an important part, as the instructions (written by Dalrymple?) for his slightly later survey of the Indian coast demanded:

> We would have the Vessel proceed along the Coast from Bombay to Surat, determining carefully the Latitude and Longitudes of the various *Points*, as well as of the *Peaks* and *Hills* inland, with explanatory Views of the Lands, taking *Altitudes* for determining the *Time* by Chronometer every hour, and taking the *Bearings* and *Altitudes* of the *Lands*, &c. by the Hadley at such Time.[38]

En route McCluer sent back to London a painting by the Chinese artist, Spoilum, of three Palauan Islanders that he was returning home from Macao, a rich example of the complexities of cultural exchange informing the production of visual imagery within the imperial context at this period.[39] We might see, as the culmination of this sequence of voyages in south-east Asia, the 1792 embassy to China, led by Lord Macartney, with Thomas Hickey and William Alexander as accompanying artists: although a state mission and not an East India Company voyage, it was keenly backed by the Company, and Macartney's ship, the *Lion*, sailed in convoy with Company vessels.[40]

The standard history of exploration of this period, together with the associated visual imagery, and their consequent combined impact on understandings of environmental history, ethno-history and historical geography, has focused overwhelmingly on Cook's voyages (understandably), seeing them either from a postcolonial perspective as part of the history of European perceptions of the world, or treating the voyages as essentially scientific enterprises, state-sponsored and formative to the rise of geographical knowledge and the discourse of science. It is clear that this picture needs to be revised and amplified: the activities of the East India Company during the same period demonstrate the complex interactions between commercial interests and artistic practise in eighteenth-century Britain, particularly in relation to voyaging, exploration and Western perceptions of south-east Asia and the Pacific. Focusing attention on the East India Company both complicates the standard history of the art of Cook's voyages as being discrete practices uniquely tied to state uses of art through the Admiralty, and also points to a much more systematic and under-analysed role of the Company in British art, that amplifies our knowledge of the uses of art in eighteenth-century Britain, for the purposes of the Company, the nation and the empire.

Notes

1. The story of Lee Boo is told in Daniel J. Peacock (1987), *Lee Boo of Belau: A Prince in London*, Honolulu: University of Hawaii Press; the epitaph is transcribed on p. 119.
2. On the history of Mai in London, see Michelle Hetherington (2001), *Cook and Omai: the Cult of the South Seas*, Canberra: National Library of Australia; Harriet Guest (2007), *Empire, Barbarism, and Civilisation: James Cook, William Hodges, and the Return to the Pacific*, Cambridge and New York : Cambridge University Press.
3. For an overview of non-Western visitors to eighteenth-century Britain, see Jocelyn Hackforth-Jones (ed.) (2007), *Between Worlds: Voyagers to Britain 1700–1850*, London: National Portrait Gallery.
4. Nicholas Thomas (2002), 'The Pelew Islands in British Culture', in George Keate, *An Account of the Pelew Islands*, ed. Karen L. Nero and Nicholas Thomas, assistant ed. Jennifer Newall, London and New York: Leicester University Press, p. 27.
5. On this subject generally, see Howard T. Fry (1970), *Alexander Dalrymple (1737–1808) and the Expansion of British Trade*, London: Frank Cass, published for the Royal Commonwealth Society, pp. 150–65 *et passim*.
6. Thomas, 'Pelew Islands in British Culture', p. 28. Bernard Smith (1985), *European Vision and the South Pacific*, New Haven: Yale University Press.
7. This has been the subject of considerable scholarship: for a summary, see Nicholas Thomas (2003), *Discoveries: The Voyages of Captain Cook*, London: Allen Lane, pp. 152–7.
8. Keate, *Account*, p. 215.
9. Thomas, 'Pelew Islands in British Culture', p. 31.
10. The literature on this subject is too vast to include here. For useful accounts of the relation of commerce and commercial ideology to art, aesthetics and eighteenth-century visual culture in general, see David H. Solkin (1993), *Painting for Money: The Visual Arts and the Public Sphere in Eighteenth-Century England*, New Haven and London: Yale University Press; David Bindman (2002), *Ape to Apollo: Aesthetics and the Idea of Race in the Eighteenth Century*, London: Reaktion Books; Matthew Craske (1997), *Art in Europe 1700–1830: A History of the Visual Arts in an Era of Unprecedented Urban Economic Growth*, Oxford: Oxford University Press.
11. Thomas, 'Pelew Islands in British Culture', p. 33.
12. Keate, *Account*, pp. 221–2.
13. George Forster (2000 [1777]), *A Voyage Round the World*, ed. Nicholas Thomas and Oliver Berghof, Honolulu: University of Hawaii Press, vol. 2, p. 505.
14. On the impeachment of Warren Hastings, see P. J. Marshall (1965), *The Impeachment of Warren Hastings*, Oxford: Oxford University Press; and within the wider context of East India Company corruption, see Nicholas B. Dirks (2006), *The Scandal of Empire: India and the Creation of Imperial Britain*, Cambridge, MA: Harvard University Press.
15. Thomas, 'Pelew Islands in British Culture', pp. 29–30.
16. Thomas, 'Pelew Islands in British Culture', pp. 27–8.
17. Keate, *Account*, p. 29.
18. Keate, *Account*, p. 25.

19. Keate, *Account*, p. 160.
20. Alexander Dalrymple (1769), *A Plan for Extending the Commerce of this Kingdom and of the East-India-Company*. London: Printed for the Author; Fry, *Alexander Dalrymple*, pp. 66–93.
21. Alexander Dalrymple (1783), *General Collection of Nautical Publications by Dalrymple*, London: G. Bigg, p. 12.
22. Dalrymple, *General Collection of Nautical Publications*, pp. 12–13.
23. Thomas Forrest (1780), *A Voyage to New Guinea, and the Moluccas, from Balambangan: including an Account of Magindano, Sooloo, and other Islands; and Illustrated with Thirty Copperplates. Performed in the Tartar Galley, belonging to The Honorouable east India Company, during the Years 1774, 1775, and 1776, by Captain Thomas Forrest. To which is added, A Vocabulary of the Magindano Tongue*, 2nd edition, London: G. Scott, p. 2.
24. Fry, *Alexander Dalrymple*, p. 138.
25. Fry, *Alexander Dalrymple*, p. 138.
26. Forrest, *Voyage to New Guinea*, pp. 5–6.
27. Forrest, *Voyage to New Guinea*, p. xii.
28. See James Cook (1777), *A Voyage towards the South Pole and round the World: Performed in His Majesty's Ships the Resolution and Adventure, in the Years 1772, 1773, 1774, and 1775*, London: W. Strahan and T. Cadell.
29. Forrest, *Voyage to New Guinea*, pp. 95–7.
30. Forrest, *Voyage to New Guinea*, p. 106.
31. Forrest, *Voyage to New Guinea*, p. 44.
32. Forrest, *Voyage to New Guinea*, p. 45.
33. Forrest, *Voyage to New Guinea*, pp. 170–1.
34. This updated portrait serves as the frontispiece to Thomas Forrest (1792), *A Voyage from Calcutta to the Mergui Archipelago*, London.
35. William Russell (1778), *The History of America, from its Discovery by Columbus to the Conclusion of the Late War*, 2 vols., London, vol. 1, p. 62.
36. Russell, *History of America*, p. 63.
37. John McCluer (1786), *An Account of the Navigation between India and the Gulph of Persia, at all Seasons, with Nautical Instructions for that Gulph, by Lieutenant John McCluer. Published at the Charge of the East India Company by Dalrymple*, London: George Bigg, p. v.
38. John McCluer (1789), *Description of the Coast of India, by John McCluer, 1787, & 1788. Published at the Charge of the East India Company, by Dalrymple*, London: George Bigg, p. i.
39. This is thought to be the painting now in the collection of the British Museum, formerly in the Museum of Mankind, BM no. Oc2006, Ptg. 23: see Peacock, *Lee Boo*, p. 131.
40. The convoy was possibly commemorated in a large oil painting by Thomas Luny now in the National Maritime Museum: *The East Indiaman 'Hindostan' and other Vessels*, BHC3403.

9
Unlikely Partners: Malay-Indonesian Medicine and European Plant Science

Jeyamalar Kathirithamby-Wells

Introduction

The biological and strategic importance of the Malay-Indonesian region – synonymous with the biogeographical zones of Sunda and Wallacea – placed *materia medica* at the forefront of regional and international commerce in the pre-European era.[1] It thus became the target of East India Company and imperial plant prospecting aimed at appropriating both the resources and the less tangible knowledge associated with them. I argue that, notwithstanding European political hegemony, indigenous *materia medica* remained autonomous and inaccessible except through avenues of social discourse and collaboration.

Part I outlines the pivotal role of Malay-Indonesian pharmaceuticals in early international trade. The trans-regional mediations which the trade generated added transplantations to a broad range of endemic stocks. The interchange of exotics, transplantations and associated knowledge within a free market economy shaped *materia media* as a distinct feature of the region's culture and identity.

Part II describes the enhanced importance of Malay-Indonesian *materia medica* in the European quest for trade commodities and cheap, efficacious remedies for tropical disease. I examine the intrusions of the English and Dutch East India Companies beyond the traditional boundaries of market exchange and the challenges this posed.

Part III traces the maturing of Company plant prospecting initiatives under imperial power as exemplified by the inauguration of the colonial scientific service and the overall effect of colonial ascendance on indigenous *materia medica*.

Part I: The foundations of Malay-Indonesian *Materia Medica*

Wealth of resource and knowledge

The affinity between biotic knowledge and healing as a universal phenomenon since ancient times is attested in Egypt's *Ebers Papyrus* (c. 1500 BCE), India's Vedic *Sushruta Samhita* and the third-century *Charaka Samhita*, Dioscorides' *De Materia Medica* (CE c. 77), and China's legendary *Shen Nung Pen Ts'ao Ching* recorded in the Sui (589–618) literature register. These medical legacies constituted systematic recording of knowledge and experience distilled and preserved over time in popular memory through religio-mystical beliefs and culinary uses. Thus, as an integral feature of culture and civilization, *materia medica* enhanced the literary, aesthetic and philosophical dimensions of good living.

Greek pharmaceuticals laid particular emphasis on plants from the warm climes of the tropics accessed through West Asia. Theophrastus (c. 371–286 BCE) who, with Aristotle (384–322 BCE), laid the foundations for the study of natural history in the West, was familiar with the medicinal properties associated with pepper, cinnamon, myrrh and frankincense. In the herbal compiled c. 1150 at medieval Europe's first medical school in Salerno, out of the 273 drugs described by Matthaeus Platearius, 229 were plant-derived and included many from the tropics.[2] Hence, visions of a paradisal East inspired pioneer European explorations seeking profit from plants with pharmaceutical and culinary properties. Alexander the Great's conquests in Egypt and India informed Greek knowledge of tropical botany while the Roman quest for spices pioneered maritime trade between the West and Asia.[3] The expanding demand for tropical spices and pharmaceuticals and the inter-Asian trade it spurred was manifested in the emergence of the fourth-century medical school in Edessa, on the northern edge of Syria and, later, in Djundishapur in Persia, where Neoplatonists and Nestorians among Greeks, Persians, Jews and Hindus exchanged herbal knowledge.[4]

Human preoccupation with the search for biotic material for the improvement of health and cure for disease proved a compelling incentive for international trade in the pre-modern era. From at least the early centuries of the first millennium mega-diversity and a strategic location thrust the Malay-Indonesian region into the forefront of Indian Ocean pharmaceutical exchange. Practitioners of Malay-Indonesian herbal practices ranged from shamans and medicine men (*bomoh/pawang* and *dukun*,[5] respectively) of a pre-literate origin serving tribal and peasant communities, to court physicians whose knowledge derived from Indian classical texts.

The medicinal simples used and traded originated in the remote recesses of the Malay-Indonesian forests where foraging aboriginal and other tribal communities were custodians of extensive plant knowledge. The 'medicinal hut' of the Malayan aborigines attested to the importance of plant medicine in the life of the community. Through barter with coastal middlemen, they exchanged plant substances, including medicinal plants, for salt and other necessities.[6]

In contrast to the extensively recorded Arab, Chinese and Indian *materia medica*, the dominance of the oral over the literary tradition in the Malay-Indonesian world rooted plant knowledge in the experience of daily encounter and cultural transmission. The aboriginal communities of Peninsular Malaysia (Orang Asli), for example, are heirs to an extensive vocabulary for ferns, which formed an important part of their daily diet. Of some 50 ferns and fern-allies in the Temuan vocabulary, at least a dozen are ascribed medicinal properties.[7] Similarly, the wide use among the Malays of the areca palm with pharmaceutical properties (see below) was well served by a vernacular nomenclature covering every part of the tree: the leaves, trunk, husk, root, shoot and nut (both ripe and unripe).[8]

Medical knowledge accumulated over time was transmitted orally. Prescriptions or *jamu*, derived from the word *jampi* (sacred recipe), belonged to the domain of cumulative experience and closely guarded oral legacies. The common custodians were women, adept at tapping the oft dual merits of herbs for culinary use and domestic health care.[9] On the professional level, practitioners were shamans, often synonymous by way of knowledge and experience with community elders. Association of the efficacy of plants with magic inextricably bound shamanistic practices with the enhancement of secret remedies through supernaturally evoked ritual.

Among the Malays, the shaman (*pawang*) customarily solicited the cooperation of the 'tree spirit' before collecting the aromatic eaglewood (*Aquilaria malaccensis; gaharu*) and camphor (*kapur*) (from *Dryobalanops aromatica*).[10] Their high market value, commensurate with their wide dispersal, difficulty of collection and easy depletion was protected, in part, by customary taboos, royal prerogatives and licensed harvesting.[11]

One of the lead products in early international trade originating from wide indigenous use in the Indo-Malay region was benzoin, or gum Benjamin (from *Styrax benzoin; kemenyan*). Used for fevers including malaria, it also played a key role in the rice harvest ceremony of the aboriginal Semang of north-central Peninsular Malaysia as a fumigant, preceding grain storage. The ritualized use of benzoin, which was burnt in a censer by the shaman in the imprecation of spirits, resonated Brahminical and Christian ritual with the use, respectively, of camphor and frankincense (see below). The magical and mystical properties associated with aromatics are believed to have enhanced their efficacy.[12] Such curative properties were associated, for example, with the aromatic lemon grass (*Cymbopogon citratus*; Malay *serai*). The Besisi of Selangor planted it near paddy fields to protect crops, and around graves to ward off spirits, while the Malays used it for renal disorders.[13]

Market pre-eminence

Low bulk, high value *media media*, constituting items equivalent to the value of precious metal, nourished the growth and flowering of Southeast Asia's early states, principally Funan, Srivijaya and Majapahit. Predominant in Southeast Asian exports to South Asia were clove (*lavanga* from *Eugenia aromatica/ caryophyllata*) and sandalwood (*Santalum album*) from eastern Indonesia. Clove entered Indian vocabulary and medicine around the second century CE and was probably transmitted in small amounts to the West through the Roman trade with the Malabar Coast for pepper (from *Piper negrum*).[14]

In the case of sandalwood, which occurred in east Java and the Lesser Sunda Islands, especially Timor, its ancient importance is suggested by its common use in funereal purification in the region. Apart from its pharmaceutical and cosmetic value, it gained an important place in religious worship among Hindus and Buddhists. Exported to China and introduced into the Indian sub-continent, it entered the Red Sea trade probably as early as the sixth century CE.[15]

Apart from dried and preserved *materia medica*, trade provided opportunity for the transplantation of seeds, rhizomes and even live plants to compatible climes. The spread of the endemic areca nut palm (*Areca catechu*) to South Asia is an outstanding example. It soon bred the ubiquitous habit of chewing the betel quid, comprising the betel-nut, wrapped in betel-leaf (*Piper betle*), with a touch of lime. Besides its attraction as a stimulant, the betel quid was favoured for its anti-bacterial properties because of arecolidine contained in the nut and contribution to general good health through preventing intestinal infections and dental decay. The dual function of betel chewing as a stimulant and an aid to good heath enhanced its cultural value and gave it a high place in social interaction, and ceremonial and religious ritual.[16]

The counter-flow of trade from India to comparable climes in the Malay-Indonesian region saw the introduction, under Hindu-Buddhist influence, of the *nagasari* (Javanese) or *penaga* (Malay) (*Mesua ferrea*) and *perawas* (*Litsea odorifera*), as well as the sweet flag (*Acorus calamus*) – all reputedly of medicinal value.[17] The magical properties attributed to the *nagasari* and the *perawas* are believed to enhance their pharmaceutical properties. Successfully introduced into Java, both plants remain popular, especially for aroma therapeutic uses.[18] In the Peninsula, where the *Mesua ferrea* does not flourish so well, substitution of the endemic *Schima naronhae* (*cangkok*), demonstrates the dynamic evolution of indigenous *materia medica*.[19] Probably also introduced during the same period of Hindu-Buddhist influence was neem, mambu (*Azadirachta indica*), which became widespread, principally as a febrifuge, and from which the modern bio-insecticide is derived.[20] Among South Asian transplants, the sweet flag, mentioned in the *Sushruta Samhita* won particular favour, its rhizome used for ailments, including malaria.[21] An introduction of considerable significance was *Piper nigrum*, endemic to the Western Ghats. Cultivated in the Malay-Indonesian region from the fourteenth century onwards as a culinary spice of prime commercial importance, its specific medicinal use is exemplified in the still-popular Singapore tonic (*ubat jamu* or *ubat majun*), an aphrodisiac and treatment for indigestion and liver complaints.[22]

While India shows some ecological overlaps with the Malay-Indonesian region favouring transplants, China's temperate climate – except on its southern border with Indochina – accounted for its spectacular volume and variety of Southeast Asian pharmaceutical imports. In this regard Chinese sensibility to the ecological underpinnings of plant life informed the insight, for example, of the fourth-century CE estate owner and poet Xie Lingyun. He perceived trees within his environment as 'seek[ing] their particular requirements, and having their own specificities' of climate, location and soil conditions.[23] Consonant with the bewildering wealth and commercial value of its Southeast Asian pharmaceutical imports, China evolved a high level in nomenclature (involving the transliteration of foreign names) as well as botanical description, uncommon in the largely oral traditions of the Nanyang.[24] Lin I, an envoy to Champa during the third century, for example, recorded a detailed morphological description of the areca-nut palm (*Areca catechu*) which, with other Southeast Asian *naturalia*, left a deep imprint on Chinese knowledge production.[25]

Seventh-century Tang expansion of the Nanyang trade, following completion of the Grand Canal, broadened the constituency of the once-elite market to include a wide range of imports to serve medicinal, ritual and culinary uses including Southeast Asian aromatics and spices, principally cloves, mace, nutmegs, and cardamom.[26]

Development of the Nanyang trade under the Tang intersected with the rise of Srivijaya and its role in the expansion of Arab maritime trade in Malay-Indonesian *materia medica*. Arab trade introduced the fragrant and curative camphor (*Dryobalanops aromatic*) of Barus (in Sumatra) to the markets of China, where its efficacy was deemed 'immediate' for alleviating labour in child-birth. Given the trade name '*kapur* Barus', as distinct from the product of Borneo and southern Peninsular Malaya, it was deemed superior in quality to the product from Iranian and Syrian sources.[27]

Similarly, Arab trade promoted the substitution of the reputedly superior Sumatran benzoin, under the trade name *laban jawa*, for depleting sources of West Asian frankincense (*Boswellia* spp.; *laban*), earlier introduced to China via the Levant and known as *franhunziang*.[28] *Laban jawa*'s special medicinal properties, not associated with the more mystical properties of frankincense, accounted for its greater preference and market value.[29]

Sumatra's exports to China included a number of other special resins and aromatics, which the Malay-Indonesian region shared with the mainland Indochinese biographic zone. Among them, 'dragon's blood' (*jernang*), identified with the resin from the rattan *Daemonorhops* spp. was believed to treat pain and blood clotting.[30] Borne westwards, like the 'kapur Barus' by Arab trade, it later entered Western medicine for treatment of diarrhoea and dysentery, besides use as an astringent in tooth powders.[31]

Lac, the secretion of the female scale-insect (*Laccifer* spp.), though generally used as a dye, also joined the list of Chinese pharmaceutical imports.[32] By the twelfth century, scented woods, pre-eminently *akar laka* (*Dalbergia parviflora*), sandalwood and eaglewood, valued for their cosmetic and medicinal properties, were among Chinese imports from Southeast Asia.[33] The same trade flows from the Nanyang included animal products, primarily ivory and rhinoceros parts, prized for their perceived medical properties. Though rarity lent many Southeast Asian medicinal simples the cloak of elite luxury in China, the common scrub grass *Imperata arundinacea/ cylindrica* (Malay *lalang*), earned a place alongside other medicinal imports.[34]

Subsequent Ming commercial expansion in the 'Southern Regions' boosted China's appetite for pharmacopoeia, epitomized in the early fifteenth-century maritime expeditions of Zheng He. It was probably during this period that edible birds'-nests from the swifts of the genus *Aerodramus* spp. entered the Nanhai trade, increasing China's investment in Southeast Asia's *materia medica* for the perceived improvement of health and quality of life.[35] Pharmaceutical products of contemporary vogue were lead items of tribute sent to China in exchange, principally, for Chinese silk and porcelain. In 1157 Melayu-Jambi presented 111,615 catties of *ju* (pine resin) and sandalwood and, in 1382, the Javanese mission conveyed an estimated 74,000 catties of its new commercial pepper.[36] The proliferation of smuggling and piracy in the coastal waters of South China attested to the low bulk, high value of *materia medica*.

Despite the plant diversity of the Malay-Indonesian region, there were some borrowings from China's rich pharmaceutical tradition. Among transplants was the prized 'Ngai camphor' from *Blumea balsamifera* (Malay *capa*) mentioned in *The Medical Book of Malayan Medicine* (see below) for a variety of treatments. Endemic to the warm climes of southern China, its use spread via Indochina into the Malay Peninsula.[37]

Trade flows to the Nanyang included some Chinese pharmaceuticals of international repute. The dry root and powder of Chinese liquorice, *Glycyrrhiza* spp. (Malay *akar manis Cina*), next in importance to ginseng in Chinese *materia medica*, won a prominent place in Malay medicine.[38] Another popular import was the rhizome of the Chinese *galangal* (Lesser Galangal: *Languas officinarum*), containing cineole and deemed of greater curative value than the native *Alpina galanga L. (Greater Galangal)*.[39] The equally popular *Smilax china* or 'China root' (Malay *gadong Cina*) in Malay medicine was used in the treatment of syphilis.[40] Carried westwards, the study of its properties by the Flemish doctor Andreas Vesalius marked the historic convergence of Oriental and Occidental *materia medica*.[41]

Part II: European plant prospecting

Venturing beyond the market place

Less than a century after Zheng He's Indian Ocean expeditions, the same bio-prospecting impulse spurred the European voyages of discovery in search of spices and tropical plant remedies. In contrast to Chinese pharmaceutical consumption contained within tributary trade, the Portuguese capture of the spice capital of Melaka in 1511 marked a historic shift towards a more aggressive European intrusion into the Indian Ocean.

Fundamental to the aims of Portuguese commercial expansion was knowledge of the trans-Indian Ocean market network convergent on Melaka. With this objective, the Portuguese crown appointed Tomé Pires, apothecary and factor at Cananore, as *veador das drogarias* (overseer of drugs) at Melaka. Pires's *Soma Oriental* (1515) and the complementary

Enformacão by the lesser-known apothecary Simãi Alvares constituted groundbreaking studies of the wealth and variety of Melaka's products, including *materia medica*.[42]

The Portuguese desire for monopoly soon moved *materia medica* from the market place to the arena of European commercial and territorial rivalry. European 'plant capitalism', spearheaded by the British and the Dutch in South- and Southeast Asia, implied going further than the inventorying of Pires and Alvares to match products in the market place with their sources of origin, uses, and prescriptions. A prerequisite for European commercial ascendancy was co-option of indigenous plant knowledge – tantamount to socio-economic intrusion – hazarded a negative response, unless skilfully negotiated. The template for addressing this challenge was pioneered by the Spanish physician Garcia da Orta (c. 1501/2–1568), a servant of the Portuguese government in Goa.

Orta set out for Goa in 1534 with 'a great desire to know about the medicinal drugs ... as well as all the fruits and pepper ... their names in all the different languages, as also the countries where they grow and the trees and plants which bear them and likewise how the Indian physicians use them'.[43] Orta's commitment to explore indigenous knowledge was endorsed by the Goan government, which was compelled by the shortage of European doctors to turn to local medical practitioners, especially for the treatment of tropical disease.[44]

Local knowledge, whether in the form of sacred texts or oral tradition, was communally shared and guarded. This problem Orta circumvented, as did other Europeans after him, by cultivating a network of local informants. Orta's friendship with the ruler of Ahmednagar, Burhan Nizam Shah, gave him access to the Muslim court physicians (*hakims*), profiting from the commonality between their *yunani* and Western medical traditions.[45] Equally, though knowing no Sanskrit, his medical and scholarly credentials eased interactions with Hindu *panditos*. He also gained access to the practical knowledge and actual medical practices prevalent among Malayali physicians (*vaidyas*) of the Ayurvedic tradition.[46] Faithful to practical observation, consonant with the spirit of the Age of Exploration, Orta wrote: 'For me the testimony of an eyewitness is worth more than that of all the physicians, and all the fathers of medicine who write on false information.'[47]

The knowledge Orta gathered from informants, combined with his extensive travels in Western India and Ceylon, and his experimentation in his private botanic garden near Bombay, culminated in the *Colóquois dos simples, e drogas ... da India* (1563). The wide scope of Orta's compendium was based, according to his own proud claim, on a synthesis of Arab, Hindu and European knowledge.[48] The *Cóloquois* – the first European botanical account of the plants of the sub-continent and beyond – described 59 plants, including information on Malay-Indonesian aromatics, sandalwood and spices, long traded in the markets of the Mediterranean but little understood.[49]

VOC: Emulating Orta in the East Indies

Orta's Indian Ocean plant exploration was expanded during the seventeenth century under the bold initiatives of the Vereenigde Oost-Indische Compagnie (VOC) and English East India Company (EEIC). Their rival ambitions converged in the Malay-Indonesian region, reiterating its historic pre-eminence as a resource pool. The abiding importance of *material medica* for commerce and health was enhanced by a curiosity to understand the natural world. Company surgeons doubled as collectors and traders. Plant prospecting attracted a wide array of other actors including military men, sailors, traders, adventurers and even the buccaneering William Dampier (c. 1651–1715).[50] *Materia medica*, among other exotic *naturalia*, were coveted objects of lucrative investment and furnished European cabinets of curiosities (*kunstkammeren*), popularized by rulers and patricians as symbols of wealth and status. Books on herbs were also among the most popular printed works.[51]

Apart from competing for goods for the European market, the VOC and EEIC were committed to exploring the full commercial and pharmaceutical potential of tropical *naturalia*. To this end they actively supported research in metropolitan museums and gardens through furnishing herbal collections and requested sample specimens. In fact, plant prospecting and collecting in the East was a vital lifeline for metropolitan research and experimentation. Chairs in botany were established in leading European universities, the first in the medical school at Padua in 1533, with affiliated experimental botanical gardens and herbaria. Reputedly, Malayan specimens furnished by Francis Drake supplemented the bulk of Dutch collections in Leiden, where the Flemish doctor and doyen of Asian botany, Carolus Clusius, was professor (1526–1609).

As well as responding to metropolitan scientific demands, it was the professional duty of surgeons and apothecaries to discover cheap, effective and readily available herbal remedies. In addition to seeking cures for common ailments, they investigated treatments for tropical diseases, which accounted for high mortality among Company employees. Surgeons and collectors approached medicinal plant prospecting with a shared conviction that remedies for diseases would be found within the same natural environment that bred them. As Jacobus Bontius (1592–1631) the VOC surgeon in Batavia put it: 'Where the diseases ... are endemic, there the bountiful hand of Nature has profusely planted herbs whose virtues are adapted to counteract them'.[52] For Rumphius (G.E. Rumpf 1627–1702) in Ambiona, the link between man and nature took a deeper religious meaning. He believed, in common with the local physicians (*dukun*), that God in his wisdom had provided appropriate herbs to cure endemic diseases.[53]

Vital to the task of plant prospecting – as Orta, Rumphius, Bontius, and Hendrik Adriaan van Reede tot Draakenstein (1636–91) amply demonstrated – was indigenous knowledge. In India, Nicholas L'Empereur (c. 1660–1742), Chief Surgeon at the French settlement at Balasore, invested in Indian medical texts in addition to conducting field research.[54] The Italian traveller and medical expert, Filoppo Sassetti, who lived in Goa (1583–6) and was the only European of his time who knew Sankrit, consulted ancient manuscripts including *Nighantu*, an Ayurvedic compendium on medicinal plants and their uses.[55]

Similarly, Van Reede, as Dutch commander in Cochin, consulted palm leaf texts in Malayalam, helped by the famous physician Itty Achuden who translated and interpreted them.[56] However, in the Malay-Indonesian region the scarcity of medical texts and experts to interpret them presented a different situation. Here, Europeans were obliged to rely largely on the non-elite sector and its more elusive but dynamic pool of orally transmitted knowledge, based on vernacular practices which Orta had favoured.

VOC surgeons soon came to respect the plant knowledge of ordinary people. Bontius, a proponent of the value of indigenous knowledge, was keen on dispelling popular assumptions of native ignorance. He was humbled by the plant knowledge of the Gujarati and Coromandel people, who 'sagaciously distinguish between medicinal, edible, and poisonous herbs better than the most expert botanist in our country [the Netherlands]'. He noted similar plant knowledge among Malayan women and condemned the superior attitude of European medical practitioners.[57]

Accessing indigenous knowledge, however, proved not entirely easy. On arriving at Banten, the first Dutch fleet was able to record 55 items of herbs and spices with their medicinal uses, all freely vended at the market, mainly by women. These vendors were equipped with the marketing skills of correct identification and freely communicated their products' uses.[58] But the more accurate and carefully guarded prescriptions beyond the market place could not so easily be accessed. Language and social barriers stood in the way of winning the confidence and cooperation of local informants generally reluctant to part with prescriptions. In fact, to gain a proper understanding of herbal remedies, collectors and surgeons often were obliged to take their own ailments to local physicians at the risk of traumatic treatments and an uncertain outcome.[59]

Fundamental to the creation of a vital area of interaction or 'biocontact zone'[60] were the acquisition of linguistic skills and a basic understanding of local customs and habits. For, as L'Empereur noted from his own experience in India, 'speaking directly without interpreters' swept away the reticence of a fakir who revealed to him the remedy for leprosy.[61] In Ambiona, Rumphius held his local Arab informant on plant resources, Iman (?Imam) Rati, in high regard.[62] Rumphius's social interaction with the island's multi-ethnic informants was facilitated by his familiarity with Arabic, Malay, the Amboinese dialects, and a smattering of Chinese. He thus adopted plant nomenclature in a variety of local languages.[63] Furthermore, his marriage to a local woman, Sussana, was conducive to cultivating links with the local community. A testament to the early Euro-Asian collaboration they forged was the orchid he named *Flos susannae*, 'in memory of her, who during her life was the first spouse and helpmate in the finding of herbs and plants, and because she discovered it'.[64] Rumphius's aim of making indigenous remedies available to a wider public purpose was shared by the merchant-physician Robert Padtbrugge (1637–1703) who opened a medicine shop in Batavia for dispensing indigenous substitutes for imports.

VOC plant exploration within an interactive Indian Ocean network culminated in three seminal publications. These comprised *Hortus Indicus Malabaricus* (1678–1703) resulting from Van Reede's investigations; the *Thesaurus Medicus Insulae Ceyloniae* ['The Medical Treasury of the island of Ceylon'] (1677) by Hermanus Nicolaas Grimm; and the posthumous publication of the fragmented remains of Rumphius's work, the *Herbarium Amboinense* (1741–55).[65] They unanimously subscribed to Batavia's quest of indigenous sources of herbal medicine.[66] Within a vibrant VOC botanical network already set in place, the manuscripts of Van Reede and Grimm were circulated in Europe preceding their publication.[67] These complemented the later initiatives of the English East India Company under Joseph Banks.

The English East India Company and the Banksian project

Eighteenth-century cameralism and its influence on agricultural experimentation for national good spurred bio-prospecting. Joseph Banks

(1743–1820), as a member of the Privy Council of Trade, promoted the investigation of 'drugs and dyes' for the home market. His commercial project intermeshed with his role as President of the Royal Society and member of the Republic of Letters, which spearheaded the European Enlightenment. Plant prospecting was for him part of a wider agenda of scientific research and discovery.[68] Among the many academics he sponsored was Dr Johann Gerhard Koenig (1728–85), a pupil of Linnaeus. Following his service as state naturalist to the Nawab of Arcot, Koenig was appointed Professor of Botany and Natural History in Madras. His subsequent botanical exploration of the Bay of Bengal included the earliest survey of the west coast of the Malay Peninsula. He took time during the course of his travels to work in the private gardens of the surgeon C. de Vendt, in Melaka, with its many medicinal plants.[69]

Banks's patronage of Koenig formed part of a wider investment in the natural history of the Malay-Indonesian region. Coincident with fast-expanding British influence in the region, Banks gave significant support to William Marsden (1757–1836) and Stamford Raffles (1781–1826) in their pursuit of natural history. Thomas Horsfield, who conducted scientific research under Raffles in Java, recorded the botany of the districts south of Batavia (Jakarta), including the Latin and local names of medicinal plants and their therapeutics uses.[70]

Banks's founding of the Calcutta Botanic Gardens in 1786, with the aim of encouraging economic botany, had implications for the development of official British support for investigation into *materia medica* in Sumatra. It spurred experimental planting in Benkulen (Bengkulu) of products of a medicinal-cum-culinary value including cloves, ginger, turmeric and nutmeg smuggled from the Moluccas (Meluku).[71] Banks' death in 1820 abruptly ended these exploratory initiatives. For most of the remaining century scientific botany gave way to the commercial preoccupations of the English Company administration in India and in the Straits Settlements (Singapore, Penang and Melaka), a trend replicated in the Netherlands Indies.[72]

Part III: Colonial science and indigenous *materia medica*

Plant collectors, collections and post-Linnaean science

The British withdrawal from Benkulen (1824) and the abolition of the Penang Government Nursery (1828) and the Singapore Botanic Gardens

(1829) anticipated retrenchments in the Calcutta Botanic Gardens. Like Joseph Hooker's Himalayan journey, plant exploration in the Malay Peninsula came to rest largely on personal initiative and private enterprise. Company surgeons, officials and members of the merchant community were united in an effort to sustain the momentum of plant exploration as a means to improving trade.[73]

In the notoriously unhealthy Batavian environment the search for ready and cheap sources of medicine drew much of the attention of medical men and botanists. But in the generally salubrious climate of the Straits Settlements (comprising Singapore, Penang and Melaka) it was plant exploration and experimentation for commercial spice production that preoccupied the surgeons. The Singapore Agricultural and Horticultural Association, founded in 1836 by the medical fraternity in association with the European merchant community, focused its attention on the experimental cultivation, especially of nutmeg, prized for its culinary and medicinal uses. It was replaced in 1860 by the Agri-Horticultural Association, chaired by Governor Orfeur Cavenagh, foreshadowing official sponsorship and the 1880 revival of the Botanical Gardens.

In Melaka, following his term as Professor at the Calcutta Botanic Gardens (1842-5), William Griffiths returned as surgeon and resumed his collection of medicinal plants. He employed a local Eurasian, Emanuel Fernandez, and two Indians, 'Verapah' (Verappa) and Ningul, probably recruited for their knowledge of herbal medicine through his contacts in India. Reputedly, Griffiths' Malayan collection was surpassed only in size by that of the Melaka magistrate A. C. Maingay (1862-8).[74]

The recruitment of salaried local assistants rather than reliance, as previously, on the informal exchange of information on an ad hoc basis, came with the transition from Company administration to imperial rule. The inauguration of the Netherlands East Indies (1820) and British rule in the Straits Settlements (1857) prejudiced easy Euro-Asian interactions for plant prospecting in a number of ways. These were: the alienating influence of imperial power; perceptions of the superiority of European race and intellect; the hardening of social and cultural barriers with the arrival of European wives; and the progress of Enlightenment science. The rupture of previously shared Greco-Arab ideas, for example, that disease emanated from humours and miasma, and the development of the germ theory were symptomatic of the growing epistemological divide between Western and non-Western systems of knowledge.[75]

By the early nineteenth century European interactions with the locals became difficult. Frustrated by the circumspection of potential informants, Francis Buchanan, Company surgeon and Superintendant of the Calcutta Botanic Gardens (1814–15), complained:

> I found no native who could or rather who would inform me of the name of plants. The obstinacy of the people of Malabar is astonishing and every man you meet suspects you have an evil design in every question you ask.[76]

Some decades later, the Singapore surgeon Thomas Oxley spoke of the 'professors of medicine', generally old women, who were reluctant to share their knowledge. His contemporary J. R. Logan, a keen amateur naturalist, was compelled to rely on the secondhand information of an Indian grocer who, in common with his Chinese counterpart, customarily stocked medicinal herbs as well as spices.[77] Similarly, the ubiquitous Chinese *sinsehs* (Chinese medicine men) in colonial townships, who reputedly had remedies for tropical diseases such as malaria, cholera and leprosy, shrouded their art in secrecy to protect their business.[78]

The co-option of indigenous knowledge was complicated by the emphasis placed by Enlightenment Science on accurate information and empirical evidence. In the fast-evolving field of plant science there were the new taxonomic demands of description, classification and illustration, which called for greater circumspection on the part of plant prospectors. Reliance for information on verbal communication with barely literate market vendors, medicine men/women (*dukun*), mid-wives (*bidan*) and aboriginal traders risked a wide margin of error.[79] I. H. Burkill, Director of the Singapore Botanic Gardens (see below), speaking from his own experience, warned about the need 'to avoid unexpected questions, for they beget gusts of fancy and incorrect assertions'.[80]

Responding to Linnaean science, naturalists, collectors and medical men made a beginning with the rigours of plant taxonomic description and identification according to the new binomial nomenclature. Dr Nathaniel Ward utilized his knowledge of Malay, acquired while serving the Baptist Missionary Society in Benkulen, to compile a list of endemic fruits of the Peninsula, with their Linnaean nomenclature, and a description of their indigenous medicinal uses.[81] In Batavia, the medical practitioner Cornelis Leendert van der Burg dedicated the third volume of his *Materia Indica* (1887) to the scientific distillation and interpretation of indigenous herbal knowledge.[82]

The Colonial Botanical Service

The waning of informal collaborations under imperial control was compensated, in part, by the development of the colonial scientific services initiated by Governor Cavenagh in Singapore (1859–67) and Governor-General C. F. Pahud (1856–61) in the Netherlands Indies. By the turn of the century official sponsorship for economic botany was fully reinstated under M. Treub at the Botanic Gardens in Buitenzorg and H. N. Ridley in Singapore. Important for medical science was the experimental acclimatization of Peruvian cinchona in west Java by the medical doctor and plant geographer Franz Wilhelm Junghuhn (1809–64).[83] The virulence of malaria had escalated since fish ponds were established around Batavia in the 1770s[84] and provided a strong incentive to secure the prized cinchona remedy. In 1854 seeds were 'stolen' by Justus Charles Hasskarl, Superintendent of the Buitenzorg gardens, pre-empting the British in breaking the Spanish monopoly. The rivalry over the procurement and acclimatization of cinchona illustrated the impediments to free movement and exchange which had affected circuits of plant exchange since European commercial and political ascendancy.[85]

Cinchona acclimatization earned Buitenzorg scientific authority under Pahud's patronage. In contrast, in the Peninsula, botanical exploration and plant collecting served the metropolitan ambitions of William Hooker, Director (1841–55) at Kew Gardens. His innovative 'Colonial Floras' scheme emphasized phytogeography and expanded the aims of the Museum of Economic Botany he had already set in place.[86] His son and successor at Kew, Joseph Hooker (1855–85), saw in the Malay Peninsula an attractive site for giving form to the Kew project. Here colonial intervention in 1874 opened an exciting field of unexplored hinterland. Recruiting Kew-trained personnel, Joseph Hooker set out to establish the Singapore Botanical Gardens as the regional plant capital for his fast-expanding global network.[87]

The Directorship of the Singapore Botanic Gardens successively under Ridley (1888–1912) and I. H. Burkill (1912–24), covered the heyday of collecting in the Peninsula. Burkill, in particular, was keen on ethno-botany, a task made possible through recruiting salaried local collectors. Among these was Alfred Dent Machardo, a Eurasian with a wide field experience acquired through a varied career as police officer, miner and planter. Employed briefly during 1902–3 in the Singapore Botanical Gardens, he assembled a collection of medicinal plants subsequently deposited in the Perak Museum as part of its distinctive ethnological collection.[88]

Burkill's extensive knowledge of medicinal plants, bequeathed to posterity in his monumental *Dictionary of Economic Produce of the Malay Peninsula* (1936), marked the culmination of long years of collaboration with indigenous collectors, principally his assistant, Mohamed Haniff (1872–1930). His pioneer study with Haniff, *Malay Village Medicine* (1930), laid the foundation for the *Dictionary*. Haniff began his career, aged 18, as a botanical apprentice and specimen collector at the Penang Waterfall Gardens established in 1884. He was later placed in full charge, though never advanced beyond the position of Field Assistant. Working both with European botanists and local collectors, he added substantially to the herbarium as well as to the live collections of the Gardens' Department of the Straits Settlements.[89] Haniff, who used his field knowledge to describe plants and their locations, is commemorated in the genus *Haniffia* (Zingiberaseae), of which a species of *Zingiber* is a key medicinal plant.[90]

Nur Mohamed Gosh, another outstanding Malayan employed by the Singapore Botanic Gardens, collected extensively, partly on behalf of Dr E. D. Merrill of Harvard University.[91] His protégé Kiah bin Haji Mohamed Salleh worked with eminent international botanists during his long service (1920–57) that spanned the formative years of ethno-botany in the Peninsula. Poorly credited for their contribution to European plant prospecting are the Orang Asli, often the best guides on the location, identity and use of herbs which straddle the uncertain boundary between medicines and poisons.

The viability of the pharmacology laboratory established at Buitenzorg at the turn of the century rested, no less, on the recruitment of indigenous collectors, botanical assistants and illustrators.[92] The competence of native assistants such as Lidan and Mario who served under Melchior Treub as Director (1880–1909) and earned the gratitude of visiting research scientists was to the credit of technical training received within the scientific service, which enabled them to bring their private knowledge to the purposes of science.[93]

Acknowledging the value of indigenous collaboration, Junghuhn, expressed the desirability of bringing the methods of natural science to the Indonesian elite for building a new kind of colonial society.[94] A. G. Vorderman, ethno-botanist and inspector of the Civil Health Service in the 1870s, contributed to the same thinking. He envisaged productive collaboration through enlisting the help of medical students as informants on indigenous *materia medica*; but their elite backgrounds and distance from village medicine stood in the way of such ambitions. No more realistic was the plan entertained by W. G. Boorsma (1867–1937) at the pharmacology laboratory at Bogor to draw indigenous practitioners into the realm of Western medical science.[95] It was thus left to the colonial botanical and health services to find a means of bridging the gap between the two systems of knowledge through ethno-botanical research. In this they were assisted, on an informal level, by the vibrant Eurasian community of Java.

Village medicine for Enlightenment science

Within the large *peranakan* community of mixed ethnic origin, the Dutch Eurasians were potential agents for rendering indigenous *materia medica* comprehensible to Europeans. Drawing from their Asian origin, Eurasian women brought to scientific purpose the close affinity between indigenous culinary, curative and health-care traditions. Moreover, in some cases they claimed the ability to interpret indigenous medicinal practices *sans* their superstitious accretions.[96] Such useful knowledge was compiled by Johanna Kloppenburg-Versteegh, a woman of Indies extraction, and circulated as a popular manual both among ordinary Europeans and the medical fraternity (Kloppenburg-Versteegh 1911). Her endeavour was tantamount to a personal mission to promote indigenous remedies following the death of her daughter through incorrect medical diagnosis.[97]

Indigenous herbal medicine provided a substitute for European medicine, particularly among the Dutch resident in remote locations with no easy access to European doctors. Trust in the efficacy of some indigenous practices and prescriptions was also not uncommon among European doctors. The nineteenth-century German physician Franz Epp, generally dismissive of the Javanese as victims of superstition, rated indigenous midwifery practices prevalent in Tegal and Pekalongan as superior to those administered by doctors in Batavia.[98] F. A. C. Waitz, who served the colonial health service in the 1820s, was himself an early exponent of indigenous medicinal herbs that passed the test of his own experimentation. These he documented with their local names and their European equivalents, for use by European patients and physicians.[99] In fact, the medical handbooks of indigenous treatments in Western format written by Eurasian women became popular in Java for the guidance of government-trained midwives.[100]

During the course of the early nineteenth century, European interest in indigenous medicine continued to increase rather than diminish. T. Geerlof Wassink, for many years Director of the Netherlands Indies colonial health service, urged physicians to experiment with specific herbs used in indigenous medicine, the results of which he published in the 1852 *Medical Journal of the Dutch East Indies*.[101]

Compared with the keen borrowing of indigenous knowledge by Europeans, Malay-Indonesian medicinal practitioners, like their South Asian counterparts, expressed a robust confidence in their distinctive traditions and often reacted negatively to Western influence. Under the shared hybrid influence of Sanskrit medical literature, *Unani Tibb* (Graeco-Arab medicine), and indigenforous beliefs and folklore, they resisted reform, fearing marginalization or assimilation of their individual traditions, which they duly reinforced in the face of the European challenge.[102] Tony Day notes a Javanese response to the Enlightenment in the Surakarta court's *Serat Centini* (1814), a comprehensive compilation of knowledge including hybrid Indo-Javanese Islamic prescriptions for *jampi-jampian* (sacred recipes for herbal medicine).[103]

Indigenous herbal knowledge transmitted textually, orally, or through everyday use against disease and for improved health and nutrition was an integral part of culture. Conducive to the survival of these traditions were colonial non-interference in rural life; promotion of urban plurality to accommodate immigrant labour; and shortfalls in Western health care. Furthermore, through stimulating trade and immigration, colonial rule effectively invigorated pre-existing exchange networks that were traditionally the lifeblood of Malay-Indonesian *materia medica*. The expanded market for plant substances both at home and abroad was well served by Singapore's pre-eminence as the regional commercial hub, emulating Melaka's role in the pre-European era.[104]

The Medical Book of Malayan Medicine by an anonymous Malay author bears unique testament to the interactions between nature, culture and international trade. Its publication in English in 1930 in Ridley's *Gardens' Bulletin* of Singapore, edited and translated by one 'Inche' (Mr) Ismail, provides a rare glimpse into a rich herbal tapestry, shot through with diverse strands of South Asian, Middle-Eastern and Chinese influence. Believed to have been compiled by a Malay resident either in cosmopolitan Singapore or Penang,[105] it incorporates local herbal knowledge broadly based on the *Yunani* tradition of the *Kitab Tib* (Book of Islamic medicinal knowledge) transmitted probably via India. It records a total of 543 medicinal substances, typically constituting endemics, imports (both dried simples[106] and transplants)[107] and a few endemic substitutes for non-endemics prescriptions.

Bearing the imprint of a dynamic, cosmopolitan, urban environment, plant names in *The Medical Book of Malayan Medicine*, like the Malay language itself, shows may borrowings from Arabic, Javanese,

Sundanese and Southeast Indian languages. Likewise, not all the names for the diseases are rendered in Malay, suggesting the cosmopolitan influences then within the urban environment. The manuscript also attests to an emerging sensibility to precision such as the classification of simples under the Malay terminology *kayu* (wood), for internal use and *kulit* (bark) for external use.[108] The compiler also attempts more accurate prescription by using weights prevalent in Penang.[109] *The Medical Book of Malayan Medicine* testifies to a discrete tradition based on Malay village medicine but one inherently open to change and adaptation at the nexus of commercial and information exchange, which the Peninsular ports represented.

Conclusion

In the pre-European era Malay-Indonesian *materia medica* flourished within the framework of trans-regional commercial exchange, including tributary trade. Dried and preserved plant substances were readily available in the market place with information about their uses. With the exception of medical texts preserved in court circles for elite use, pharmaceutical knowledge belonged to the domain of everyday life, firmly anchored to a distinct cultural tradition and epistemology.

Compared to the pre-European era of port- and court-oriented pharmaceutical exchange, the European quest for a more comprehensive appropriation of Malay-Indonesian *materia medica* could not be subsumed within trade and diplomacy. EEIC and VOC intrusions beyond the market place, often employing coercive tools, secured the desired resources but not the intangible body of indigenous knowledge. These circumstances rendered European plant prospecting critically dependent on negotiating informal discourses with 'the other', rising above the restraints of bureaucracy and status. Following the path pioneered by Orta, surgeons and medical practitioners were in the vanguard of botanical, ethno-botanical and pharmacological explorations conducted during the subsequent centuries of European dominance. Their effort to win the trust and cooperation of common people, whom they respected as custodians of valuable knowledge, constitutes a humbling sub-text to European colonialism. Ironically, the botanical and medical services created as tools of dominance during the high noon of imperialism endorsed the value of indigenous medicinal knowledge to the progress of science and anthropology as signifiers of European triumphalism.

In the post-colonial era, *materia medica* was reconfigured as part of national culture and identity. With a burgeoning middle-class moving comfortably between two traditions, the demand for indigenous herbal medicine retains its domestic popularity.[110] On the international front, plant products of the region remain important for servicing the pharmaceutical industry, biotechnology and genetic research.[111] The entrenchment of Malay-Indonesian *materia medica* at the intersection of science and culture, modernity and tradition, forms an integral part of European colonial enterprise, irrevocably linking past and present.

Notes

1. This chapter is a revised and extended version of a paper presented originally at the 2010 Conference of the International Association of the Historians of Asia, with the generous support of the late Lady Peng McNiece (trustee WWF Malaysia) and the Wellcome Foundation. A version of the paper was also presented at the 2011 Conference in Cambridge of the Association of Southeast Asian Studies, UK. I am grateful to Hans Pols and William Gervase Clarence-Smith for useful comments on earlier versions of the chapter.
2. A. Pavord (2005), *The Naming of Names: The Search for Order in the World of Plants*, London: Bloomsbury, p. 111.
3. Those popular on the European market were pepper (*Piper nigrum*), nutmeg (*Myristica fragrans*), cloves (*Eugenia aromatica*) and cinnamon (*Cinnamomum* spp., especially *C. zeylanicum*) and cardamom (*Elettaria* and *Amomum*).
4. Pavord, *The Naming of Names*, p. 83.
5. For a discussion of the origin of the *dukun* and their role in Indonesia see Jeniffer W. Norse (2013), 'The meaning of *dukun* and the allure of Sufi healers: How Persian cosmopolitans transformed Malay-Indonesian history', *Journal of Southeast Asian History*, 44(3): 400–22.
6. W. W. Skeat and C. O. Blagden (1906), *Pagan Races of the Malay Peninsula*, London: Macmillan, Vol. I, pp. 231, 252; F. Dunn (1975), *Rainforest Collectors and Traders: A Study of Resource Utilization in Modern and Ancient Malaya*, Monograph 5, Kuala Lumpur: Malayan Branch of the Royal Asiatic Society, pp. 86–91, 181–4; J. Kathirithamby-Wells (2005), *Nature and Nation: Forests and Development in Peninsular Malaysia*. Copenhagen: NIAS Press, p. 37.
7. Dunn, *Rainforest Collectors and Traders*, pp. 81–4.
8. J. D. Gimlette (1971), *A Dictionary of Malayan Medicine*, (ed. and comp.) H. W. Thomson, first published in 1939, London and Kuala Lumpur: Oxford University Press, p. 186.
9. C. Antons and R. Antons-Sutanto (2009), 'Traditional medicine and intellectual property rights: A case study of Indonesian *jamu* industry', in C. Antons (ed.), *Traditional Knowledge, Traditional Cultural Expressions and Intellectual Property Law on the Asia-Pacific Region*, Alphen van den Rijn: Wolters Kluer, 2009, p. 369.
10. W. W. Skeat (Preface) in C. O. Blagden (1967), *Malay Magic: An Introduction to Folklore and Popular Religion of the Malay Peninsula*, first published 1900, New York: Dover, pp. 214–15; E. M. Endicott (1981), *An Analysis of Malay Magic*, first published 1970, Kuala Lumpur: Oxford University Press, pp. 11–24.

Malay-Indonesian Medicine and European Plant Science 213

11. J. Kathirithamby-Wells (1995), 'Socio-political structures and the Southeast Asian ecosystem: An historical perspective up to the mid-nineteenth century', in O. Bruun and A. Kalland (eds.), *Asian Perceptions of Nature: A Critical Approach*, Richmond: Curzon Press, pp. 29–30.
12. Skeat and Blagden, *Pagan Races*, vol. I, pp. 227, 354–6; Anon., J. D. G. Gimlette (ed. & intro.), Inche Ismail (tr.) (1930), *The Medical Book of Malayan Medicine, Gardens' Bulletin, Straits Settlements*, 6(3): 403, 415; I. H. Burkill (1966), *A Dictionary of Economic Products of the Malayan Peninsula*, first published 1926, Kuala Lumpur: Government of Malaysia and Singapore, vol. II, p. 2142.
13. Burkill, *Dictionary*, vol. I, pp. 35–6; Skeat and Blagden, *Pagan Races*, p. 108; Skeat, *Malay Magic*, p. 229.
14. Burkill, *Dictionary*, vol. 1, pp. 976–9; O. W. Wolters (1967), *Early Indonesian Commerce: A Study of the Origins of Srivijaya*, Ithaca: Cornell University Press, pp. 66, 68.
15. By the twelfth century sandalwood joined Southeast Asian exports to China, with a sharp increase in the sixteenth century due to Portuguese exports from Timor to Melaka and Macao. Burkill, *Dictionary*, vol. II, pp. 1986–90; J. Villiers (1994), 'The vanishing sandalwood of Portuguese Timor', *Itinerario*, 18(2): 86–96.
16. Indeed, not only the nut, even the roots and leaves of the areca palm were in medicinal use in the Malay-Indonesian world. Burkill, *Dictionary*, vol. I, pp. 225–9; II, pp. 1767–70; Gimlette, *Dictionary*, pp. 187, 225–6; A. Reid, 'From betel-chewing to tobacco smoking in Indonesia', in M. J. MacLeod and E. S. Rawski (eds.) (1998), *European Intruders and Changes in Behaviour and Customs in Asia and Africa Before 1800*, Aldershot: Ashgate, pp. 530–35.
17. H. Knapen (2001), *Forests of Fortune: The Environmental History of Southeast Borneo, 1600–1800*, Leiden: KITLV, p. 66.
18. Burkill, *Dictionary*, vol. II, pp. 1375–80; L. P. A. Oyen and Nguyen Zuan Dung (eds.) (1999), *Essential Oil Plants, Plant Resources of Southeast Asia* (PROSEA), No. 19, Leiden: Backhuys, p. 125.
19. Burkill, *Dictionary*, vol. II, p. 1482–3; 2800–9; Gimlette, *Dictionary*, pp. 35–6.
20. Burkill, *Dictionary*, vol. II, pp. 1467–9.
21. Burkill, *Dictionary*, vol. I, pp. 34–8.
22. Burkill, *Dictionary*, vol. II, pp. 1776–81; A. Reid (1993), *Southeast Asia in the Age of Commerce, 1450–1680*, vol. II, *Expansion and Crisis*, New Haven: Yale University Press, pp. 7–8; J. A. Duke, M. J. Bogenschutz-Godwin, J. duCellier and P. A. K. Duke (2003), *Handbook Medicinal Herbes*, Boca Raton, FL: CRC Press, p. 145.
23. M. Elvin (2004), *The Retreat of the Elephants: An Environmental History of China*, New Haven: Yale University Press, p. 355.
24. J. Needham (1986), *Science and Civilisation in China*, vol. 6, with the collaboration of Lu Gwei-Djen and a special contribution by Huang Hsing-Tsung, *Biology and Biological Technology, Pt. 1: Botany*, Cambridge: Cambridge University Press, pp. 163–5.
25. Needham, *Science and Civilization in China*, pp. 445–6.
26. Gungwu Wang (1958), 'The Nanhai trade: A study of the early history of Chinese trade in the South China Sea', *Journal of the Malaysian Branch of the Royal Asiatic Society*, 31(2): 71.
27. Wolters, *Early Indonesian Commerce*, pp. 67, 68, 122–3, 282 n. 29.

28. Needham, *Science and Civilization in China*, pp. 272–7; E. H. Schafer (1963), *The Golden Peaches of Samarkand: A Study of T'ang Exotics*, Berkeley: University of California Press, p. 169.
29. Wolters, *Early Indonesian Commerce*, p. 116; Burkill, *Dictionary*, vol. II, pp. 2139–42.
30. Wolters, *Early Indonesian Commerce*, p. 123.
31. Burkill, *Dictionary*, vol. I, pp. 758–9.
32. Burkill, *Dictionary*, vol. II, pp. 1311–15; Schafer, *The Golden Peaches of Samarakand*, p. 135.
33. Burkill, *Dictionary*, vol. II, pp. 198–204, 765–6; II, pp. 1986–90; P. Wheatley (1964), *Impressions of the Malay Peninsula in Ancient Times*, Singapore: Eastern Universities Press, pp. 41–2.
34. Wang, 'The Nanhai trade', pp. 110–11.
35. Bien Ching (2009), 'Market price, labour import, and relation of production in Sarawak's edible bird's nest trade', in E. Tagliacozzo and Wen-Chin Chang (eds.), *Chinese Circulations: Capital, Commodities and Networks in Southeast Asia*, Durham, NC: Duke University Press, p. 109.
36. Burkill, *Dictionary*, vol. I, pp. 394–6; O. W. Wolters (1970), *The Fall of Srivijaya in Malay History*, Kuala Lumpur: Oxford University Press, p. 61.
37. Needham, *Science and Civilization in China*, pp. 303–4; Burkill, *Dictionary*, vol. I, pp. 337–9.
38. Gimlette, *Dictionary*, p. 2.
39. Burkill, *Dictionary*, vol. I, pp. 328–30.
40. Anon., *The Medical Book of Malayan Medicine*, p. 437; Gimlette, *Dictionary*, p. 60.
41. Needham, *Science and Civilization in China*, pp. 160–1; Pavord, *The Naming of Names*, p. 239.
42. Tomé Pires (1944), *The Suma Oriental of Tomé Pires* (ed.) A. Cartesão, London: Hakluyt Society; A. J. R. Russell-Wood (1992), *The Portuguese Empire 1415–1808: A World on the Move*, Baltimore: Johns Hopkins University Press, p. 79.
43. S. Sangwan (1992), 'Natural history in colonial contest: Profit or pursuit? British botanical enterprise in India 1778–1829', in P. Petitjean, C. Jami and A. M. Moulin (eds.), *Science and Empire: Historical Studies about Scientific Development and European Expansion*, Dordrecht: Kluwer, pp. 281–2.
44. M. N. Pearson (2005), 'Hindu medical practice in sixteenth-century western India: Evidence from Portuguese sources', in *The World of the Indian Ocean, 1500–1800: Studies in Economics, Social and Cultural History*, Variorum Collection, Aldershot: Ashgate, p. 106; M. de Figueiredo (1984), 'Ayurvedic medicine in Goa according to European sources in the sixteenth and seventeenth centuries', *Bulletin of the History of Medicine*, 58: 225–35. De Figueiredo, 'Ayurvedic medicine in Goa', pp. 227–8.
45. D. Lach (1965), *Asia in the Making of Europe*, vol. 1: *The Century of Discovery*, Chicago: University of Chicago Press, p. 193; R. Grove (1996), *Green Imperialism: Colonial Expansion, Tropical Island Edens and the Origins of Environmentalism*, Cambridge: Cambridge University Press, p. 129. Orta's descriptions were later illustrated in Cristobal de Acosta (1578), *Tractado de las drogas, y medicinas de las Insias Orienta'es*.
46. Grove, *Green Imperialism*, pp. 130–1; De Figueiredo, 'Ayurvedic medicine in Goa', pp. 229–30.

47. Lach, *Asia in the Making of Europe*, vol. I, p. 193.
48. Grove, *Green Imperialism*, p. 130.
49. Lach, *Asia in the Making of Europe*, vol. I, p. 194; A. G. Debus (1979), *'Improvement' of the World*, New Haven: Yale University Press, p. 47.
50. W. Dampier (1931), *Voyages and Discoveries*, (ed.) C. Wilkinson, first published 1699, London: Argonout Press, vol. II, pp. 3, 110,159, 169.
51. Debus, *'Improvement' of the World*, p. 49.
52. H. J. Cook (2004), 'Global economics and local knowledge in the East Indies', in L. Schiebinger and C. Swan (eds.), *Colonial Botany: Science, Commerce and Politics in the Early Modern World*, Philadelphia: University of Pennsylvania Press, p. 103.
53. J. F. Veldkamp (2002), '15 June 2002, 300th anniversary of Rumphius' death', *Flora Malaysiana*, Bulletin 15(1): 7–21; E. M. Beekman (ed. and tr. with an intro.) (1993), *The Poison Tree: Selected Writings of Rumphius on the Natural History of the Indies*, Kuala Lumpur: Oxford University Press, p. 13.
54. Kapil Raj (2005), 'Surgeons, fakirs, merchants, and crafts people', in Schiebinger and Swan (eds.), *Colonial Botany*, pp. 256–7.
55. De Figueiredo, 'Ayurvedic medicine in Goa', pp. 228–9; M. N. Pearson (2005), 'Hindu medical practice in sixteenth-century western India: Evidence from Portuguese sources', in *The World of the Indian Ocean, 1500–1800*, p. 106.
56. H. Y. Mohan Ram (2005), 'On the English edition of Van Reede's *Hortus Malabaricus* by K. S. Manilal', *Current Science*, Bangalore, 89(10): 1677–8.
57. H. J. Cook (2008), *Matters of Exchange: Commerce, Medicine, and Science in the Dutch Golden Age*, New Haven: Yale University Press, p. 203.
58. Reid, *The Age of Commerce*, vol. I, p. 54.
59. D. Preston and M. Preston (2004), *A Pirate of Exquisite Mind: The Life of William Dampier*, New York: Walker & Company, pp. 266–7.
60. L. Schiebinger (2004), *Plants and Empire: Colonial Bioprospecting in the Atlantic World*, Cambridge MA: Harvard University Press, pp. 82–3.
61. Raj, 'Surgeons, fakirs, merchants', p. 258.
62. Cook, *Matters of Exchange*, p. 330.
63. Beekman, (intro.), *Georgius Everhardus Rumphius*, pp. 59–60; Beekman, *The Poison Tree*, p. 14.
64. Veldkamp, '15 June 2002, 300th anniversary', pp. 64–5; Beekman, *The Ambonese Herbal*, vol. I, pp. 64–5; vol. IV, p. 244.
65. Cook, *Matters of Exchange*, pp. 315–17. The collection of Paul Hermann who served the VOC in Ceylon (1672–77) was lost until brought to the attention of Linnaeus who produced it in 1747 as the well-known *Flora Zeylanica*. H. Trimen (1887), 'Hermann's Ceylon Herbarium and Linnaeus's "Flora Zeylanica"', *Linnaean Journal of Botany*, 24(160):129–55.
66. P. Boomgaard (2006), 'The making and unmaking of tropical science: Dutch research in Indonesia, 1600–2000', *Bijdragen tot de Taal-, Land-en Volkenkunde*, 162(1–2): 195.
67. Raj, 'Surgeons, fakirs, merchants', p. 269.
68. J. Gascoigne (1994), *Science in the Service of Empire: Joseph Banks, the British State and the Uses of Science in the Age of Revolution*, Cambridge: Cambridge University Press, pp. 141–51.
69. Kathirithamby-Wells, *Nature and Nation*, p. 345.

70. T. Horsfield (1990), *Zoological Researches in Java and the Netherlands Archipelago, with a Memoir by J. Bastin*, first published 1824, Singapore: Oxford University Press, p. 9.
71. A. P. Thomas (2006), 'The establishment of the Calcutta Botanic Garden: Plant transfer, science and the East India Company', *Journal of the Royal Asiatic Society*, Ser. 3, 16(2): 165–77; Kathirithamby-Wells, *Nature and Nation*, p. 28; Jeyamalar Kathirithamby-Wells (2009), 'Peninsular Malaysia in the context of natural history and colonial science', in Ooi Keat Jin (ed.), *Themes for Thoughts on Southeast Asia, New Zealand Journal of Asian Studies*, Special number, 11(2): 293–4.
72. D. Arnold (2008), 'Plant capitalism and Company science: the Indian career of Nathaniel Wallich', *Modern Asian Studies*, 42(5): 911, *passim*; Grove, *Green Imperialism*, pp. 412–14; Kathirithamby-Wells, *Nature and Nation*, p. 31.
73. In Bengkulu, the Agricultural Society which Raffles set up with the assistance of Dr Nathaniel Ward of the London Missionary Society undertook crop experimentation for nutritional improvement. C. E. Wurtzburg (1954), *Raffles of the Eastern Isles*, London: Hodder and Stoughton, pp. 576–7. In Singapore, Dr José a-Almeida, Dr William Montgomerie and Dr Thomas Oxley experimented with the cultivation of spices under the auspices of the Agricultural and Horticultural Society. C. M. Turnbull (1972), *The Straits Settlements 1826–67*, Oxford: Oxford University Press, p. 146; Kathirithamby-Wells, 'Peninsula Malaysian in the context of natural history', p. 36.
74. M. J. van Steenis-Kruseman (1985), *Flora Malesiana: Being an Illustrated Systematic Account of the Malaysian Flora...*, series I (ed.) C. G. G. J. van Steenis, first published 1950, Koenigstein: Koeltz Scientific Books, vol. l, p. 201.
75. C. Liebeskind (2002), 'Arguing science: Yunani-tibb, hakims and biomedicine in India, 1900–50', in W. Ernst (ed.), *Plural Medicine, Tradition and Modernity, 1800–2000*, London: Routledge, p. 59, *passim*.
76. Sangwan, 'Natural history in colonial contest', p. 289.
77. T. Oxley (1850), 'The botany of Singapore', *Journal of the Indian Archipelago*, 4: 439–40; J. T. Thompson (1881), 'A sketch of the career of the late James Richardson Logan of Penang and Singapore', *Journal of the Straits Branch of the Royal Asiatic Society*, 7: 76–7.
78. L. Hesselink, 'Crossing colonial and medical boundaries: Plural medicine in Java, 1850–1910', in A. Digny, W. Ernst and P. B. Muhharji (eds.) (2010), *Colonial Historiographies: Histories of Colonial and Indigenous Medicines in Transnational Perspectives*, Cambridge: Cambridge Scholars Publishing, p. 129; L. Hesselink (2011), *Healers on the Colonial Market: Native Doctors and Midwives in the Dutch East Indies*, Leiden: KITLV, pp. 276–7.
79. Oxley, 'The botany of Singapore', pp. 439–40.
80. I. H. Burkill and Mohamed Haniff (1930), *Malay Village Medicine, The Gardens' Bulletin, Straits Settlements*, 6(2): 165.
81. J. Cameron (1965), *Our Tropical Possessions in Malayan India*, first published 1865, Kuala Lumpur: Oxford University Press, pp. 397–408.
82. H. Pols (2009), 'European physicians and botanists, indigenous herbal medicine in the Dutch East Indies, and Colonial networks of mediation', *East Asian Science, Technology and Society*, 3: 179, 182, 184.

83. A. Goss (2008), 'Decent colonialism? Pure science and colonial ideology in the Netherlands Indies, 1910–1929', *Journal of Southeast Asian Studies*, 40(1): 189–90; A. Goss (2011), *The Floracrats: State-Sponsored Science and the Failure of Enlightenment in Indonesia*, Madison: University of Wisconsin Press, pp. 37–40.
84. I. Bruijn (2009), *Ship's Surgeons of the Dutch East India Company: Commerce and the Progress of Medicine in the Eighteenth Century*, Leiden: Leiden University Press, p. 80.
85. Bruijn, *Ship's Surgeons of the Dutch East India Company*, p. 80; Goss, 'European physicians and botanists', pp. 36–7; R. Drayton (2000), *Nature's Government: Science, Imperial Britain, and the 'Improvement' of the World*, New Haven: Yale University, p. 208.
86. Drayton, *Nature's Government*, pp. 193, 178–9, 203–4.
87. Kathirithamby-Wells, *Nature and Nation*, pp. 48–9.
88. Van Steenis Kruseman, *Flora Malesiana*, Ser. 1, vol. I, p. 342.
89. Mohd Nor Jamalul Lail (2000), ' Mohamed Haniff (1872–1930) of the Penang Botanic Gardens: A biographical tribute to a pioneer botanist', *Flora Malaysiana*, 2: 27–32.
90. Burkill, *Dictionary*, vol. II, pp. 2335–43.
91. Van Steenis Kruseman, *Flora Malesiana*, Ser. 1, vol. I, p. 358.
92. Pols, 'European physicians and botanists', p. 187.
93. Goss, *The Floracrats*, pp. 71–2.
94. Goss, *The Floracrats*, p. 20.
95. Pols, 'European physicians and botanists', pp. 185, 187.
96. Pols, 'European physicians and botanists', p. 179.
97. Pols, 'European physicians and botanists', pp. 191–8.
98. M. Somers Heidhues (1995), 'Dissecting the Indies: The 19th century German Doctor Franz Epp', *Archipel*, 49: 36–7.
99. Pols, 'European physicians and botanists', pp. 181–2.
100. L. Hesselink (2010), 'Crossing colonial and medical boundaries: Plural medicine on Java, 1850–1910', in A. Digny, W. Ernst and P. B. Muhharji (eds.), *Colonial Historiographies: Histories of Colonial and Indigenous Medicines in Transnational Perspectives*, Cambridge: Cambridge Scholars Publishing, p. 129; L. Hesselink (2011), *Healers on the Colonial Market: Native Doctors and Midwives in the Dutch East Indies*, Leiden: KITLV, pp. 127–8.
101. Pols, 'European physicians and botanists', p. 184.
102. Liebeskind, 'Arguing science', pp. 60–65.
103 T. Day (2003), *Fluid Iron: State Formation in Southeast Asia*, Honolulu: University of Hawai'i Press, pp. 122–4; Susan-Jane Beer (2012), *Jamu: The Ancient Indonesian Art of Herbal Healing*, Singapore: Periplus, pp. 15–17.
104. L. K. Wong (1960), 'The trade of Singapore, 1819–69', *Journal of the Malayan Branch of the Royal Asiatic Society*, 33(4), *passim*; Skeat and Blagden, *Pagan Races*, vol. II, pp. 63–70.
105. Pieroni and Vandebroek, for example, highlight the role of urban centres in ethno-botanical knowledge exchange. A. Pieroni A. and I. Vandebroek (eds.) (2007), 'Introduction' in *Travelling Cultures and Plants*, Oxford: Berghahn, pp. 1–3.
106. Illustrating the continued importance of medicinal imports from China are the dried insect fungi *Cordycepts sinensis*, a de-worming agent that grows on the caterpillars of *Thitarodes* moths, and the China root (*Smilax china*, Malay

gadong Cina), a prescribed remedy for syphilis. Anon., *The Medical Book of Malayan Medicine*, pp. 432, 437; Burkill, *Dictionary*, vol. II, pp. 2073–4.
107. Indigenized medicinal plants include those of an earlier provenance such as the Indian *nim* or *neem* (*Azadirachta; Melia indica*), a febrifuge; the West Asian henna (*Lawsonia inermis*); the tannin (*kacu*) producing *Acacia catechu*, a nineteenth-century Dutch introduction; and the post-Columbian transplant, the New World papaya (*Carica papaya*). Anon., *The Medical Book of Malayan Medicine*, pp. 423, 441, 444.
108. Anon., *The Medical Book of Malayan Medicine*, p. 445.
109. Anon., *The Medical Book of Malayan Medicine*, p. 325.
110. C. Antons and R. Antons-Sutanto, 'Traditional medicine and intellectual property rights: A case study of Indonesian *jamu* industry', in C. Antons (ed.) (2009), *Traditional Knowledge, Traditional Cultural Expressions and Intellectual Property Law on the Asia-Pacific Region*, Alphen van den Rijn: Wolters Kluer, pp. 363–7; H. H. de Beer and M. J. McDermott (1989), *Economic Value of Non-Timber Forest Products in Southeast Asia, with Emphasis on Indonesia, Malaysia and Thailand*, Amsterdam: Netherlands Committee for IUCN, p. 32.
111. In Malaysia, by the 1990s the demand for herbal medicine – not helped by forest clearance for plantation agriculture – had outstripped supply, resulting in an unprecedented rise in imports. Raw Materials, Tropical and Horticultural Products Service (2004), *Trade in Medicinal Plants*, Rome: Food and Agriculture Organisation of the United Nations, pp. 9–10. Internet resource downloaded from ftp://ftp.fao.org/docrep/fao/008/af285e/af285e00.pdf (last accessed 12 May 2014).

10
Plants, Animals and Environmental Transformation: Indian–New Zealand Biological and Landscape Connections, 1830s–1890s

James Beattie

Elizabeth Muter (1832–1914) began working on her two-volume *Travels and Adventures of an Officer's Wife in India, China, and New Zealand*, while sailing from China to England. She continued drafting the manuscript in New Zealand and completed it 'on the way from Dunedin to Calcutta', from where she sent it to be published in London.[1] The writing and publication of *Travels and Adventures*, just as much as its content, speaks volumes to the transitory lives of women like Muter and men like her husband (Figure 10.1) – Colonel Dunbar Douglas Muter (1824–1909) – in the British Empire. The work evinces also the importance of print culture and letter-writing as means of cultivating and giving shape to the imagined space of the British Empire.

In letters that criss-crossed imperial territory, connecting everywhere from Dunedin to Delhi, Sydney to Saskatchewan, friends and acquaintances exchanged gossip and debated the pressing local and imperial issues of the day. Where possible, they visited each other, sometimes even moving to be closer to one another. As much as military and political power, it was these cultural spaces and the friendships sustained from afar that created and sustained a sense of the British Empire.[2] As Muter highlighted in her book:

> Mrs. Smith will ask Lieutenant Brown, 50th Bombay Native Infantry, just from India, if he knows young Smith, in some Bengal regiment, whose number she cannot at the moment recollect; and Mr. Smith will write to her cousin in Kurrachee [*sic*] to look out for his married daughter going to Calcutta.[3]

Like many others from the East India Company (EIC) and Europe, Muter and her husband (see Figure 10.1) came to New Zealand to benefit from

COLONEL AND MRS. DUNBAR DOUGLAS MUTER

Frontispiece

Figure 10.1 Colonel and Mrs D. D. Mutter, from Elizabeth McMullin Muter, *My Recollections of the Sepoy Revolt (1857–58).* London: John Long Ltd, 1911.

its healthy climate. Like many others, too, the Muters attempted to remake parts of New Zealand's environment in light of their experiences in India. This chapter examines some of the environmental dimensions of Empire in considering how the exchange of plants, animals and environmental attitudes connected India and New Zealand, as well as other places. Men and women associated with the EIC, it shows, played a prominent role in introducing Indian plants and animals into New Zealand. They also oversaw and participated in settler acclimatisation societies and in the naming and modification of the environment in ways that drew together the landscapes of New Zealand and India.[4]

In addition, money earned while in the employ of the EIC helped to remake New Zealand's landscapes using the biological resources of other parts of the world, not just India.

This chapter stresses the importance of informal imperial networks in driving colonial environmental modification, in part because scholars have paid so much attention to state actions in imperial environmental history to the extent of perhaps neglecting the activities of individual settlers. Despite the overwhelmingly important role of settlers in leading imperial environmental transformation and with the exception of studies of certain topics – such as acclimatisation societies – when it comes to plant and animal introductions, scholarly attention has been devoted almost exclusively to the examination of state botanical and zoological gardens, as well as state plant nurseries. This chapter corrects this imbalance in three main ways: first, by examining the commercial and private exchange of plants and animals and their role in remaking New Zealand's environment; second, in following how money earned in EIC employ was used to fund environmental modification beyond the sub-continent; third, in presenting the argument that India could be considered a sub-imperial hub at the centre of broader Australasian environmental networks between the 1830s and the 1870s.

Environmental exchanges during this period and afterwards can only be understood within both the broader pattern of Australasian–Indian trading networks and in relation to fears over India's climate. In examining these economic, environmental and health connections, the chapter proposes that India fulfilled a similar role in the Pacific Ocean to that which it played in the Indian Ocean. According to Thomas R. Metcalf, India functioned in Indian Ocean networks as 'a nodal point from which peoples, ideas, goods and institutions ... radiated outwards', a similar role it also took on in the Pacific.[5] In this respect, Tony Ballantyne's research into nineteenth-century New Zealand–Indian intellectual and material connections, like that of James Broadbent *et al.* and David Walker on India and Australia, has significantly complicated our perceptions of India's role in the Pacific region. Ballantyne, for one, has encapsulated the shifting nature of imperial cultural, intellectual and material exchanges and connections through the notion of 'webs of empire'.[6] My own work has considered Australasia as a sub-imperial hub of India within the webs of empire generated over shared anxieties about health, climate change and resource decline.[7] Fears of the enervating effects of the sub-continental climate explains why so many families whose members worked as EIC officials or military made their way to New Zealand, a country presented as a very healthy migrant destination. Many who came promoted the acclimatisation of Indian plants and animals into New Zealand and the pursuit of landscape comparisons between New Zealand and India.

EIC–Australasian trade networks, 1788–1840s

The EIC's control of the highly lucrative China and India trade to Britain earned it massive profits for several centuries. EIC trading connections established hybrid cultures in late-eighteenth-century colonial entrepots like Bengal and Calcutta. Intermarriage between European traders and Indians resulted, as did a genuine scholarly appreciation of each other's culture. By the early decades of the nineteenth century, British Orientalist attitudes were being replaced by far less sympathetic attitudes towards India and Indians. Seen through the eyes of most British evangelicals, Indians represented a fallen people desperately in need of Christianity and other trappings of 'civilisation'. The British military presence in the area also stepped up as a result of the power vacuum left by the collapse of the Mughal Empire, the intensification of Anglo-French rivalry and the loss of the thirteen colonies. The EIC's territorial aggrandisement changed forever the face of the sub-continent, and the nature of Indian–British relations. With territorial conquest and the consolidation of the right to earn taxes, the British presence in the sub-continent increased.[8]

These associated factors of growing trade and the increased presence of British merchants and military in India sent ripples and occasionally tidal waves crashing onto the shores of other regions bordering the Indian and Pacific Oceans. In the Pacific, the establishment of a penal colony at Botany Bay in 1788, Australia, opened up new profit-making opportunities for the EIC. From 1788 until well into the nineteenth century, Australian–EIC trading connections, although dwarfed in scale and volume by British–Indian exchanges, assumed immense importance for eastern and later western Australia. Such trading considerably shaped the culture, economy and, from the 1820s, settlement patterns of early colonial Australia. In the 1790s, Indian food supplies kept the Botany Bay settlement going, without which the settlement would have likely failed. Even in prosperous times, commodities from India flooded colonial markets while local Australian fashions and building styles followed those of Bengal or Calcutta. Along with goods, colonists traded in live animals, plants and seeds. In the 1790s, for example, privately chartered vessels from Calcutta, contravening the EIC monopoly on trade, landed Bengal sheep in New South Wales (NSW). Early in the next century, the direction of the exchange of the thriving export market in stallions reversed, as Australian studs became established and were sent to India.[9] Introductions of other Indian animals, as well as plants, also took place.[10] The enthusiasm for acclimatisation in Victoria, for example, saw not just the introduction of Cashmere goats from Simla, but also jungle fowls, and unspecified numbers of other seeds, including of Indian pines and ornamentals.[11]

In 1823, the establishment of the colony of NSW, encouraging the immigration of free settlers, made it an attractive proposition to many retiring from EIC service. Over the following decades, migration and trade between India and parts of Australia reached the other newly founded colonies of Van Diemen's Land (established as a colony in 1825 and now known as Tasmania), Western Australia (1829) and South Australia (1834). The nexus of trading power also extended into the spiritual realm. Until 1835 Calcutta's archdeacon headed the Anglican Church of NSW.[12] As Beverley Kingston notes of this period from the late eighteenth century into the mid-nineteenth:

> A vast network of imperial connections in government, administration, the army, the church, the law, education, and enterprise, extended from India to the Australian colonies. Most families engaged on imperial business, whether officially or privately, knew someone in India.[13]

From the 1790s, new frontiers of resource extraction also expanded into the southern ocean, drawing in New Zealand through the demand for trees, seals and, later, whales.[14] Until its formal colonisation in 1840, New Zealand participated in the Indian trade as an adjunct to NSW. Through the 1790s until 1801 many EIC vessels called into various parts of northern New Zealand searching for spars, trading with local Maori and gaining an appreciation of the potential resources of this area. For example, in 1794, the East Indiaman *Fancy* (150 tons) spent three months in the Coromandel, northern New Zealand, obtaining 200 trees for later shipment to India.[15] In 1801, another EIC vessel, *Royal Admiral*, on the way to its final destination in China, gathered spars while en route from NSW to Tahiti. Along the way, four convicts escaped in New Zealand's Cape Colville area.[16] These vessels – and especially those involved in whaling – also offered opportunities for Maori and Indians to travel. In 1809, for example, the daughter of a Maori chief and her European husband landed up in Calcutta.[17] And, in the early 1820s, two Maori chiefs visited Bengal.[18] Travellers and the early colonial press also reported several instances of 'Lascars' living among Maori tribes after having jumped ship. In 1813, six did so in Otago Harbour, southern New Zealand, and three later became members of the local Maori tribe.[19] Through the trade in goods, irregular shipping networks connected New Zealand with India, very often via Australia. Such networks also facilitated the travel of Europeans, as well as sometimes Indians, Maori and other peoples.

India–China–New Zealand plant connections

In 1831, Thomas McDonnell (1788–1864), a former free mariner in India most likely involved at one time trafficking opium in China, began operating a trading entrepôt in northern New Zealand. McDonnell made extensive use of his EIC networks in importing goods and exporting raw products to this region, a commerce which also extended to the introduction of Asian plants into New Zealand. McDonnell's career began in the Royal Navy (c.1804–1815).[20] In 1816, he purchased a license permitting him to trade as a free mariner at the EIC settlement of Fort William, Calcutta, where he lived with his wife, Dorothy.[21] He spent the next decade or more trading in South, East and South East Asia. In 1821, for example, he commanded a vessel conveying an official trade mission to Siam and Cochin China. Later he skippered clippers running opium into China. And, by the late 1820s, he is recorded as trading at Port Jackson, and various places in China and the Pacific.[22]

In 1831, McDonnell purchased the shipyard and timber trading entrepôt at Horeke, Hokianga, in northern New Zealand (see Figures 10.2 and 10.3).[23] There, his extensive garden showcased rare ornamental plants from India and China. This garden served as a conspicuous statement of McDonnell's wealth and social aspirations at a time when non-food-producing gardens were extremely rare. McDonnell's garden, complemented by a large collection of exotic plants, dwarfed those of the only other ornamental gardens of the time: the Wesleyans' garden, in the next bay from McDonnell's in the Hokianga Harbour, and that of Government House, Waitangi, on the eastern coast of New Zealand, but still only some 50 km from Horeke.

McDonnell's house and gardens were indeed 'of some pretensions'.[24] One visitor commented that McDonnell's large expenditure on the 'layout of his garden and grounds' was undertaken 'with great taste, stocking them with the choicest shrubs and flowers, grapevines, hothouses & in fact all the appliances of what is called "a very pretty place"'.[25] McDonnell 'independently imported many Asian plants in

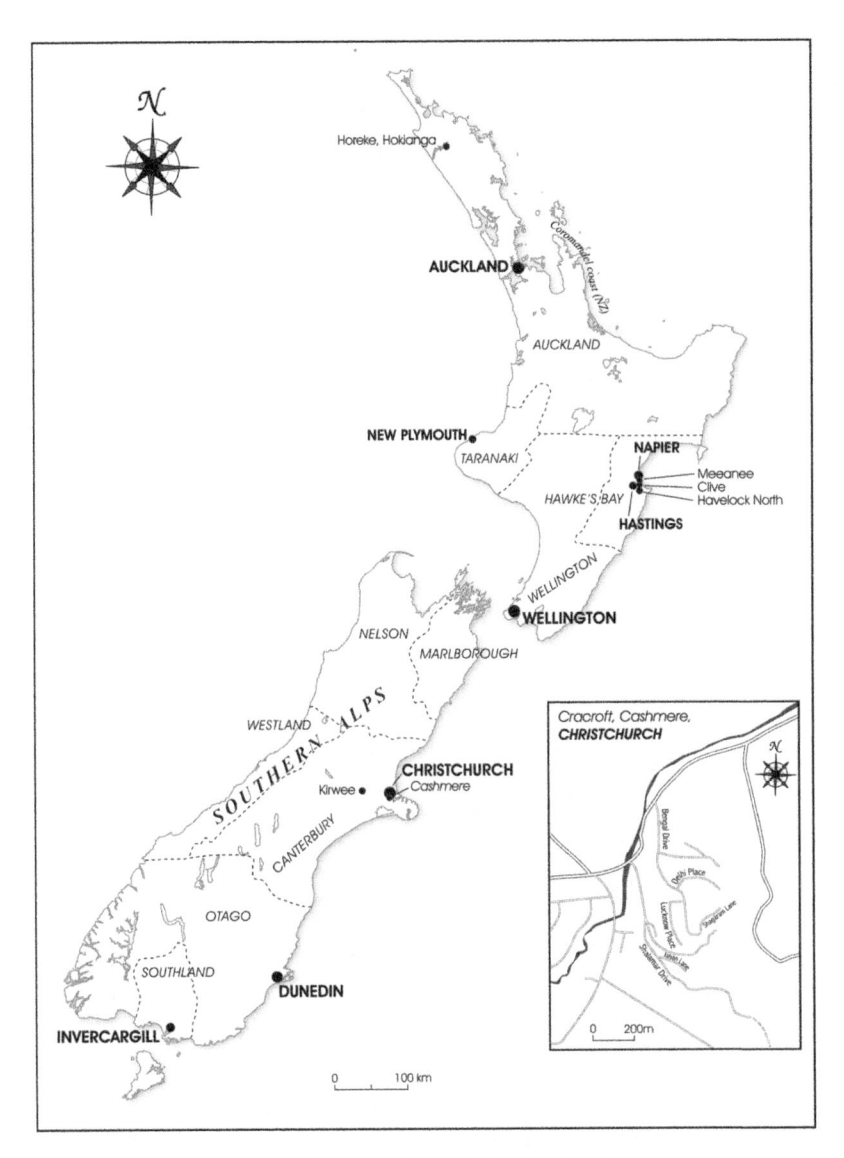

Figure 10.2 Location map of places discussed in the chapter.

226 *James Beattie*

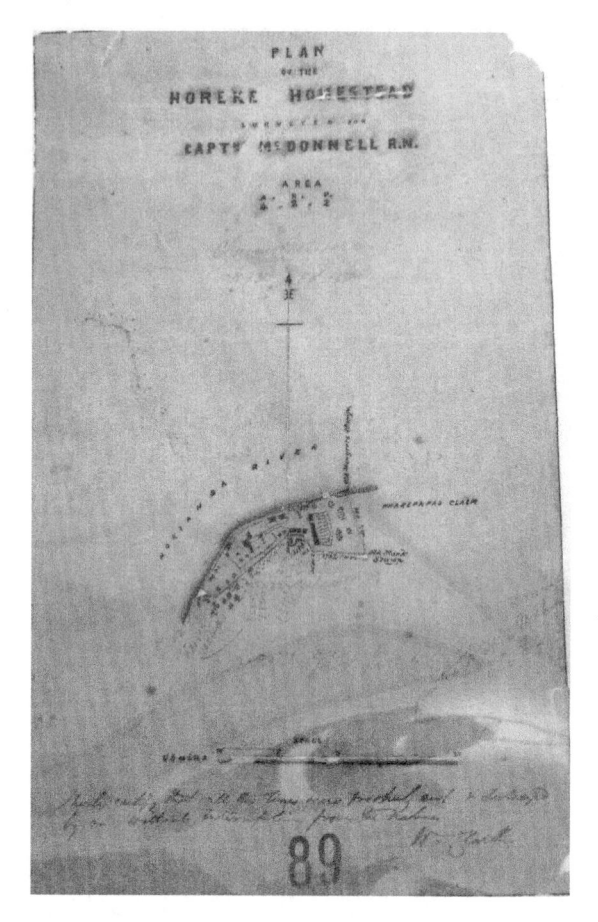

Figure 10.3 Map of the layout of McDonnell's garden.
Source: Old Land Claims 89: Plan of Horeke Homestead surveyed for Captain McDonnell in c.1857: Archives reference: BA12 23908 A1708 2811/ OLC 89, Archives NZ, Auckland.

connection with the flourishing timber trade' to create this garden. *Kalanchoe grandiflora* – native to Mysore and which boasts large yellow flowers – was, as botanist David Given suggests, 'probably in cultivation in New Zealand decades before its introduction into Europe'.[26] Other plants, like Indian strawberry, now growing as garden escapees near his former residence and shipyard, may also have been introduced by McDonnell.

McDonnell had a variety of sources from which to obtain these exotic plants. Some may have been gathered by him during his voyages to India and China. His last trading trip, most probably carrying opium into China, took place in 1832, giving him direct access to Chinese and Indian plants after the establishment of his Horeke entrepôt.[27] McDonnell's interest in plants from that region may have developed during his time as a free mariner, as it was commonplace for skippers of tea and opium clippers to be paid to carry live plants from China and India to Britain.[28] McDonnell may also have obtained Asian plants from the EIC vessels calling into New Zealand or during his regular business visits to Sydney. In Sydney, several Chinese and Indian plants were commonly available from both private and public sources.[29] Furthermore, from 1816, Sydney's Botanic Gardens (later Royal Botanic Gardens, Sydney) facilitated the introduction of many Chinese and Indian species. It received plants directly from Canton until the mid-nineteenth century, and through Calcutta Botanical Gardens for much of the nineteenth century.[30]

By the late 1830s, however, the Royal Botanic Gardens, Kew, likely became McDonnell's major source of plants. McDonnell would order boxes of seeds from Kew and return 'them filled with those of New Zealand'.[31] A paucity of records, compounded by the loss of all of McDonnell's papers in a fire, means we shall never know the full extent of McDonnell's introductions, but a surviving record of plants sent to him from Kew Gardens provides some clues. From this 1845 document we learn that McDonnell received plants from around the world. European plants comprised ten of the 36 varieties sent. Ten also came from East Asia and probably five came from the India/Himalaya region (*Rhododendron ponticum, Cedrus deodara, Jasminium revolutum, Jasminum pubigerum* and *Leycesteria Formosa* [now a significant invasive plant in New Zealand]), a reflection perhaps of McDonnell's interests and knowledge of plants from this region.[32] The EIC trading networks snaking around the south Pacific enabled an individual like McDonnell with the means and inclination to develop a flourishing garden stocked with many colourful varieties of Asian plants, several in fact in advance of their appearance in Britain.

Climate, colonisation and India, 1840s–1880

During McDonnell's residence in the Hokianga, the Treaty of Waitangi (1840) formally made New Zealand a part of the British Empire. Formal colonisation made New Zealand attractive for a large-scale European settlement. More established – and ever quicker – shipping connections quite literally also opened up the biological floodgates to new plant and animals introductions while a rapidly expanding migrant population, bringing into New Zealand the British love of gardening and passion for exotics, established a demand for the introduction of exotic plants, including those from India.[33]

The scale of emigration to New Zealand is apparent when one examines the rapid rise of the European population evident over the nineteenth century. In 1840, New Zealand's population comprised about 100,000 Maori and 2000 non-Maori. The New Zealand Company (NZC), a private settlement concern, added a further 10,000 settlers over the next decade or so from 1840.[34] Alongside non-NZC settlers, New Zealand's non-Maori population grew to over 26,000 by 1851.[35] Over the next decades, discoveries of gold attracted ever more Europeans and significant numbers of Chinese, such that by 1871 the colony's non-Maori population stood at over a quarter of a million. From the 1870s assisted immigration schemes led to a substantial population increase: New Zealand's non-Maori population reached three quarters of a million by 1900 just as its Maori population dipped to a low point of 42,000, though one from which it would later recover.[36]

A significant part of the appeal of New Zealand to migrants lay in the presentation of both easily available land in the colony and a healthful climate.[37] Countless migrant handbooks rhapsodised on the healthiness of its climate while doctors and statisticians eagerly confirmed this – often by conveniently ignoring that New Zealand's low death-rates reflected its young immigrant population rather than any innate healthiness of the climate. At this same time, searching for a healthy climate had become a matter of life and death for EIC officials, traders and military stationed in India, reflective of escalating concerns about the effects of the sub-continental climate on Anglo constitutions. De-facto colonialism in India heightened anxieties as it seemed to throw Europeans at the mercy of cholera, plague and a host of other diseases against which they had no immunity. As a consequence, fears of death, disease and lasting debility hung over all Europeans settlements in India. Confidence in the ability of the British to acclimatise to places different to the ones they were born in was also evaporating, leading to an urgent search for healthier and more temperate places in which to live.[38] John Turnbull Thomson captured the mood of many Anglos in India when, in 1865, he declared that 'nature wars in the tropics against the white man and his institutions'.[39] Retreat to hill stations offered Britons a temporary fix to the problems created by India's climate, but migration presented a safer and more permanent solution.

New Zealand writers eagerly encouraged such migrants, and specifically tried to attract EIC retirees, especially in the wake of the 1857 First Indian War of Independence, or 'Uprising' as the British termed it at the time.[40] Many EIC retirees in New Zealand in turn played a role in encouraging friends, relatives and acquaintances to settle in New Zealand. Articles such as this one, from *The New Zealand Journal* (1842), were typical of the appeals designed to entice India-based Europeans to the southern Pacific colony. According to the article, '[t]he sickly Nabob, the childless wife, and the attenuated object of consumption, will soon be eager to reach' New Zealand and experience its salubrious climate, where 'they may be restored to the blessings of health and enjoyment'.[41] Several similar advertisements extolling the virtues of New Zealand and its climate appeared in publications in India. For example, in 1852 *Saunders' Monthly Magazine for All India* carried a 50-page article rhapsodizing over the benefits of the South Island province of Canterbury, including those of its climate.[42] Several ex-EIC migrants to New Zealand also produced books promoting the colony – and its climate – as a settlement destination for ex-EIC officials. In 1854 Sir John L.C. Richardson (1810–1878) wrote one such manual. Bengal-born, Richardson had served with the military in India and Afghanistan and retired in 1851 with the rank of Major. Soon after, he emigrated to New Zealand for health reasons, and later become a prominent politician in the colony, serving as Otago Provincial Superintendent (1861–1863) during the gold rushes, which transformed the province economically, culturally and politically. Based on his extensive travels throughout New Zealand, Richardson published *A Summer's Excursion in New Zealand: With Gleanings from Other Writers*, a work paying keen attention to the benefits of New Zealand's climate.[43]

Medical testimony supported the writing of individuals like Richardson. One such testimony came from the highly respected A. S. Thomson (c.1817–1860), who served as surgeon to the 58th Regiment, which came via India and Afghanistan to New Zealand in the late 1840s. Thomson published several medical geographies extolling the healthiness of New Zealand for troops previously stationed in India. As he observed in 1855:

> To the Indian who has suffered from no disease, but whose mind and body are exhausted and enervated by the high temperature and restless nights, which residence in the tropics produces, New Zealand will be found a peculiarly agreeable residence. I speak of this from my own personal experience, and that of one or two others who have suffered from the exhaustion of an Indian life.[44]

The events of 1857 magnified Anglo fears of India's climate and heightened their sense of the vulnerability of their rule. Several even suggested that India's unhealthy climate had not only lessened the effectiveness of European and Indian troops, but had also perhaps encouraged rebellion in the first place.[45] Nor were concerns about India's climate limited to Europeans. In the 1820s, a Maori chief attempted to dissuade another, Titore, from visiting Bengal. 'Brian', reported the writer – who had named him such – represented 'the Indian climate ... as very unhealthy; saying it was intolerably warm, and so much infested with mosquitoes as to prevent sleep'.[46]

As far as healthy countries to retire to, the options were fairly limited. As one author explained in a New Zealand newspaper, when an Anglo-Indian commonly retires to Britain, he

> arrives in the country he calls home, and finds it a strange land; his friends are dead, dispersed, or receive him coldly. ... he sits in a draught, and gets a cold in this head: he is caught in a shower, and gets rheumatism in his shoulder: and he concludes the climate of England has changed.[47]

Medical advice reinforced these perceptions, by cautioning retiring EIC military and officials against the immediate return to such a cold climate as Britain's following residence in the tropics.[48] Health matters aside, there were other compelling social and economic reasons not to return to the British Isles. In England, the returning Company man 'is a mere nobody'. 'What influence [has he] on the affairs of even a village?'[49] In contrast to the disadvantages posed to Anglo-Indians of residence in Britain, for a brief period, the New Zealand government offered advantageous land grants for EIC officers and men, especially those from the military who could be called upon to fight Maori.[50]

Possibly dozens or more officials and troops with Indian experience took up these, and other offers, in settling in New Zealand. Over the nineteenth century, many also encouraged their friends, relatives and acquaintances to join them.[51] As noted, the events of 1857 in particular boosted migration. An anonymous 1858 correspondent to a Canterbury newspaper from the Hill Station of Murree captured British fears and explained why places like New Zealand seemed suddenly so much more attractive: 'The shock which the mutiny and rebellion has given to [the British in] India can scarcely be understood in your part of the world.' As a result: 'Numbers here are turning their eyes wildly about looking for a land in which they can live in peace, without a chance of their wives and children being cut into ribbons.' He expressed confidence in his ability to 'direct a real emigration from India to Canterbury', noting how: 'Whenever I get an opportunity I always introduce New Zealand as the subject of conversation. People are invariably interested and anxious for information.'[52]

EIC biota barons in New Zealand

From the 1850s until the 1880s, several of the wealthier ex-EIC officials who retired to New Zealand served in national and provincial politics. Some also introduced into New Zealand environmental policies and ideas shaped by their time in the EIC.[53] Because of their noteworthy environmental impacts as private individuals, either through plant and animal introductions from India or through other significant landscape changes, several can be described as 'biota barons'. This term, coined by environmental historian Paul Star, describes 'those who were influential in the business of shifting biota from place to place'.[54] These biota barons, along with colonial surveyors with experience in India, are characteristic of the 'imperial careerists' identified by David Lambert and Alan Lester – individuals whose colonial experiences in one or more places shaped attitudes and experiences elsewhere in Empire.[55]

Canterbury politician, runholder and former EIC Judge, Sir John Cracroft Wilson (1808–1881) was one such biota baron.[56] Wilson sought out opportunities in Canterbury in 1854, but only settled there permanently with his family after the 'Indian Uprising'. Born in Onamore, India, Wilson spent over twenty-five years in EIC service. Before his role in suppressing the 'Mutiny', he had played a prominent role in fighting Thuggism in the 1830s, subsequently serving as a Magistrate and Collector in Moradabad.

Like several other ex-EIC retirees in the colony, Wilson penned a manuscript

> designed for the use & information of the Members of the Civil & Military services of the Honorable the East India Company ... many of whom are anxiously revolving in their minds ... in what country they must eventually settle and end their days.

Although acknowledging the challenges of living in a 'newly settled' country such as New Zealand, 'there are', he wrote, 'many "good men and true" among the Senior Members of the East India Company's services, who are fit for better things than dragging out a useless existence in England as an Emancipated Indian; men who, in a good climate, are fit for the performance of any duties, however arduous'.[57] In describing the retired Indian officer in England 'as a very reluctant John Bull', Wilson echoed the sentiments of others in ruing the sometimes socially and economically circumscribed lifestyle this group experienced in that country by comparison with their life of luxury in India. He also perhaps alluded to the cool reception received by wealthier EIC retirees from among the British upper classes.[58]

Notwithstanding that 'the climate of the Canterbury Province is not always that Heavenly climate which it has been designated', Wilson felt that most of the time it could be compared favourably with 'the atmosphere of the Himalaya Mountains at an elevation of 7000' feet. More particularly, he likened Canterbury's climate to that of the hill stations of Nainee Tal, Munsooree and Simlah.[59] This description would have resonated strongly with readers in India, for whom a visit to such places represented relief from the maddening heat of the plains and a welcome opportunity to restore one's health.

But Wilson went well beyond merely seeing similarities between landscapes. He firmly marked Canterbury's climatic association with Indian hill stations by naming the hill immediately above Christchurch, 'Cashmere'. Moreover, as he explained, the view from his house in Cashmere, New Zealand, extended over 'a plain very like the Moradabad Terrace [but] without its Mango Groves'.[60] The climatic similarity of New Zealand's 'Cashmere' of course recalled its namesake Kashmir, a hill station popular among British officials. New Zealand's Cashmere, like its popular Indian namesake, also rose abruptly over flat plains. Wilson probably chose to live at a higher situation because of prevailing fears of swampy Christchurch as a source of miasma – unseen effluvia popularly believed to cause disease. (Interestingly, long after Wilson's death, Cashmere's association with health continued through the establishment of a tuberculosis sanatorium there.[61])

Wilson's naming and environmental modifications illustrate 'the intertwining of imperial landscapes of health'.[62] Wilson sought to do this in Canterbury by remaking Cashmere, New Zealand, in the image of its Indian namesake through the introduction of Indian plants and animals. His actions in bringing with him to New Zealand from Calcutta (via Sydney) 'a menagerie for the public good', as a friend described it, also evinced the importance he placed on environmental transformation accompanying colonisation. This menagerie from India arrived with many Indian seeds and plants.[63] The vessel Wilson charted, *Akbar*, had on board:

> A high cast very powerful Arab
> Two Bokhara Assess
> Two Chinese pigs, Spotted deer, Hog Deer, Antelope.
> Five Goats from the Agrah District
> Eight Peacocks and peahens
> Ten Hares
> ...
> Some Rohillah Game Fowls
> Some Guinea Fowls
> Two boxes of Grey partridges
> One box of Black Partridges
> One box containing three French partridges
> Three Ward's cases of Scarlet Rhododendron
> One Dozen cases of Bamboos
> Various kinds of seeds.[64]

For his fellow Indian military officer, Captain (later Colonel) Muter, resident in New Zealand in the 1850s, Wilson's introductions promised to open the floodgates to immigration hitherto 'impeded by the barrenness of these Islands in animal life'.[65] Here, Muter identified one of New Zealand's perceived deficiencies: its lack of game animals. For Anglo-Indians like Muter and Wilson, this deficiency in particular represented a problem. In India hunting – *shikar* – was not merely a pasttime of the upper and middle classes and regal Indians (from whom the concept and its name was taken), but an incredibly important aspect of masculine identity, at once a statement of class pretensions and of racial or caste superiority. A contest against a wild animal tested the mettle and skill of the European hunter, but also testified to the innate notion of British fair play through the skilful and 'sporting' nature of the hunt. Unlike lower-caste Indians or lower-class British poachers who merely hunted for food, the true hunter's reward was the challenge of man against beast and the glory symbolised by a mounted lion's head or beast's stretched-out pelt.[66] As Muter wrote, 'the pursuit of game not only furnishes amusement, but also, in a great measure, forms the character of a people'.

How did Wilson's animals fare in their new home? Even before reaching New Zealand, his stock had suffered considerable losses. In Sydney, he noted how he landed 'the unfortunate remnant of my once beautiful flock of 1220 ewes and 50 rams', and horses.[67] At least, he observed, the Arab Horse arrived 'safe and well' in Christchurch, winning him first prize at the December cattle show. Jenny, the surviving Bosehard Ass, he recorded, was in constant employment 'carrying a Lady or more ignoble load of flour to the farm or Christchurch'. Among the Agrah breed of goats he introduced, 'one male and four females reached Canterbury in safety'. But 'for a wild dog killing them I should have possessed in Decr 1854 eight kids whereas I possess only two'. 'The Rohillah Game fowls, the Pintados ... and the rabbits are thriving'. Two of the last escaped and were to be noticed by Wilson among an ever-growing number of offspring. 'A Chinese Boar and Sow are doing very well, obeying Nature's first Law, "Increase and Multiply".' In contrast, none of the partridges made it to Christchurch, nor did any of the three kinds of deer, while only a single peacock survived.[68] Whether the failures were due to the perils of on-board transportation or their unsuitability to Canterbury's climate is unclear.

Wilson's plant introductions had a similarly mixed success. Dr Hugh Falconer (1808–1865), Director of the Calcutta Botanical Garden, had supplied Wilson with several different species of bamboos before his departure. All of Falconer's bamboos reached Christchurch alive, but 'frost killed them' despite Wilson having placed them under the shelter of the veranda of his house. Other bamboos did not even make it that far. A fracture in the glass of the Wardian case killed '[t]he small hill bamboo (Nilgala)' he had brought.[69] (Effectively a mini-glasshouse, the Wardian case was invented in the 1830s although its use only took off after 1845, following the repeal of the Glass Tax, which reduced the case's cost.[70]) These losses plunged Wilson into despair, especially given the special care he had taken to ensure their survival. On his arrival he had given large amounts of the seed of the large hill bamboo to the well-known local gardener and nurseryman, William Wilson (1819–1897).[71] 'I kept them with the greatest care in my writing desk', Cracroft Wilson confided dejectedly to his diary, but '[n]ot one seed germinated, and the loss of this plant, which would be perfectly invaluable in New Zealand, caused me more vexation than all my other losses in the horticultural line.' As Wilson's experience showed, notwithstanding the Wardian case, the live transportation of plants remained a chancy affair, subject to the whims of inclement weather, sometimes indifferent care and the ever-present likelihood of loss occasioned by every transferral from one form of transportation to another.

Not all the losses were accidental. Immediately upon his arrival into New Zealand, Wilson deliberately destroyed the doab grass (*Cynodon dactylon*), 'being fearful lest it should become a curse to the country'. His action was motivated by his experiences in Australia, where Wilson found the grass 'all over Sydney & the Hunter River' and considered by locals 'detrimental under the name of Kooch grass'. Wilson's actions, however, were to no avail, as by the early twentieth century, the grass was widespread in northern South Island and the North Island.[72] Contrasting with his disappointment over the bamboo and his decision to destroy the 'kooch grass', the three young Himalayan rhododendron he brought were not only alive, but 'flourishing under the care of' Wilson's 'friend Mr Davie in a garden adjoining the house of Mr. T.T. Brown in Christchurch'. Of the garden seeds and creepers which he distributed, several also fared well.[73]

Five years later, following his involvement in the events of 1857 in India, Wilson and his wife returned to the colony in 1859. They chartered the *Armenian*, a fine vessel described as belonging 'properly to the Calcutta and China trade'. The journey of the vessel illustrates the complex nature of the Indian–Australasian trade. The *Armenian*, 'full rigged and fitted with auxiliary [steam] engines', made record time on its journey from Calcutta, via Mauritius and Sydney, to Lyttelton, Christchurch's port. On the way, the vessel transported 500 coolies from Calcutta to Mauritius, picked up sugar for Sydney, and then, in Sydney, embarked 55 horses and various cargoes for New Zealand. A participant in the lucrative Sydney–Calcutta horse trade, Wilson then returned with the vessel to Sydney. There, he embarked 150 brood mares to be sent on to Calcutta for breeding. On this voyage, Wilson had intended to bring 'specimens of deer and other game and animals' from India into New Zealand, a plan thwarted by the still-unsettled nature of the subcontinent. Nevertheless, he was able to introduce from India into New Zealand 'two hares and a Bokhara jackass'.[74]

Wilson's activities in introducing new plants and animals into New Zealand were not unusual. Acclimatisation in the so-called settler lands of Australasia, Canada and the United States, as historian Thomas Dunlap has observed, became something of a colonial obsession. It appealed at once to biblical injunctions to improve and re-stock the earth with useful plants and animals. It reminded settlers of other homes through the introduction of familiar species. It gave colonists an opportunity to engage in the pastime of hunting. And, it broadened the settler economy by introducing economically useful plants and animals.[75]

In Canterbury, Wilson's passion for acclimatisation found expression in various forms. He was in 1864 a founding member of the Canterbury Horticultural and Acclimatisation Society (shortened to Canterbury Acclimatisation Society in 1866), and later served as its President. As an acclimatiser, Wilson released trout and birds into New Zealand, and oversaw the transportation of salmon ova. His Cashmere estate, for example, received kangaroo and deer from various sources. He also maintained on his estate large fish ponds of sufficient size to accommodate over 1000 trout. Aware of the benefits as well as the drawbacks of acclimatisation, he wryly observed in 1866 that he would willingly sell his Cashmere goats if only someone could first round them up.[76]

As a landowner of three very extensive estates in Cashmere, Rangitata and Culverden, Wilson also oversaw massive environmental changes across the Canterbury plains. This included the drainage of swamps and the laying down of pasturage in place of native grasses as well as the planting of trees and the introduction of cattle. The extent of these changes, underwritten, in part, by wealth earned in the employment of the EIC is quite astonishing, and underlines the significance of such biota barons in inaugurating large-scale environmental change in New Zealand using overseas funds. Upon his death in 1881, Wilson's various land holdings, which included leaseholds and freeholds, amounted to over 48,600 acres; while his total estate was valued at a staggering £197,000. For example, Culverden Estate had 5500 acres laid down in pasture on which 22,347 sheep ran. Other parts of the estate produced 3300 bushels of oats and 70 tons of oaten hay per annum.[77]

Almost singlehandedly, noted a contemporary, Wilson had transformed 'dismal swamp ... into magnificent pasture country'.[78] Several of the Indian retainers Wilson had brought with him from the subcontinent helped undertake these changes alongside locally hired labour.[79] Until his death, too, Wilson maintained his enthusiasm for the introduction of plants from India. For example, in May 1871, Wilson entertained Christchurch's mayor and councillors and gave them 'a tour of the gardens and stables'. The reporter covering the visit observed that the tour afforded evidence of 'the efforts of Mr Wilson in the way of planting and general cultivation having evidently been of very unusual extent. The great number and variety of ornamental trees and shrubs are worthy of all praise, and would take very extensive space to note in anything like detail.' The reporter, however, singled out two species from the sub-continent for special comment: 'an extensive avenue of *Cupressus torulosa*, which are from twenty to thirty feet in height, and have a most beautiful effect. A number of Deodars, or sacred trees of India, also claimed great attention.' These were Himalayan cypress/Bhutan cypress, and would, most likely, have been introduced by Wilson in the late 1850s, given the height they were recorded as reaching in 1871. More significantly, perhaps, Wilson was willing to distribute the seeds of his for free among settlers to encourage the transformation of Canterbury. 'Mr Wilson has quite a nursery of valuable shrubs of this kind [that is, Deodars], and we understand that with a view to the general good of the province he is prepared to distribute seed gratuitously.'[80]

Wilson's involvement in importing organisms from India modifies some of the interpretations of plant and animal movement made by historians such as Thomas Dunlap and Alfred Crosby. In introducing plants and animals as a reminder of India, Wilson's activities complicate Dunlap and Crosby's assertions that New Zealand's environmental transformation took place largely with European species as a reminder, in part, of Britain.[81] The routes by which Indian plants took to reach New Zealand also demonstrate much greater complexity than Crosby ever recognised. For Crosby, plants, animals and microorganisms came directly from Europe to New Zealand – only in a footnote to the second edition of *Ecological Imperialism* does he mention an exception: the introduction of the Australian eucalyptus genus in the so-called Old World.[82] Instead, this chapter clearly demonstrates that plant and animal introductions took many routes before reaching New Zealand and were not solely European in origin, even if their immediate source was from that continent. Introductions by private and public actors such as commercial nurseries and botanical gardens, including exchanges of seeds and animals among friends and acclimatisation societies, highlight the sometimes multiple stages of movements of plants and animals into New Zealand.

The sources and motivation for such introductions varied greatly, too. Direct family or personal connections with India served as a pathway for the introduction of some Indian plants and animals into New Zealand, as witnessed in the case of Wilson and, earlier, McDonnell. Others – as I explore below – included acclimatisation societies sourcing Indian plants from Australia and Hawai'i, or commercial nurseries sourcing them from Britain. While the overall thrust of Crosby's thesis – that human disturbance created ideal conditions for introduced organisms in parts of the neo-Europes – is valid, both the pathways of introductions and the origin of those plants requires reconsideration. For example, of the 399 plants estimated to have naturalised in New Zealand by 1937, 306 of them were common to Asia and Europe. This figure, of course, is tentative: representing as it does an estimate. Additionally, it is an estimate of plants which had successfully naturalised by this date, rather an estimate of all of the species settlers tried to introduce, successfully or otherwise.[83] As I have written elsewhere, given this complexity, it is perhaps less accurate to describe the British Empire as the 'empire of the dandelion', as Crosby coined it, than it is to describe it as 'the empire of the rhododendron', given the importance of plants from Asia.[84]

Other Indian plant and animal acclimatisation

With their blazing colours, attractive scents and delicate flowers, Indian rhododendrons and azaleas proved immensely popular in colonial New Zealand.[85] Eagerly collected by private settlers, state botanical gardens and commercial nurseries, they were obtained from a variety of sources; from individuals, commercial nurseries and botanical gardens in Australia, Britain, North America and India, among other places. The early Wellington settlers Thomas and Selina Drake, for example, expended much energy in developing a fine garden in the early 1840s. To do so, they received rhododendrons and azaleas directly from their uncles in Darjeeling, plants which had somehow managed to survive a whole year in transit.[86] Indian plants were also cultivated by commercial nurserymen and acclimatisation societies in New Zealand. Dunedin nurseryman, William Martin (1823–1905), introduced the first rhododendrons and azaleas into the province of Otago. By about 1880, his catalogue listed 19 varieties of Indian rhododendron.[87] Of these, Martin was especially proud of the 'rich yellow blossoms' of *R. Falconeri*,[88] a bush spreading 'seven or eight feet high and fully as wide'.[89] Every November when they flowered, Martin's 'Azalea Walk' attracted as many as 500 visitors a day.[90] The 'Walk', as Martin's grandson recalled, comprised of 'a long curved path margined with azaleas and backed by the fine rhodoendrons, eight feet or more tall'.[91] Martin senior also earned himself a world-wide reputation through his hybridisation of rhododendrons, most notably the 'Marquis of Lothian' (*R. falconeri ssp. falconeri* and *R.*), which in turn was sold overseas.[92] As the *Otago Witness* observed in 1893, the appeal of rhododendrons and azaleas, as well as other plants, is easily explained when considering that 'India has perhaps a greater variety of plants than any other country in the world, having 15,000 native species, while the flora of the entire continent of Europe only embraces about 10,000.'[93]

Just as rhododendrons and camellias flourished in New Zealand's cooler southern climes, so too did northern New Zealand's subtropical climate give acclimatisers hopes of being able to successfully introduce some of India's tropical plants.[94] In 1869, the Auckland Acclimatisation Society received Indian plants from Dr Neill (65th Regiment), Mooltan.[95] Two years later it was offered unspecified numbers of rare Indian plants from Hawai'i, where many Indian plants had apparently been introduced.[96] And, in 1883, Dr Hector, Director of Wellington Botanic Garden, and arguably New Zealand's most influential scientists of the late nineteenth century, exchanged New Zealand seeds with Calcutta Botanical Gardens for Indian ones in return.[97] These exchanges underline the complexity of colonial plant transfers, and are several among many such examples of exchanges engaged in by private and public institutions. For example, the plantsman T. W. Adams (1842–1919), of Canterbury, New Zealand, received acorns and seeds from India, some of which he then passed on to David Tannock (1873–1952), Dunedin's Superintendent of Reserves and head of its Botanic Garden, for planting around that city. This included specimens of the *Quercus Dalhousie* [sic].[98] Among commercial nurseries, *Cedrus deodar* was widely available by the 1870s, with seeds on sale in plant nurseries from the early 1860s, if not earlier.[99]

While of a much smaller scale by comparison with the flow of Indian plants into New Zealand, as early as 1859, the medic and forester Hugh Cleghorn (1820–1895) published a report on the acclimatisation of 'the Kaurie [sic][100] pine [*Agathis australis*] from New Zealand' at the gardens established at the Lal Bagh in Bangalore.[101] In 1868, G. Bidie, Honorary Secretary to the Agri-Horticultural Society, Madras, recorded that New Zealand flax (*Phormium tenax*) was found to thrive well in its gardens. With 'every reason to believe that it will do the same at places of lower elevation', the Society's Committee 'think, therefore, it would be a great acquisition to coffee planters for cultivation in land in which the coffee has died out'. With that in mind, it requested 'the Government to have plants distributed from the Ootacamund Gardens for trial'. Great difficulty, however, was met with in sending the seed 'to any distance without impairing its vitality'. It is unknown what became of the trial.[102]

Despite the activities of Wilson and the anonymous author of 'The Canterbury Colony', who expressed his intention of introducing a variety of Indian animals, including Chitta-gong fowl and, for ornamental purposes, Brahmin cattle, Indian animals did not enjoy anywhere near the same popularity as Indian plants in New Zealand.[103] Some of the more unusual attempts at introduction included the importation in 1877 by C. Basstian, of Dunrobin Station, Southland, of 15 mongooses from India in the hope that they might rid the station of its rabbit infestation.[104] No record exists of their fate, and it can be assumed that the introduction did not succeed. Game animal introductions from India were relatively few and far between. Yet one of the exceptions to a general history of acclimatistion failures was the Himalayan Thar (*Capra jemlaicus* or *Hemitragus jemlaicus*). Intended to satisfy the needs

240 *James Beattie*

of recreational hunters and to boost the region's developing tourist industry, numbers of the animal increased rapidly following its early introduction into the Mt Cook/Aoraki area of central South Island in 1904 and the West Coast.[105] Today, it is necessary to undertake culling to deliberately restrict their range to the West Coast and Canterbury regions, with around 8000 of the animals estimated to be in New Zealand in 2010. Of birds, the Indian or common mynah (*A. tristis*) was introduced from Australia into many different places in New Zealand from the 1870s,[106] in the hope that it would aid in keeping down insect numbers.[107] By the late nineteenth century, the birds seemed to be thriving only in the central North Island. A scientific belief at the time held that the mynah preferred living on the margins of large forested areas, of which many were created through the large-scale forest clearances of the North Island in this period.[108] Nevertheless, by the twentieth century they had become a pest species in many parts of northern New Zealand; but by contrast, probably died out in the South Island by the 1890s.[109]

Indian–New Zealand landscape connections

The desire by ex-EIC migrants in New Zealand to recall their life in India through the introduction of plants and animals from the sub-continent extended also to the naming of New Zealand landmarks and towns after those of India. I have already discussed Wilson's naming of Cashmere (Figure 10.2, insert), but there are also many other examples where naming in New Zealand recollected aspects of British India. Alfred Domett (1811–1887), New Zealand Premier and poet, named most of the towns in the Province of Hawke's Bay, eastern North Island, after prominent British associated with India (Figure 10.2). The town of Napier commemorates General Sir Charles Napier, whose victories paved the way for the conquest of Scinde, but who interestingly opposed its annexation. Napier also has Scinde Island and Scinde Heights. Other towns in the province associated with India are Meanee (named after the battle of 1843), Hastings (after Sir Warren Hastings), Havelock North (after Sir Henry Havelock) and Clive (after Sir Robert Clive).[110]

Further south, in Canterbury, and after nearly 36 years of active service in India, Colonel James De Renzie Brett (1809–1889) named the region he farmed, 'Kirwee', after the Fort of Kirwee (now, Karwi, Uttar Pradesh), which he had helped to capture in 1857. Brett also imprinted his Indian experiences on Canterbury's landscape in several other ways. One was through a water race – still in use to supply water for stock – modelled, so Brett argued, on his experience of irrigation works in Central India. At Kirwee town, a miniature monument of the Taj Mahal straddles the water race, built after Brett's death to commemorate his role in its construction. By far the most unusual landscape monument to India Brett established was a plantation in which each tree was said to represent the disposition of Brett's troops during the storming of the Fort of Kirwee – plans of the plantation from this period support this interpretation.[111]

Travellers and settlers also drew comparisons between India and New Zealand landscapes. In line with most other nineteenth-century travellers, the romantically coded language of the sublime and the picturesque allowed travellers to find similarities in landscapes, not only among European and colonial environments, but also among different colonies, including India and New Zealand.[112] Travel, too, could evoke associations between places. For example, during J. D. Hooker's (1817–1911) famous Himalayan exploration, Hooker likened a 'large square stockade' he came across near a village in the Monai valley to 'a New Zealand "Pa [fortified village]"'. Not only that, but 'the whole country hereabouts much recalls', he wrote, 'the grassy clay hills, marshy valleys, and bushy ridges of the Bay of Islands', New Zealand.[113] Hooker had visited the Bay of Islands in the early 1840s during the voyage to the southern ocean of HMS *Erebus* and *Terror*, from 1839 to 1843. In another example, Elizabeth Muter regarded the long approach to Calcutta up the Hooghly River with hope by recalling similar such journeys in New Zealand. But on landing, she 'soon missed' 'the clear bracing atmosphere of New Zealand, its snow-covered mountains and blue streams'. Instead of New Zealand, she had come to 'a climate of degenerate animals – wretched men, wretched ponies, wretched cattle'.[114] The power of imaginative geographies, expressed through naming and landscape alteration, as well as by the recognition of similar geographical forms, connected India and New Zealand in ways beyond simply the introduction of animals and plants.

Conclusion

This chapter has demonstrated how eighteenth-century EIC trading interests in New Zealand's natural resources drew this southern region and its people into networks of economic exchange and migration that later facilitated the introductions of plants and animals from India, as well as limited exchanges the other way. Retired EIC employees who became New Zealand colonists brought with them Indian organisms, as well as environmental ideas and aesthetics shaped by their Indian experiences. The garden-making of Thomas McDonnell over the 1830s and 1850s, for example, demonstrated its owner's desire to possess Indian plants despite the many difficulties in doing so. That McDonnell could acquire Indian plants was because New Zealand was linked with the wider EIC trading network of the Asia-Pacific region. New levels of interaction with India and New Zealand developed mid-century as fears of India's deadly and debilitating climate drove EIC military, office mandarins and merchants to search for healthy places to retire to. Many EIC migrants who came to New Zealand for health reasons actively introduced plants and animals from India, alongside organisms from other places. They also introduced environmental policies and environmental management techniques shaped by their experiences on the sub-continent. Such was the environmental impact, that some, like Sir John Cracroft Wilson, became 'biota barons', responsible for introducing Indian plants and animals into the colony, and using money made in India to fund these and other environmental transformations in New Zealand. Yet, just as lasting, perhaps, have been the geographies of the mind, as EIC settlers named, planted and wrote their Indian experiences into parts of the New Zealand landscape. All of these examples underline the importance of India to the history of New Zealand's environmental transformation. Charting this formerly forgotten history recovers some of the fascinating aspects of nineteenth-century colonial interconnections, which can also serve to enrich and broaden the environmental historiography of India.[115]

Notes

1. E. Muter (1864), *Travels and Adventures of an Officer's Wife in India, China, and New Zealand*, Vol. 1. London: Hurst and Blackett, pp. v–vi.
2. John M. MacKenzie (1986), *Imperialism and Popular Culture*. Manchester: Manchester University Press.
3. E. Muter (1997), *Travels and Adventures of an Officer's Wife in New Zealand*. Originally published 1864, facsimile edition Christchurch: Kiwi Publishers, p. 277.
4. The migration of EIC employees and their families also opened up a raft of other environmental links, not explored in this chapter: from EIC surveying and forest conservation models, to exchanges of personnel and agricultural know-how. James Beattie (2011), *Empire and Environmental Anxiety: Health, Science, Art and Conservation in South Asia and Australia, 1800–1920*. Basingstoke: Palgrave Macmillan; Beattie J. 'A "shock which ... can scarcely be understood": Health panics, migration and plant exchange between India and Australia post-1857', in Robert Peckham (ed.) (2014), *Panic: Disease, Crisis and Empire*. Hong Kong: Hong Kong University Press, pp. 87–110.

5. T. R. Metcalf (2007), *Imperial Connections: India in the Indian Ocean Arena, 1860–1920*. Berkeley and London: University of California Press, p. 1; T. Ballantyne (2001), *Orientalism and Race: Aryanism in the British Empire*. London: Palgrave Macmillan.
6. Ballantyne, *Orientalism and Race*; T. Ballantyne (2012), *Webs of Empire: Locating New Zealand's Colonial Past*. Wellington: Bridget Williams Books; D. Walker (1999), *Anxious Nation: Australia and the Rise of Asia, 1850–1939*. St Lucia, Queensland: University of Queensland Press; J. Broadbent, S. Rickard and M. Steven (eds.) (2003), *India, China, Australia: Trade and Society, 1788–1850*. Glebe, NSW: Historic Houses Trust of New South Wales.
7. Beattie, *Empire and Environmental Anxiety*; J. Beattie (2012), 'Imperial Landscapes of Health: Place, Plants and People between India and Australia, 1800s–1900s', *Health & History*, 14(1): 100–120; J. Beattie (2007), 'Tropical Asia and Temperate New Zealand: Health and Conservation Connections, 1840–1920', in B. Moloughney and H. Johnson (eds.) (2007), *Asia in the Making of New Zealand*. Auckland: Auckland University Press, pp. 36–57.
8. C. A. Bayly (1989), *Imperial Meridian: The British Empire and the World, 1780–1830*. London: Longman; R. Marks (2002), *The Origins of the Modern World: A Global and Ecological Narrative from the Fifteenth to the Twenty-First Century (World Social Change)*. Lanham, MD: Rowman & Littlefield.
9. *Argus*, 7 December 1865: 5; 26 February 1866: no page; K. R. Binney, *Horsemen of the First Frontier (1788–1900) and the Serpents Legacy*. No place: Volcanic Productions; 2005.
10. Note: S. Rickard (2003), 'Lifelines from Calcutta', in Broadbent, Rickard and Steven (eds.), *India, China, Australia: Trade and Society, 1788–1850*, pp. 64–93.
11. See: *Argus*, 22 January 1861: 5 (Cashmere goats); 16 May 1866: 5 (jungle fowls); 14 April 1862 (Indian pines); 30 October 1861; 4 (animals).
12. B. Kingston (1990), 'The Taste of India', *Australian Cultural History*, 9: 39; Beattie *Imperial Landscapes of Health*.
13. Kingston, 'The Taste of India', p. 36.
14. The EIC permitted whaling in New Zealand waters in 1789: G. A. Knox (ed.) (1969), *Natural History of Canterbury*. Wellingon: A. H. and A. W. Reed, p. 519.
15. R. McNab (1909), *Murihiku: a History of the South Island of New Zealand and the Islands Adjacent and Lying to the South, from 1642 to 1835*. Wellington, NZ: Whitcombe & Tombs, pp. 57–8.
16. 'Extracts from the Records of the HEICS Ship Royal Admiral, William Wilson, Commander, on a voyage from London to New South Wales, thence to New Zealand, Otaheite and China, 1800 to 1802, Records of the Honourable East India Company's Marine', 28 May 1801. Unpublished MS: Alexander Turnbull Library; MS-Papers-qMS-0706, p. 10.
17. See correspondence in British Library, India Office Records F/4/299/6922; T. Ballantyne and B. Moloughney (2006), 'Asia in Murihiku: Towards a Transnational History of a Colonial Culture', in T. Ballantyne and B. Moloughney (eds.), *Disputed Histories: Imagining New Zealand's Pasts*. Dunedin: Otago University Press, p. 71.
18. P. Dillon (1829), *Narrative and Successful Result of a Voyage in the South Seas*. London: Hurst, Chance and Co.
19. Ballantyne and Moloughney, *Asia in Murihiku*, p. 71.

20. J. Lee (1997), *An Unholy Trinity: Three Hokianga Characters*. Russell: Northland Historical Publications Society, p. 69.
21. J. O. C. Ross (date unknown), 'McDonnell of Hokianga: A Biographical Account of the life and times of Lieutenant Thomas McDonnell, Royal Navy'. Unpublished MS: Alexander Turnbull Library; MS-Papers-1500-05, p. 9.
22. Ross, 'McDonnell of Hokianga', pp. 9, 15–16.
23. J. O. C. Ross (1980), *Te Horeke: Pre-Colonial Shipyard and Trading Establishment, The Records of the New Zealand Historic Places Trust*. Upper Hutt: New Zealand Historic Places Trust, pp. 18–22.
24. J. Buller (1878), *Forty Years in New Zealand: including a Personal Narrative, an Account of Maoridom, and of the Christianization and Colonization of the Country*. London: Hodder & Stoughton, p. 28.
25. Morton-Jones (1851), *Journal of Hokianga, 1851*. Sydney: Mitchell Library; cited in Lee, *An Unholy Trinity*, p. 95.
26. D. R. Given, E. G. Brockerhoff and J. Palmer (2006), 'Nationally Networked Plant Collections are a Necessity', *New Zealand Garden Journal*, 9(1): 15. In Given's article the incorrect botanical name is given for Chinese Hill Cherry. Records at the Allan Herbarium, Landcare Research, confirm that Given collected Chinese Hill Cherry at the former site of McDonnell's garden. See record CHR 420411, collected September 1984, Allan Herbarium, Landcare Research. My gratitude goes to Dr Ines Schönberger for pointing out this error of nomenclature and for searching herbaria records for me. For details on the plant, see *Curtis' Botanical Magazine* 1864, 20(3): table 5460.
27. Ross, 'McDonnell of Hokianga', p. 53.
28. J. Kilpatrick (2007), *Gifts From The Gardens Of China*. London: Frances Lincoln; F. Fan (2004), *British Naturalists in Qing China: Science, Empire, and Cultural Encounter*. Cambridge, MA: Harvard University Press.
29. Broadbent, Rickard and Steven (eds.), *India, China, Australia: Trade and Society, 1788–1850*.
30. 'Catalogue of plants cultivation [cultivated?] in The Botanic Gardens, Sydney, At January, 1828, Part 1', 1828–47. Royal Botanical Gardens, Sydney, Archives, B1; 'List of Plants, seeds &c distributed from the Government Botanic Garden Sydney', 1828–1847, Royal Botanical Gardens Sydney, B2.
31. J. O. C. McDonnell to W. Hooker 1840, Sep 19. Dorset Square, London, Kew Gardens: DC 15 English Letters I–Z, 1840, f. 63, Archives, Royal Botanic Gardens, Kew.
32. Goods Outwards Book, volume 1836–1847. f. 181, Archives, Royal Botanic Gardens, Kew.
33. J. Beattie (2013), 'The Empire of the Rhododendron? Re-orienting New Zealand Garden History, 1830s–1920s', in T. Brooking and E. Pawson (eds.), *Environmental Histories of New Zealand*. Dunedin: University of Otago Press, pp. 241–257.
34. P. Mein Smith (2005), *A Concise History of New Zealand*. Cambridge: Cambridge University Press, p. 78.
35. D. C. Thorns (1997), *Understanding Aotearoa/New Zealand: Historical Statistics*. Palmerston North, NZ: Dunmore Press, p. 32.
36. Thorns, *Understanding Aotearoa/New Zealand*, p. 32.
37. J. Beattie (2009), 'Climate Change, Forest Conservation and Science: A Case Study of New Zealand, 1840–1920', *History of Meteorology*, 5: 1–18.

38. M. Harrison (2002), *Climates & Constitutions: Health, Race, Environment and British Imperialism in India*. New Delhi: Oxford University Press; D. Arnold (1996), 'Introduction: Tropical Medicine before Manson', in D. Arnold (ed.), *Warm Climates and Western Medicine: The Emergence of Tropical Medicine, 1500–1900*. Amsterdam: Rodopi, pp. 1–19; D. Arnold (1993), *Colonizing the Body: State Medicine and Epidemic Disease in Nineteenth-Century India*. Berkeley: University of California Press.
39. J. T. Thomson (1865), *Sequel to Some Glimpses into Life in the Far East*. London: Richardson and Company, p. xii.
40. Beattie J. 'The shock which ... can scarcely be understood': Health panics, migration and plant exchange between India and Australasia post-Uprising'. Conference paper. 9–10 December 2012. University of Hong Kong.
41. Anonymous (26 November 1842), no title, *New Zealand Journal*, p. 279.
42. Anonymous (1852), 'The Canterbury Colony – Its Site and Prospects', *Saunders' Monthly Magazine for All India*; 1: 357–373, 465–485, 563–587. Republished as: *The Canterbury Colony: Its Site and Prospects, Reprinted from Saunders' Monthly Magazine 1852*. Dunedin: Hocken Library, 1976.
43. J. L. C. Richardson (1854), *A Summer's Excursion in New Zealand: With Gleanings from Other Writers*. London: Kerby and Sons.
44. A. S. Thomson (1851), *Climate of New Zealand*. Enclosure No. 35, 1850 Oct 16. P.114. In *British Parliamentary Papers and Papers relating to native inhabitants; the New Zealand Company and other affairs of the colony*, Colonies: New Zealand, p. 55.
45. J. Beattie (2014), '"shock which ... can scarcely be understood": Health panics, migration and plant exchange between India and Australia post-1857', in Robert Peckham (ed.), *Panic: Disease, Crisis and Empire*. Hong Kong: Hong Kong University Press, pp. 87–110.
46. Dillon, *Narrative and Successful Result of a Voyage in the South Seas*, p.196.
47. Anonymous (1976), 'The Canterbury Colony: Its Site and Prospects', Reprinted from *Saunders' Monthly Magazine 1852*. Dunedin: Hocken Library, p. 4.
48. Board of Commissioners (1858), 'Military Sanatarium' [sic], *Report of the Board of Commissioners, 7 September 1858*. Tasmania: no publisher. In *Tasmania: Miscellaneous 1857–1897*. National War Memorial Museum of Australia, Canberra, p. 5.
49. Anon, 'The Canterbury Colony: Its Site and Prospects', p. 4.
50. Beattie, *Empire and Environmental Anxiety*, pp. 57–59.
51. J. Beattie (2011), 'Making Home, Making Identity: Asian Garden-Making in New Zealand, 1850s–1930s', *Studies in the History of Gardens and Designed Landscapes*, 31(2): 139–159; J. McCabe (2008), 'Letters from Kalimpong: A British Tea Planter's Journey Towards "Home" with his Anglo-Indian Children' [Hons. Dissertation]. Dunedin: University of Otago; H. Drysdale (2006), *Strangerland: A Family at War*. London: Picador.
52. 'Pahari' to Editor, Murree (8 August 1858); (12 August 1858), *Lyttelton Times*, 22 December 1858, p. 4.
53. Beattie, *Tropical Asia and Temperate New Zealand*; Beattie, *Empire and Environmental Anxiety*, pp. 150–176.
54. P. Star (2011), 'New Zealand's Biota Barons: Ecological Transformation in Colonial New Zealand', *Environment and Nature in New Zealand*: 6(2): 1.

55. D. Lambert and A. Lester (2006), 'Imperial Spaces, Imperial Subjects', in D. Lambert and A. Lester (eds.), *Colonial Lives across the British Empire: Imperial Careering in the Long Nineteenth Century*. Cambridge: Cambridge University Press, p. 2.
56. Sir John Cracroft Wilson (1854), Transcript of Diary/Recollections, 1854, of Canterbury, typed transcript by Ron Chapman, 1989, Canterbury Museum, ARC1989.80.
57. Wilson, 'Diary', p. 2.
58. M. Jasanoff (2005), *Edge of Empire: Lives, Culture, and Conquest in the East, 1750–1850*. New York: Knopf/Fourth Estate.
59. Wilson, 'Diary', p. 41.
60. Wilson, 'Diary', p. 13.
61. T. O. Enticott (1993), *Up the Hill: Cashmere Sanatorium and Coronation Hospital, 1910 to 1991*. Christchurch: Canterbury Area Health Board.
62. Beattie, 'Making Home, Making Identity', p. 141.
63. Muter DD to Editor (date unspecified), *Lyttelton Times*. 12 November 1853: 9.
64. Wilson, 'Diary', p. 3.
65. Muter DD to Editor (date unspecified). *Lyttelton Times*, 12 November 1853: 9.
66. John M. MacKenzie (1997), *The Empire of Nature: Hunting, Conservation and British Imperialism*. Manchester: Manchester University Press.
67. Wilson, 'Diary', p. 10.
68. Wilson, 'Diary', p. 24. For later official introductions, note G. Bidie, Honorary Secretary to the Agri-Horticultural Society, to the Acting Secretary to the Board of Revenue, 18 August 1868, in File 7071930: Internal Affairs 1 1870/1930, National Archives (NA), Wellington.
69. Wilson, 'Diary', p. 23.
70. M. Campbell-Culver (2004), *The Origins of Plants: The People and Plants that have Shaped Britain's Garden History*. London: Eden Project Books, p. 350.
71. On William Wilson, see C. Challenger (1978), 'Studies on Pioneer Canterbury Nurserymen: (1) William Wilson', *Royal New Zealand Institute of Horticulture Annual Journal*, 6: 139–162.
72. T. R. O. Field (1990), 'Ford MB. Effects of Climate Warming on the Distribution of C4 Grasses in New Zealand', *Proceedings of the New Zealand Grasslands Association*, 51: 48.
73. Wilson, 'Diary', p. 23.
74. *Lyttleton Times*, 9 April 1859: 6.
75. T. R. Dunlap (1999), *Nature and the English Diaspora: Environment and History in the United States, Canada, Australia, and New Zealand (Studies in Environment and History)*. New York: Cambridge University Press.
76. R. C. Lamb (1964), *Birds, Beasts & Fishes: The First Hundred Years of the North Canterbury Acclimatisation Society*. Christchurch, NZ: The Society, pp. 17, 27, 29, 60, 91, 96.
77. Department of Justice, High Court, Christchurch, Item CH 511/1881 – Wilson Cracroft John, Box Location: L1, 1a – L4, 31c and L7, 64a – 67i. Deeds – L7, 67i-j. Books of Wills – U1, 3c-e, National Archives, Christchurch.
78. *Otago Daily Times*. 5 March 1881, p. 2.
79. G. Oglivie (1991), *The Port Hills of Christchuch*. Christchurch and Dunedin: Philip King Bookseller, pp. 162–168.

80. *Star*, 6 May 1871, page 2. I thank Louise Beaumont for alerting me to this reference.
81. Dunlap, *Nature and the English Diaspora*, p. 53.
82. Only in a footnote to the second edition of *Ecological Imperialism* does Crosby acknowledge the introduction of eucalyptus throughout the world. A. W. Crosby (2004), *Ecological Imperialism: The Biological Expansion of Europe, 900–1900 (Studies in Environment and History)*. 2nd ed. Cambridge and New York: Cambridge University Press.
83. H. H. Allan (1937), *The Origin and Distribution of the Naturalized Plants of New Zealand*, Proceedings of the Linnaean Society of London, 150th Session, Part 1: 32.
84. Beattie, '"Empire of the Rhododendron?"'. On other introductions, see A. Grey (1984), 'North American Influences on the Development of New Zealand Landscapes, 1800–1935', *New Zealand Geographer*, 40: 66–77; J. Beattie, M. Heinzen and J. P. Adam (2008), 'Japanese Gardens and Plants in New Zealand, 1850–1950: Transculturation and Transmission', *Studies in the History of Gardens & Designed Landscapes*, 28(2): 219–236.
85. On their popularity in India, see the superb book by E. W. Herbert (2011), *Flora's Empire: British Gardens in India*. Philadelphia: University of Pennsylvania State Press.
86. T. Parker (1987), *And Not to Yield: The Story of a New Zealand Family, 1840–1940*. Auckland: David Bateman, p. 26.
87. William Martin & Son (1880), *Catalogue of Plants Cultivated for Sale by William Martin & Son, Nurseryman and Seedsman, 'Fairfield'*. Dunedin: Mills, Dick and Co., p. 10.
88. W. Martin, 'Early History of Fairfield', November 1963, typewritten, in Martin (MS) in Toïtu Otago Settlers Museum (hereafter OSM), Reference DC-0320 OSMN.
89. W. Martin (date unspecified). 'Some Notes on the Rhododendrons at Fairfield', in Garden History Box 5 Nurseries, OSM.
90. William Martin (1953), 'Mr William Martin, a Pioneer Horticulturist of Otago', handwritten notes by Wm. Martin (grandson) 3 February 1953, OSM.
91. Martin, 'Some Notes on the Rhododendrons at Fairfield'.
92. William Martin, 'Mr William Martin, a Pioneer Horticulturist of Otago', handwritten notes by Wm. Martin (grandson) 3 February 1953, OSM.
93. *Otago Witness*. 24 August 1893: 4. Of course, China, with around 30,000 species, has the largest.
94. *New Zealand Herald*. 18 August 1883: 4.
95. *New Zealand Herald*. 5 August 1869: 3.
96. *Daily Southern Cross*. 6 June 1871: 3.
97. *New Zealand Herald*. 25 July 1883: 5.
98. T. W. Adams to David Tannock, Greendale, 13 March 1915, 'Superintendent of Reserves: Correspondence', Series PR 3/2 (1915), Dunedin City Council Archives, Dunedin.
99. William Wilson's nursery offered packets of *Cedrus* seed for sale at 2 shillings, 6 pence per ounce. *Lyttelton Times*. 1 January 1862: 6.
100. *Agathis australis*.
101. H. Cleghorn (1861), *The Forests and Gardens of South India*. London: W. H. Allen & Co., pp. 330–334.

102. Internal Affairs File 7071930: IA 1 1870/1930, National Library of New Zealand, Wellington.
103. Wilson, 'Diary', 68.
104. *Inangahua Times.* 4 June 1877: 3.
105. A. H. Clark (1949), *The Invasion of New Zealand by People, Plants and Animals: The South Island.* New Brunswick: Rutgers University Press, p. 278.
106. J. Drummond lists the following dates for introductions of the mynah. 'Awakino, South Auckland, about 1893; Brightwater, Nelson, 1880; Cape Egmont, about 1882; Carnarvon, about 1893; Christchurch, 1879; Dunedin, 1875; Havelock North, about 1885; Hawke's Bay, 1877; Kimbolton, about 1902; Marton, 1895; Motu, Poverty Bay, about 1890; Ngatimaru Survey District, 1895; Patutahi, Poverty Bay, about 1890; Rongomai, 1900; Te Rangitumau, 1895; Upper Wangaetu, 1900; Waituna, 1899; Waiapu, 1889; Waikouaiti, about 1885; Waverley, about 1883; Weber County, Hawke's Bay, about 1896.' J. Drummond (1906), 'Dates on which Introduced Birds have been liberated, or have appeared, in different Districts of New Zealand.' *Transactions and Proceedings of the New Zealand Institute*, 39: 507.
107. *Wellington Independent.* 26 March 1868: 3.
108. W. W. Smith (1910), *Notes on the Saddleback of New Zealand (Creadion carunculatus). Transactions and Proceedings of the New Zealand Institute*, 43: 168.
109. *Review of the Biology and Ecology of the Common Myna (Acridotheres tristis) and some implications for Management of this invasive species* (2009), Auckland: Pacific Invasives Initiative. The mynah, for instance, had been introduced into Melbourne in the 1860s.
110. *Auckland Star.* 3 October 1936: 20.
111. Beattie, 'Making Home, Making Identity', pp. 143–147.
112. D. Arnold (2005), *The Tropics and the Travelling Gaze: India, Landscape, and Science, 1800–1856.* Delhi: Permanent Black; J. Beattie (2011), 'Wilderness Found, Lost and Restored: The Sublime and Picturesque in New Zealand, 1830s–2000s', in R. Reeve and M. Abbott (eds.) (2011), *The Future of Wilderness in Aotearoa New Zealand.* Dunedin: Otago University Press, pp. 91–105.
113. J. D. Hooker (1854), *Notes of a Naturalist in Bengal, The Sikkim and Nepal Himalayas, The Khasia Mountains, &c.* [Internet resource]. [updated 2 November 2002; accessed 15 October 2012]. Available from: http://www.gutenberg.org/cache/epub/6478/pg6478.txt
114. Muter, *Travels and Adventures of an Officer's Wife in New Zealand,* pp. 312–313.
115. The author thanks the following for their comments and help: Betty Gilderdale, Ondine Godtschalk, Ines Schönberger, Paul Star and the editors of this volume. Research was supported by a Faculty of Arts and Social Sciences Contestable Research Grant, University of Waikato.

11
St Helena as a Microcosm of the East India Company World

A. T. Grove

Introduction

Some of the first colonisations of the East India Company were not surprisingly on oceanic islands, as these were important stopping points for ships. The case of St Helena is an important story in this history of colonisation and significant in the history of the emergence of various scientific networks in the eighteenth century. Little attention has been paid to the influence of islands in the shaping of environmental history writing. This chapter hopes to fill this obvious gap by tapping to some useful environmental accounts of the island of St Helena in the early modern period.

St Helena lies 2000 km west of Angola and 3000 km from Brazil in latitude 16° S. The island is the tip of an enormous ancient volcano that emerged from the South Atlantic Ocean 14 million years ago and last erupted about 7 million years ago. Since then it has been colonised at intervals of thousands of years by plants and animals carried by the South Easterly Trades and by ocean currents from south-west Africa and, possibly, from the southern Indian Ocean. In the course of millennia the newcomers gradually adapted to the local environment and are now endemics – species found naturally only on St Helena. So in 1502, when the island was first discovered by the Portuguese, it was a little natural world on its own, uninhabited and lacking mammals and serpents. It is easy to see why, in the discourse of the time, it was conceptualised as a Garden of Eden before the arrival of Adam and Eve.[1]

For 150 years after its discovery St Helena was visited by Portuguese, Spanish, Dutch and English ships calling for water on their return voyages from the Indian Ocean and landing sailors suffering from scurvy and other ailments. 'The King of Spain is said to have expressly forbidden anyone to be left there except the sick – for fear they should make themselves masters and take possession of the island.'[2]

The East India Company took possession of St Helena in 1659 when a fleet under the command of Captain John Dutton arrived from England with soldiers to provide a garrison plus civilian settlers. Early in the preceding year the Company had ordered all homecoming ships to provide one ton of rice on their arrival at the island, so it was evidently expected that St Helena would not be self-sufficient in food supplies for some time.[3]

Dutton, appointed Governor by the Company, was instructed to select three individuals to form a Council to assist him. One of them was to write down the proceedings or consultations, copies of which were to be sent to the Directors of the Company in London.[4] Company rule of St Helena persisted until 1834.

Given the long history of Company rule on St Helena, the island provides a useful case study for examining the environmental impacts of colonialism in this period. St Helena was the subject of the writings of many visiting naturalists and of many works of history, some of which have focused specifically on the environmental aspects. For Richard Grove, St Helena was extremely significant in the scientific networks of the eighteenth century. Philip and Myrtle Ashmole have written a natural history of St Helena[5] and Ascension, in which Chapter 7 on the 'Ecological history of St Helena since 1502' includes references to the contributions by William Burchell and William Roxburgh on the plant life of the island and to several important recent papers by Quentin Cronk. More recently, Barry Weaver, a geologist at the University of Oklahoma, has provided on the web an electronic version of pre-1900 books and miscellaneous documents referring to St Helena, plus early maps and views of the island.[6] Geographer Stephen Royle's *The Company's Island,* which appeared in 2007,[7] includes a table listing the first mentions of plants introduced to the island, together with products sent by the EIC to St Helena to 1698. In this chapter, I will draw on these previous works and on a survey of the East India Company records that remain on the island to discuss the climate, environment and wildlife of the St Helena and its alterations over the period of Company rule.

Climate and environment of St Helena

In the century and a half before the coming of the East India Company to St Helena, comments made by visitors to the island point to environmental degradation becoming increasingly serious. The newcomers had introduced various plants, especially citrus trees, and numerous animals, notably goats, sheep, pigs, cats and rats. According to Beatson,[8] an early nineteenth-century Governor of the island, Captain Quendol, had related in 1588 that there were thousands of goats on the island and that 'they were seen one or two hundred together', 'sometimes in a flock almost a mile long'. The imported animals proceeded to destroy the indigenous fauna, mainly birds, and to feed on the plants and young trees. When the English navigator Lancaster made a return visit to the island on 16 June 1603 to get meat and fresh water, he remarked that the goats had become very wild and difficult to procure.[9] Pyrard in 1610, also on a second visit, was sadly disappointed. 'Everything is broken and spoiled', he remarked,[10] 'even the greater part of the trees have not been spared.' He added that, 'the Hollanders, now that they go there regularly, would seem to make a clean sweep' of the animals. He concluded:

> The consequence is that now fruits are found only by chance, and most of the trees are broken down or cut to pieces; for the passing ships take away the fruits though still in flower, on the plea that it is better thus than to leave them for the Hollanders and English: which peoples act in same sort toward the Portuguese.

It is evident that the initial environmental destruction on St Helena involved deliberate destruction by visiting mariners and that the depredations of introduced animals long preceded East India Company rule.

St Helena's plant cover continued to suffer under Company rule. However, accounts of the situation on the island differ considerably at intervals of only a few years. Deterioration of the environment was especially marked in drought years and also on occasions when heavy rain, falling on the upper slopes of the island, generated floods which caused massive erosion and destruction in the valleys at lower levels. Between such events, conditions often seem to have improved surprisingly quickly.

St Helena's climate is dominated by the Benguela Current that runs northwards from the Southern Ocean alongside the west coast of southern Africa. North of the Tropic of Capricorn, the cool upwelling water generally swings westwards to surround the island and influence its climate. The surface of the ocean thereabouts is usually about 19 to 23°C and the prevailing winds are the Southeast Trades. In Jamestown, the capital, at sea-level on the northern, leeward side of the island, temperatures seldom exceed 33°C or fall below 15°C, so climatic conditions for the garrison of the fort were pleasant enough and amongst seamen St Helena had the reputation of being a very healthy place. However, temperatures on the island diminish with height above sea level at a rate of 1.3°C per 100m of ascent, twice the usual rate, with the result that Hutts Gate, 620m above sea level, is on average 7°C cooler than Jamestown. Crops ranging from sub-tropical to temperate can be grown between 300m and 600m, but the settlers at these higher levels often had to put up with cool, cloudy conditions and their journeys to Jamestown by way of steep footpaths were long and difficult.

The mean annual rainfall at sea level on St Helena is only 200mm (137mm at Jamestown) and in consequence the coast is not only rugged but also desert-like with trees and pasture confined to valley bottoms watered, and sometimes flooded, by streams rising at much higher levels. Above 300m, where slopes are gentler, the mean annual rainfall is much greater, exceeding 1000mm at 600m (814 mm at the high ridge of Hutts Gate) and it rains on about half the days in the year. The first half of the year from February to July receives on average about 50% more rain than the later months from August to January, but in some years, 2013 for instance, there may be very little rain from March to July.

The early years of Company rule

Dutton's fleet took provisions in 1659 sufficient to last the colonists fourteen months, including two dozen different kinds of fruits and vegetables. Evidently the newcomers were disappointed in their expectations of St Helena for in 1661, when Captain Dutton was sent off to be Governor of Polu Run (one of the Banda Islands, now in Indonesia), all except two of the settlers decided to go with him. Others replaced them but numbers remained low, about 70 in all, for the next ten years or so.

The new Governor, Stringer, was ordered in 1661 to give each settler a portion of land. Acting on these orders, Stringer divided up the island into 150 parts, reserving 15 parts for the Company, 5 for himself, and allotting one share to each planter, his wife and his servants. In return, the landholder had to assist in maintaining the newly built fortifications, take his turn in the watch and pay a small rent.[11]

The settlers had difficulty in maintaining their food supplies and a visitor in 1665, Nicholas Buckeridge,[12] described the island as being in disorder with time-expired servants clamouring to be sent home to England. However, Rennefort, visiting the island in a French ship in 1666, gives an account of life at the Governor's residence that appears to have been comfortable enough.[13] (England and France had been at war since the beginning of the year, but the news had not reached the South Atlantic.) According to Gosse:

> Rennefort admired the quantities of peas, beans, turnips, beetroot, cabbages, bananas, lemons, oranges, grenadines and melons, all most carefully cultivated, even grapes ripen and there was nothing obnoxious to the amenities of life except vast quantities of rats, on which the Governor wages a sanguinary war. There are great numbers of goats. They did import horses, but these had become so wild that when they were pursued to the ends of the island they threw themselves off the rocks into the sea rather than be caught. Partridges and guinea fowl provided sport for the guns. Mr Stringer had 24 cows, looked after by his negros, while four women milked and made the butter.[14]

Robert Barlow in 1671 mentions that the East India Company had sent out a stock of cattle which had increased very much; 'the very good grass in some places which keep the cattle very fat and in good case, they multiplying very much on it'.[15] He considered the soil to be very fertile and remarked how the inhabitants grew quantities of good potatoes, beans and Indian corn as well as colewort and other herbs such as parsley, 'but bread corn they have none, for they cannot sow by reason of the roughness of the ground'. A little while before his visit, the English had planted some banana and plantain trees, and he found very good yams, 'a thing like potato but far bigger'.

Towards the end of 1672, the Dutch at the Cape landed 500 men and briefly occupied the island. Governor Beale, who had escaped to Brazil on New Year's Day 1673, sailed back to St Helena in May and by good luck met up with an English squadron under Munden that had been sent from England to protect ships homeward bound from India. By June the island was back in English hands. The Company was now more conscious than it had been of the value of St Helena to its activities.

On 16 December 1673 King Charles granted the Company a fresh charter. Two ships were promptly sent out with 110 soldiers and settlers and all sorts of stores. These included large quantities of pickled beef, brandy, guns and gunpowder, plus a wide range of clothing for soldiers and civilians, building materials, books and agricultural implements.

The Directors of the Company continued to take a close interest in the island's progress. A letter from England in 1675 noted:

We have been advised from Bantam that the Governor and Council have sent you several plants for the improving of our island, of which you make no mention in your letter to us. We hope you have been careful in their disposal.[16]

They wished: 'to have an account of what these plants and goods are which came into your hands'. Evidently not realising the limitations of the island's environment, they were anxious that sugar cane, indigo, cotton and other such commodities should be planted and put on sale.[17]

In March 1676 the Directors referred to the purchase of eight Carmenian goats being sent from India[18] and a year later wrote 'we hope the Connemara goats have arrived'.[19] They objected to wild goats being killed, writing in 1678 that several persons had 'taken the liberty to hunt and kill many of the goats that are wild',[20] claiming that all of them were the property of the Company. Evidently the Directors were still not as concerned as they should have been by the damage goats had already done to the island's tree cover.

Seventeen different kinds of fruit trees and fruit bushes were sent in 1678.[21] By then, the island's population had increased to 390. Families settling on the northern slopes were each assigned 20 acres of land and two cows, those on the southern, more exposed windward side were granted an additional 20 acres. Land was also granted to soldiers of good character and the settlers were required to take their turn as lookouts or in the garrison.

The astronomers Halley and Maskelynne on St Helena

On St Helena, the East India Company's contribution to knowledge of natural conditions was greatest in the early years of its administration and again in the final years. In November 1676, at the requirement of King Charles, the Company provided Edmond Halley, then 20 years of age, with a passage to St Helena, primarily to observe the transit of Mercury. During the voyage out, Halley kept himself well occupied, improving the sextant, collecting a number of valuable facts relative to the ocean and atmosphere, and noting the equatorial retardation of the pendulum.[22] The Company constructed an observatory for him high up on the island and Halley stayed for 18 months. To his dismay he found the horizon almost always covered by cloud. Furthermore, 'the night-time air on the high mountain upon which he set up his astronomical instruments deposited a constant film of moisture on his lenses, and even made his note-paper unable to bear ink'.[23] Nevertheless, he catalogued for the first time 341 southern hemisphere stars, discovered a star cluster in Centaurus and, on 7 November 1677, using a refracting telescope 24 feet long, made the first complete observation of a transit of Mercury across the face of the sun. He realized that simultaneous measurements of such a transit from different places on the earth would enable the size of the earth's orbit to be measured and that, from this, the orbits of all the other planets could be calculated.

A lesser known fact is that Halley also recognised the ability of water to erode the soil, observing streams on St Helena carrying so much into the sea as to discolour the water around the island. Later, in 1715, he used this knowledge, together with measurements of salt in ocean water and lakes, in his attempts to calculate the age of the earth.[24]

Halley was to return to St Helena on the *Paramore* in 1700 in the course of his second voyage to map the pattern of magnetic variation in the Atlantic region. At that time, ships intending to call at St Helena still sailed on a course that would take them well to the east of the island and then, at the appropriate latitude, they turned to sail west. Halley hoped that the magnetic variation would enable longitude to be determined with an accuracy similar to latitude, but in this he was disappointed.

Almost a century after Halley's first visit to St Helena, an observatory was erected for Nevil Maskelynne and Robert Waddington and when they came for the transit of Venus on 6 June 1761 they were 'accommodated in a suitable manner with diet and apartments at the Company's expense'.[25] While Maskelynne was there he used Meyer's lunar tables and the lunar distance technique to find the island's longitude. In a letter to the Earl of Macclesfield, President of the Royal Society, he expresses his disappointment at the accuracy of his observations of the transit of Venus. This was due in part to the cloudy weather and in part to the nearness of sun and planet to the horizon so that both were 'exceedingly ill defined'. Maskelynne expressed the hope that in 1769, when the next transit of Venus was expected, it would be possible 'to do justice to Dr Halley's noble proposal, and to settle, with the last and greatest degree of exactness, that curious and nice element in astronomy, the sun's parallax, and thence determine the true distance of the planets from the sun, and from each other'.[26]

Problems of water, woodland and wildlife

By 1679, the Governor, Sir John Blackmore, and his Council were coming to realise that the island's resources were deteriorating. Lemons, effectively a wild resource, had become very scarce.[27] Pigs in Chapel

Valley, in which Jamestown stands, were polluting water intended for visiting ships. The Great Wood was being overrun by swine and it was proving impossible to find and catch them. They had turned wild and multiplied, unmarked with no one knowing who their owners were, 'so that everyone thinks that all unmarked swine may as well be his own...whereupon many have endeavoured to seize, kill and convert to their own use as many as they can catch' while others complained at 'losing both stock and increase'. Henceforth, the Governor ordered, no swine were to be turned into the Great Wood and parts adjacent without being marked. Owners of cattle and swine in Tombstone Wood, Manatee Bay and the parts adjoining were ordered to remove them speedily and dispose of them to other places.[28]

Timber was needed on the island in large quantities for many purposes. For instance, in early December 1678, named inhabitants of the East Division were ordered to be present with axes for cutting, felling and barking 240 pieces of gumwood timber, 10 feet long and 5 inches by 5 inches, brought from the adjacent wood, to protect the Crane gun batteries where falling rock had killed two soldiers. At the end of the month, all the inhabitants able to bear arms were ordered to help bring the timber down into Chappell Valley. But it was becoming increasingly difficult to obtain such timber. Henceforth, it was ordered, only fallen trees were to be used to build and repair houses.[29]

Climate variability on St Helena

Living conditions on St Helena were dominated by droughts, some of which seem to have lasted several years, and by floods in the intervals between the droughts. The forts on the island were damaged by floods in 1691[30] and a letter tells of 'the most dreadful storm ever known' that lasted 9 days, probably in July 1701.[31] Richard Grove has stated that the very long drought of 1682 followed a strong El Niño in 1681 and preceded another in 1684. He evidently suspected that there was some connection between the essentially Pacific Ocean phenomenon and climatic events on St Helena.

Table 11.1 lists years of strong, very strong and extremely strong El Niño and La Niña years, according to Gergis and Fowler,[32] plotted against years with droughts and floods on St Helena. It can be seen that the droughts of 1721–3, 1737 and 1792 occurred in years with very strong or exceptionally strong El Niños and the floods of 1715, 1732, 1742 and 1763 in years with strong or very strong La Niñas. However, only a quarter of the drought years appear to have coincided with

Table 11.1 Years of strong, very strong and extremely strong El Niños and La Niñas and years with droughts and heavy rains on St Helena

El Niño years E, VS and S	Droughts on St Helena	Floods and storms on St Helena	La Niña years E, VS and S
			1676 S
	1682		
			1685 S
1687 VS			
		1691	
1694 S			
			1696 VS
	1698		
		1701	
		1705, 1706	
		1709	1708 S
	1712–14	1714	
		1715	1715–16 SS
1718–19 ES		1719	
1723 E	1721–3		
		1724	
1728 S			
	1729–31	1732	1733 VS
	1734	1734, 1735	
1737 E	1737		
	1739–40	1742	1739–43 VS VS S E VS
			1745 S
	1747–50	1747	1750 S
	1751–2		1752–3 VS S
	1755	1753–4, 1756–7	1755 S
		1763	1763 S
			1765 S
1770 VS			
			1779–80 S S
		1781	
		1787	1786–8 S VS
1791 VS	1791–2		1790 S
1799 S		1797	

strong to exceptionally strong El Niños and only a quarter of the floods with strong to exceptionally strong La Niñas.

In 1715 (when Gergis and Fowler do not list a strong El Niño) Governor Pyke wrote to London that the Cape of Good Hope and Mauritius, like St Helena, had both been suffering from drought. 'We have had a sickly season lately here but we hear that general sickness has reigned both at the Cape of Good Hope and all those coasts.' Captain Litter touched at the island called Don Mascarenas which lies in the latitude 20° S. between the Great Island of Madagascar.[33] When he went on shore, he reported that: 'it rained which it had not done in 15 months before, which dry time has exceedingly decreased their cattle of every sort so that they have been as incapable to provide for their shipping as we have been'.[34]

Currently, in 2013, a drought in St Helena lasting 3 months coincided with a severe drought in Namibia and southwest Angola. Many of the more extreme anomalies in southern and eastern Africa, such as droughts, floods and hurricanes, have strong teleconnections to ENSO events and in some years Indian Ocean currents and winds are much influenced by El Niño. In early to mid-2013 however, El Niño conditions were neutral and statistical evidence shows ENSO events can account at most for about 50% of the interannual rainfall variance in eastern and southern Africa.[35] However, a more recent study has found links between South African summer rainfall and temperature variability of the Benguela and Agulhas Current systems, the Agulhas Current bringing around the Cape from the Indian Ocean a quantity of warm water that varies greatly from one year to another.[36]

The impact of droughts and storms on St Helena

The Company does not appear to have appreciated the scale of the climatic difficulties on St Helena. No doubt, this was partly because of the time lag between events taking place on the island and knowledge of them reaching London. 'Why have the Company's cattle decreased so much?' asked the Directors on one occasion.[37] They went on to say:

> We have at his (Mashbone's) instance allowed him to buy several seeds and plants for trees and hedges and several other seeds for garden trade, bettering the ground and improving the husbandry also divers implements for the same purpose together with other utensils of wood and iron as you list. Send us an account how the seeds and plants thrive and which most and what you shall annually count – with proper directions about them. Write also as you have opportunity to all parts of India for any seeds or plants from thence proper for St Helena.[38]

On another occasion, they wrote:

> We do earnestly recommend to you all to encourage the improvement of the vines at St Helena so that if possible quantities of wine may be made for the benefit of the inhabitants which will be far more wholesome than arrack or any of your distillations from potatoes.[39]

But, on the island, it was reported to the Directors, 'It having pleased Almighty God not to have sent us any rain for nigh 10 months past', 2500 head of cattle had died. St Helena 'suffers from hunger on account of drought and servants of the company at the lower table ask for and are granted 2 quarts of Arack each day'.[40]

The drought came to an end with a great flood on 3 February 1714[41] and when a new Governor, Pyke, arrived on 8 July that year he found the island still

> in a very poor and deplorable condition, your plantations and stock upon examination and our views very much gone to ruin and bare of all sorts of provisions. The livestock left by the late Governor being 60 Black cows and 23 hogs. No goats, sheep, deer, turkeys, geese, ducks, fowl or rabbits,[42]

the people impoverished, they and the soldiers owing the Honourable Company £7500 11s 13/4d.

Pyke relates that, on his voyage out:

> [E]lms we carried out of England throve at first but spent themselves too fast and the heat killed them ere we got here. We carried out also a box of willows and they grew prodigiously at first but they likewise spent too fast and died. We carried out three rose trees. The biggest produced two seasons of roses or rather two roses at very difficult and different times but that also when we came 30 [i.e. to latitude 30° N] it withered away and died, so did 2 apple trees and 6 gooseberry bushes but we with cool air in latitude 29 carried two small rose trees safe which flourish now and we brought 12 coconuts which died but two of the pineapples, one at First garden and the other in the Country are both like to thrive and we have planted some pomkins (pumpkins) which are likely to do well from the St Iago [Santiago in Cape Verde] seed.[43]

He adds, 'We carried two bottles full of all the seeds we had at St Iago, oranges, lemons, limes and water melons some of which came up but by a (wind) blast about three weeks since were all cut off and lost.'[44]

Plants arriving from South Africa survived more readily. The Governor received by the *Susanna* 11 sorts of kitchen garden seeds from the Cape of Good Hope. They were immediately planted and all came up well, as they 'being fresher than the Europe seeds were, thus they take more kindly'. As he wrote:

> We are in great need for some pumps to raise the water to some parts where without vast charge we can't make it run. Then we hope to have garden trade in shipping enough to furnish and supply our little market.[45]

He added: 'A great drain is needed to carry off flood water such as that of February 3rd 1713. Such another but bigger happened about 8 year before.'[46] In March and April 1715, seas were so high that stone from Sandy Bay could not be unloaded. Construction of the new aerodrome on St Helena has experienced similar difficulties. Now, as Pyke wrote, there was a prospect of a good season. Everything was beginning to thrive:

> [B]ut we have not had a good success with those seeds we brought out of England with most of them being so dried they rotted in the ground but the Governor had some seeds from the Cape of Good Hope that came here by the *Susanna* which do all thrive here very well.[47]

By 1717, Pyke was pointing out to the Company how much things had improved since his arrival, admitting this was largely due to the weather. The island was now in a state where it could supply all the returning ships.[48] All the planters were being supplied 'with seeds, slips, stocks and plants to encourage their propagation of garden trade for the refreshment of your shipping'.[49] But as for vine plants: 'only five of these which came by the *Cardonnell* do grow and by the *Success* we received none at all. So the want of such things is the same as for several years past.'[50] Evidently the efforts made to stimulate wine production had not been very successful.

Firewood for Plantation House, Pyke's residence, now had to be fetched from over four miles away.[51] The settlers told Pyke that their fertility had declined over the years with the cutting down of the trees:

> The soil we think was impoverished by cutting down the wood for by that means the rains being unrestrained which fall here are sometimes with great impetuosity the upper surface of the ground is

often washed away as we see every rainy season and it has not done so where wood grows thick. So that now to improve the ground even only to make it healthy as formerly there must be many acres of land planted with wood but first of all the ground fenced in, also the goats and cattle which graze on the wasteland (as we call all that is not enclosed) will destroy it as fast as it is planted and because this is a thing as necessary as any for bringing back the island to as flourishing estate as formerly and will be some time before it is grown up large eno to be useful, we have begun with it and have planted wood about your Plantation House to prevent that loss of time and labour for futurity in fetching wood from so great a distance as at present.

Attempts were made to repair the damage done by soil erosion:

> Some of the guts or narrow valleys are worn out to the clay but we have in one of them carried in soil in bags and given the ground a new shirt of earth but this being an incredible labour requires more than all our hands. We doubt not but that it will answer our ends, the Governor following Mr Evelyn's directions in his book[52] on gardening therein, and as we have time and can spare the blacks we shall do so in several other places and we have in the garden begun to improve that ground with sea sand which we find succeeds very well.

Some consideration was also given to the soil types most suitable for yams, which by this time had become a staple crop:

> Yam suckers are planted in moist areas and then some are planted out on drier soils. The Governor is now taking in some ground around the Peak that never was planted yet which we think will hold about 300,000 yams when full. But there are some springs on that land which we think will produce suckers enough to plant the dry ground in Bamboo Gut. [If yams are planted in September/October they are ready in 20 months; in February/March they are ready in 25/26 months].[53]

Bamboo Gut (now known as Sandy Bay), once the Governor's only plantation, had been planted up for 30 years and then abandoned for 8 years to lie fallow. It was now improved with soil and sea sand and was expected to produce 200,000 yams to feed the Governor's newly arrived slaves.[54]

Drought returned in the early 1720s:

> The backwardness of our rainy season and the want thereof for upwards of four years past has several times been made mention of. The island now being in a very miserable condition even in a greater calamity than when the drought was in 1713 and part of 1714, all sorts of provision being so scarce that the poor people are quite dejected and caste down.

Even 'the goats which will shift the best of everything are very poor and not eatable did not a necessity oblige'.[55] The island was still in a deplorable state in January 1724.

Matters improved with the appointment of Byfield as Governor. By March 1727 progress was being made in fencing the Great Wood and a New Plantation was completed in Chappell Valley.[56] Byfield writes to London: 'We have great quantities of barren land in almost every part of the island which we are apt to think would yield us tolerable crops if we had hayseed that was very fresh and good – please to order some.'[57] Four pastures totalling 148 acres were enclosed to provide grazing for the Governor's stock and this gave time for pastures in other places to recover.[58]

By 1729, the Great Wood was reported by the Governor to be providing a great quantity of hay and potatoes and grazing for cattle. Seeded grass, protected by furze (gorse) hedges and trees, was doing very well. The plantation gardens at the Governor's residence were now surrounded by apple, mulberry, bitter lemon and orange trees, and the interior of the house was neat and clean.[59] 'Apple trees from England had not much root so they were grafted on to other trees, and pears were grafted onto quince.' In 1733, Green Tipped Bourbon Coffee seeds were brought from Mocha in Yemen in a Company ship, the *Houghton*, and were planted at various places around the island.[60] Thousands of gumwood and redwood trees were also planted:

> The last is excellent timber for many purposes, is of a good colour and fine scent and much resembles a Red Cedar and although is very serviceable yet it was nearly lost to the island but about five years ago the Governor got a couple of young plants, neither of them above an inch high, set them in his garden, took great care of them and they now produce seed in such great abundance that from these two trees alone we shall be able to satisfy all the island and we will encourage the increase of trees all we can. They will grow almost anywhere and those we have planted surprisingly fast.[61]

Only 28 years later redwood was being exported from the island, for in 1757 the *Queen Sophia* 'was loaded with bale goods, pepper, salt petre, and redwood, bound for Copenhagen'.[62] Coffee also enjoyed some limited success on the island, where it is still grown in small quantities.

At a meeting on 30 January 1730, the planters voted to kill their sheep and goats within two years. The Company's sheep and goats, except for a flock of tame sheep, were also to be killed. The weather continued to be dry, cattle were dying but the goats survived.[63] Next winter, again, there was no rain. 'Wood is become universally scarce', the Governor reported:

> Yet there is scarcely a man amongst them has planted a stick these two years. What was formerly planted has been trod down and destroyed by their goats and cattle and if great care is not speedily taken about this matter this island within a compass of a few years will become desert and uninhabitable unless it were generally stocked with a better sort of people your Honours would be better without them than with them.[64]

Three years later the Governor writes:

> The wood has greatly decayed in quantity in this place and the preservation of it too much neglected even though every holder of land is required to plant one acre in ten but they usually turn in their cattle on it. Unless the cattle be kept off the wood will not grow and is trod down and eaten up. Several hundred acres have become entirely barren with no trees or grass and the soil is all washed away by the great rains and left original rocks appearing on all the surface of the land.

He goes on to comment:

> We have many instances of this in history from divers parts of the world. The Bermuda islands which have become famous for exceeding fruitfulness and a healthy air is now become an unhealthy air as well as less fruitful than formerly it was and that is chiefly attributed to the cutting down of the trees to enlarge their pasturage and plantation grounds. There is the same account from Jamaica and other parts of the West Indies and there they are alleged for the present barrenness of Mount Libanos and great part of Turkey is a stonily testimony of the same.[65]

Pyke died and was replaced by John Goodwin who wrote to London in early 1739:

> This winter has been favourable for the planting of wood and furze (gorse) and we did not let the opportunity slip...The Great Wood when we have long heavy rains produces very large quantities of good pasture and at such times it is of great service and will graze your whole stock were their numbers double to what they now are for many months together by which means your pastures in other places recovers and affords much feed but in dry seasons it is in all parts totally barren and hardly of any use at all.

He advises the Company that it should not be deceived as formerly 'with deceitful boastings of great improvements there made which in fact were solely owing to the bounty of heaven'.[66]

The summer rains failed in 1739 and in July 1740 it was 'still too dry for the sixth year running'. Goodwin died and in 1741 was replaced by Jenkins who reported that the island is in a deplorable state, the people 'forced to eat fish'.[67] Then, in 1742, there was 'a lot of rain'.[68] That same year Jenkins died and Major Lambert was made Governor. He died, possibly from plague (which was rife on the island) and Powell, a local man, acted as Governor until he was dismissed in 1744 to be replaced by Hutchinson.

Drought returned in 1747. Cattle were fed on plantain and gumwood leaves and other livestock were in poor condition; 1000 turkeys and 2000 fowles were reported lost by distemper. There was a shortage of hooks for fishing and this time the inhabitants were 'expected to survive on salt meat'. The lemon trees on the island had died, yams were burnt by the sun from lack of water, and springs never known to have failed were dry.[69] At last in March 1750 'there were some fine rains', but drought returned in 1751 and 1752.

When drought came yet again in 1770 and 1771 the Company lost 150 head of cattle and the planters 560.[70] Cattle could be imported from the Cape, but they had usually been found to be in bad condition and introduced disease to the island, so sheep were preferred.[71] In 1776 the Captain of the *Mercury* was authorised to purchase at the Cape various fruit trees, animals and birds – including canaries which could readily be sold on visiting ships.[72]

Wood was ever more scarce. Notice had been given in 1761 strictly forbidding wood to be taken from Longwood or furze hedges destroyed. In 1767, John Desfontaine complained that the great part of the wood upon Peak Hill had been cut down. In 1771, Blacks detected cutting trees down or carrying hatchets in the Longwood were to receive 100 lashes. But the gumwood trees remaining on the Company's land were still

> constantly being destroyed by persons from the town who go under the pretence of fallen wood. Such gumwood will be seized. But should any planters or others have occasion to send gumwood to the valley in future from their enclosed grounds they are required to give their servants notes specifying the same.

A sensible step was taken in 1788 when leave was given to inhabitants not possessing lands to purchase coals in the Company stores.[73] Drought returned in 1791 and 1792.

The final years of Company rule and the emergence of a new spirit of scientific inquiry

In 1787, as a result of a suggestion from Kew Gardens, the Governor established a botanical garden on St Helena. At about the same time, Sir Joseph Banks, by then President of the Royal Society, was encouraging the movement of plants between the British colonies. Having visited St Helena with James Cooke in 1775, Banks favoured it as a place for ships to call when they were transferring plants between one part of the tropical world and another. For Richard Grove by the 1790s the institutional reach and complexity of the East India Company had allowed a sophisticated analysis of the 1791 events not least due to the prior existence of long runs of meteorological observations and systems of correspondence that had built up to service the new imperial botanic gardens and regulate the relationship between the East India Company and Kew. In India, St Helena and St Vincent the drought experiences of 1791 led to an unprecedented interest in the possibility of forest protection as a means of preventing drought.[74] On 24 December 1792, when Bligh arrived at the island with breadfruit, mangos and other plants from Timor and 'the South Seas' in his second attempt to ship them to Jamaica, some were sent on shore 'for planting under the direction of the Company's Botanists and in return they have been supplied with all such Plants and Trees from this Island as they wished for'.[75]

On 25 April 1797 'the most dreadful floods ever remembered' tore a gully 10 feet deep and 25 feet broad in a plantation leading down to Sandy Bay. There were 57 landslips in Peak Gutt, one of them 40 feet deep and 32 yards wide.[76] Similar inundations were experienced on 22 and 23 May 1798.

The beginning of the nineteenth century saw the emergence of a new spirit of scientific inquiry on St Helena. William Burchell who had worked at Kew Gardens and was a Fellow of the Linnean Society, arrived on the island in 1805. His intentions were uncertain. Governor Patton took a liking to the young man and appointed him school master and superintendent of the island's botanical garden. Burchell's main contribution to the knowledge of St Helena was a collection of plants and a comprehensive catalogue of them. He also made numerous sketches and water colour drawings of the island, many of which are now in the Library at Kew Gardens. Burchell became aware of the high degree of endemism of the flora and the closeness to extinction of some of the endemic plants but his work remained unpublished and so had little influence in the nineteenth century. Quentin Cronk, from his analysis of Burchell's data, has concluded that a maximum of only 80 known species can be considered native to the island.[77] As well as studying the botany of the island, Burchell took an interest in its geology and became responsible for surveying the island's natural resources.

Beatson arrived as Governor in 1808. This transformed the situation so far as conservation of the island's environment was concerned. Beatson inquired into the land-use history of St Helena as he had previously in the case of Mauritius. In 1811 he wrote to Sir Joseph Banks to inform him of the superior timber of pineaster trees growing on St Helena. In 1816, he pointed to the simultaneous occurence of drought in India, St Helena and Montserrat.[78] As Grove noted, his approach was 'strictly utilitarian; more specifically, his outlook on life was directly opposed to that of Burchell. Not surprisingly, the two men quarrelled violently and soon came to detest one another.'[79] In 1810 Burchell left for South Africa where, over the next five years, he embarked on extensive collecting expeditions.

Roxburgh, Chief Botanist of the East India Company and Superintendent of the Calcutta Botanic Garden, was on St Helena from June 1813 until March 1814. During this time he named many of the island's plants and attempted to distinguish between native and introduced species. The Ashmole's have written that his work essentially completed the discovery phase of botanical work on the island.[80]

During the Napoleonic wars St Helena was strategically important and for six years afterwards, when Napoleon was prisoner on the island, he was guarded by large numbers of troops. In those years, between 1796 and 1821, St Helena was more prosperous than at any time before or since. A thousand ships called at Jamestown every year and the island's economy benefited from the trading opportunities and from the relatively generous payments made to staff. Following the death of Napoleon in 1821, the number of troops in the garrison was drastically reduced and by the time Darwin arrived on the *Beagle* and spent a week there in July 1834, St Helena had come under British Government rule.

Notes

1. Richard Grove (1993), 'Conserving Eden: the (European) East India Companies and Their Environmental Policies on St. Helena, Mauritius and in Western India, 1660 to 1854', *Comparative Studies in Society and History*, 35(2): 318–351.
2. Pierre Bergeron, and Jérôme Bignon (ed. and trans.) (1887–1890), *The Voyage of François Pyrard, of Laval, to the East Indies*, London: Hakluyt Society.
3. Friends of St Helena Society (2013), Friends of St Helena Website, *East India Company Rule, 1658–1815*, URL: http://sthelena.uk.net/, last accessed 27 December 2013.
4. Consultations and copies of correspondence with the Directors are preserved in the St Helena archives as well as in the Public Record Office in Kew.
5. P. Ashmole and M. Ashmole (2000), *St Helena and Ascension Island: A Natural History*, Oswestry: A. Nelson.
6. A. Beatson (1816), *Tracts Relative to the Island of St Helena: Written During a Residence of Five Years*, Nicol, Booth, London. Available online at Weaver, *St Helena Virtual Library and Archive*, URL: http://www.bweaver.nom.sh/beatson/beatson.htm). Last accessed 27 December 2013. Also listed in Weaver are John Barnes (1817), *A Tour Through the Island of St Helena*, Richardson, London; J. C. Mellis (1875), *St Helena: a Physical, Historical and Topographical Description of the Island, Including its Geology, Fauna, Flora and Meteorology*, London; and H. R. Janisch (1885), *St Helena* which is available as a PDF file (http://www.bweaver.nom.sh/janisch/janisch.pdf).
7. S. Royle (2007), *The Company's Island: St Helena, Company Colonies and the Colonial Endeavour*, London and New York: Tauris.
8. Beatson, *Tracts*.
9. Clements R. Markham (ed.) (1877), *The Voyages of Sir James Lancaster, Kt., to the East Indies*, London: Hakluyt Society.
10. Bergeron and Bignon, *The Voyage of François Pyrard*, p. 297.
11. W. C. Palmer (1926), 'History of St. Helena and the Route to the Indies, 1659–1702', *Historical Research*, 3(6): 183–185.
12. British Library India Office Records, Original Correspondence 3064-1. Vol. 29.
13. S. de Rennefort (1688), *Histoire des Indes Orientales*, Paris: Arnoul Seneuze and Daniel Hortemels.
14. Philip Gosse (1990), *St Helena, 1502–1938*, Oswestry: A. Nelson.
15. Basil Lubbock (ed.) (1934), *Barlow's journal of his life at sea in king's ships, East & West Indiamen & other merchantmen from 1659 to 1703*, London: Hurst and Blackett.
16. Court of Directors to Council 7.3.1675.

17. Court of Directors to Council 20.2.1677.
18. Court of Directors to Council 8.3.1676.
19. Court of Directors to Council 20.2.1677.
20. Court of Directors to Council 30.9.1678.
21. Royle, *The Company's Island*, p. 170.
22. R. Gowing (1995) 'Halley, Cotes, and the nautical meridian', *Historia Mathematica*, 22(1): 19–32; School of Mathematics and Statistics, University of St Andrews, Scotland (2000), 'Edmond Halley', URL: http://www history.mcs.standrews.ac.uk/Biographies/Halley.html, JOC/EFR. Last accessed 27 December 2013.
23. A. Chapman (1994), 'Edmund Halley's use of historical evidence in the advancement of science', *Notes and Records of the Royal Society of London*, 48(2): 167–191.
24. E. Halley (1715), 'A short account of the saltiness of the ocean and of the several lakes that emit no rivers: with a proposal, by help thereof, to discover the age of the world', *Philosophical Transactions of the Royal Society*, 29: 296–300.
25. Letter from England 31.12.1760 and Letter to England 26.5.1761.
26. N. Maskelyne (1761), 'An Account of the Observations made on the transit of Venus, June 6, 1761, in the island of St Helena: in a Letter to the Right Honourable George Earl of Macclesfield, President of the Royal Society, from the Rev. Nevil Maskelyne, M.A. and F.R.S.', *Philosophical Transactions of the Royal Society*, 52: 196–201.
27. Council minutes 11. 8. 1679.
28. Letter to England 11. 8. 1679.
29. Letter to England 16.1.1681.
30. Consultations 8.6.1691.
31. Consultations 1.8.1701.
32. J. L. Gergis and A. M. Fowler (2009), 'A history of ENSO events since 1525: implications for future climatic change', *Climatic Change*, 92: 343–387.
33. It is difficult to understand what Pyke means by this last phrase. Diego Garcia lies far out in the Indian Ocean.
34. Letter to London by *Mercury* 1715.
35. L. A. Ogallo (1994), 'Validity of the ENSO-Related Impacts in Eastern and Southern Africa', in M. Glantz (ed.), *Usable Science: Food Security, Early Warning, and El Niño*, pp. 179–184. Proceedings of the Workshop on ENSO/FEWS, Budapest, Hungary, October 1993, Nairobi: UNEP, and Boulder, CO: CAR.
36. N. D. Walker (2012), 'Links between South African summer rainfall and temperature variability of the Agulhas and Benguela Current systems', *Journal of Geophysical Research (Oceans)*, 95(C3): 3297–3319.
37. Letter from England 5.3.1713, para. 52.
38. Letter from England 5.3.1713, para. 59.
39. Letter from England 5.3.1713, para. 60.
40. Consultations, 12.5.1713.
41. Letter to London by *Mercury*, 21.7.1714.
42. Letter to London 21.7.1714.
43. Letter to London by *Susannah*, 12.11.1714, para. 51. St Iago is Santiago, Galicia, Spain.

44. Letter to London by *Susannah*, 12.11.1714, para. 52.
45. Letter to London by *Susannah*, 12.11.1714, para. 53.
46. Letter to London by *Susannah*, 12.11.1714, para. 53.
47. Letter to London by *Mercury*, 1715.
48. Letter to England by the *Dartmouth*, 8.5.1717.
49. Letter to England by the *King William*, 6.1.1718, para. 11.
50. Letter to England by the *King William*, 6.1.1718, para. 12.
51. Letter to England by the *King William*, 6.1.1718, para. 37.
52. Possibly John Evelyn (1693), *The Compleat Gardener*, printed for M. Gillyflower: London. A translation from the French original of Jean de La Quintinie.
53. Letter to England by the *King William*, 6.1.1718, para. 60.
54. Letter to England by the *King William*, 6.1.1718, para. 56.
55. Letter to England by the *Dawson*, 31.7.1723, para. 44.
56. Letter to England by the *Grantham*, 18.3.1727, para. 26.
57. Letter to England by the *Derby*, 29.5.1727, para. 11.
58. Letter to England by the *Stanhope*, 6.1.1728, para. 7.
59. Letter to England by the *Montague*, 22.2.1729.
60. Friends of St Helena, *East India Company Rule, 1658–1815*.
61. Letter to England by the *Montague*, 22.2.1729, para. 10.
62. Ashmole and Ashmole, *St Helena and Ascension Island*, p. 141.
63. Letter to England by the *Houghton*, 16.5.1730.
64. Letter to England by the *Montague*, 11.5.1731, para. 11.
65. Letter to England 17.6.1733, p. 209, para. 5.
66. Letter to England 1.1.1739, para. 14.
67. Consultations 10.7.1741.
68. Consultations 17.3.1742.
69. Consultations 12.4.1748.
70. Letter to England 6.1.1771.
71. Letter to England 19.3.1770.
72. Letter to England 24.6.1776.
73. Consultations 20.11.1789.
74. Richard Grove (1997), 'The East India Company, the Australians and the El Nino: colonial scientists and ideas about global climatic change and teleconnections between, 1770-1930', in Richard Grove (ed.), *Ecology, Climate and Empire*, Cambridge: White Horse Press, p. 125.
75. Letter to England 24.12.1792.
76. Letter to England 27.8.1797.
77. Q. C. B. Cronk (1988), 'W. J. Burchell and the botany of St Helena', *Archives of Natural History*, 15: 45–60.
78. Beatson, *Tracts*, Section V11.
79. Richard Grove (1995), *Green Imperialism*, Cambridge: Cambridge University Press, p. 357.
80. Ashmole and Ashmole, *St Helena and Ascension Island*, p. 67.

Afterword

Vinita Damodaran

This volume has been based on the premise that modern globalisation was an unprecedented global movement requiring us to rework the idea of scale in historical writings on environmental change. In this context, the networks and empire of the East India Company can be seen here as a spatial and temporal context for organising narratives about the natural world relating to a range of field sciences, such as botany and geology in particular and environmental change in general. The natural world encountered by the EIC was dominated, not only by the its gargantuan appetite for resource extraction, but also by a conviction that increased in the nineteenth century that European methods of 'improvement' would enhance productivity and harvesting of resources. In this process, the transfer and exchange of flora and fauna that had been occurring since the seventeenth century gave way to huge plantations for a range of products that included coffee, tea, sugar and cotton. By the end of the EIC period the imperial imperative was for relentless transformation and domination of people and lands in the distant regions of an Eastern empire. However, one cannot forget that this insatiable need to explore and exploit the far-flung frontiers of empire also encompassed a discourse that gave rise to an emergent conservationist language to describe peoples and landscapes; though one that was embedded within bureaucratic, centralised and coercive practice. The linked themes of exploitation and conservation thus lie at the heart of the environmental history of empire.

In attempting to give us the big picture of environmental change, this volume has attempted to partly fulfil the vision of Richard Grove and his plans for a global environmental history project. The discussion in the volume has yielded a rich harvest of reflections on global environmental history as a paradigm for the interpretation of the past and a cultural and political repository for ideas about action in the present. The EIC operating as a global institution of change had a profound transformative effect on the environment in terms of resource extraction. At the same time, it found conservationism to its taste and economic advantage, particularly in ensuring sustainable timber and water supplies and in ensuring control of marginal subjects. The experimentally and empirically derived awareness of environmental change helped to enshrine the nascent language of environmentalism, which has clear resonances for society today in a context when the earth is threatened by deforestation, famine, extinction and climate change. The large amount of material relating to natural history generated by the EIC and now kept in repositories across Britain, India and elsewhere, provides vital resources for understanding global environmental and climate change. Scientists and naturalists in the colonial tropics collected field data on a vast scale and visualised links between climate and deforestation, between species protection and land degradation. Their official, academic and even personal papers as well as physical collections of flora and fauna and artistic representations held in museum and gallery collections are invaluable for debates in contemporary botany, medicine, zoology, geology, meteorology, archaeology and ethnography. One important task is to make available this voluminous material, thereby creating and making widely available an important archive of knowledge of the natural world. This will highlight networks never before brought to light, yet crucial to what was a renaissance in natural history and environmental understanding as a result of the encounter with an unfamiliar tropical environment. These archives and libraries dispersed in various parts of the world need to be identified, integrated and digitised as they will provide an invaluable resource for understanding global environmental change. Linking together academics, holding institutions and museums will help this project of recovery of EIC data, providing critical knowledge for the future. It is hoped that the volume will provide important indications as to the research paths a global environmental historian can follow to contribute to this field of studies.

Select Bibliography

Adamson, George C. D. (2012), '"The languor of the hot weather": Everyday perspectives on weather and climate in colonial Bombay, 1819–1828'. *Journal of Historical Geography*, 38(2): 143–154.

Adamson, George C. D., Nash, David J. (2012), 'Long-term variability in the date of monsoon onset over western India'. *Climate Dynamics*, 40: 2589–1603.

Adamson George C. D., Nash, David J. (2014), 'Documentary reconstruction of monsoon rainfall variability over western India, 1781–1860'. *Climate Dynamics*, 42: 749–769.

Addams-Williams, Christopher (1919), *History of the Rivers in the Gangetic Delta, 1750–1918*. Calcutta: Bengal Secretariat Press.

Addams-Williams, Christopher (1913), *Drainage Problems in the Ganges Delta. A Series of Six Lectures Delivered at the Sibpur Engineering College during March 1913*. Calcutta: Bengal Secretariat Book Depôt.

Agrawal, Arun (1995), 'Dismantling the divide between indigenous and scientific knowledge'. *Development and Change*, 263: 413–439.

Agrawal, C. M. (1983), *Natural Calamities and the Great Mughals*. Bodh Gaya: Kanchan Publications.

Alam, Muzaffar, Subrahmanyam, Sanjay (2012), *Writing the Mughal World: Studies on Culture and Politics*. New York: Columbia University Press.

Allan, H. H. (1937), 'The origin and distribution of the naturalized plants of New Zealand'. *Proceedings of the Linnean Society of London*, 150(1): 25–46.

Alory, Gaël, Wijffels, Susan, Meyers, Gary (2007), 'Observed temperature trends in the Indian Ocean over 1960–1999 and associated mechanisms'. *Geophysical Research Letters*, 34(2): doi:10.1029/2006GL028044.

Amrith, Sunil S. (2013), *Crossing the Bay of Bengal: The Furies of Nature and the Fortunes of Migrants*. Cambridge, MA: Harvard University Press.

Andaya, L. Y. (1993), *The World of Maluku: Eastern Indonesia in the Early Modern Period*. Honolulu: University of Hawaii Press.

Anderson, Clare (2012), *Subaltern Lives: Biographies of Colonialism in the Indian Ocean World, 1790–1920*. Cambridge: Cambridge University Press.

Antons, C. (2009), *Traditional Knowledge, Traditional Cultural Expressions, and Intellectual Property Law in the Asia-Pacific Region*. Alphen Aan Den Rijn: Kluwer.

Arnold, David (1996), *Warm Climates and Western Medicine: The Emergence of Tropical Medicine, 1500–1900*. Amsterdam and Atlanta, GA: Rodopi, 1996.

Arnold, David (2006), *The Tropics and the Traveling Gaze: India, Landscape, and Science, 1800–1856*. Seattle: University of Washington Press.

Arnold, David (2008), 'Plant capitalism and company science: The Indian career of Nathaniel Wallich'. *Modern Asian Studies*, 42(5): 899–928.

Ashmole, Philip, Ashmole, Myrtle (2000), *St Helena and Ascension Island: A Natural History*. Oswestry: A. Nelson.

Ashok, Karumuri, Saji, N. H. (2007), 'On the impacts of ENSO and Indian Ocean dipole events on sub-regional Indian summer monsoon rainfall'. *Natural Hazards*, 42(2): 273–285.

Asiatic Society of Bengal, Oriental Library, Ivanov, Vladimir Aleksieevich (1924), *Concise Descriptive Catalogue of the Persian Manuscripts in the Collection of the Asiatic Society of Bengal*. Calcutta: Printed at the Baptist Mission Press Pub. by the Asiatic Society of Bengal.

Axelby, Richard, Nair, Savithri Preetha, Cook, Andrew S., India Office Records (2010), *Science and the Changing Environment in India, 1780–1920: A Guide to Sources in the India Office Records*. London: The British Library.

Ballantyne, Tony (2002), *Orientalism and Race: Aryanism in the British Empire*. Basingstoke and New York: Palgrave Macmillan.

Ballantyne, Tony (2012), *Webs of Empire: Locating New Zealand's Colonial Past*. Wellington, NZ: Bridget Williams Books.

Ballantyne, Tony, Moloughney, Brian (2006), *Disputed Histories: Imagining New Zealand's Pasts*. Dunedin, NZ: Otago University Press.

Bandopadhyay, Arun (2010), *Science and Society in India, 1750–2000*. Delhi: Manohar.

Banks, Stephen (2010), *A Polite Exchange of Bullets: The Duel and the English Gentleman, 1750–1850*. Woodbridge and Rochester, NY: Boydell Press.

Bastin, John (1990), *Thomas Horsfield: The Natural History Researches of Dr. Thomas Horsfield (1773–1859), First American Naturalist of Indonesia*. Singapore: Oxford University Press.

Bayly, Christopher A. (1989), *Imperial Meridian: The British Empire and the World, 1780–1830*. London and New York: Longman.

Bayly, Christopher A. (1996), *Empire and Information: Intelligence Gathering and Social Communication in India, 1780–1870*. Cambridge and New York: Cambridge University Press.

Beattie, James (2011), *Empire and Environmental Anxiety: Health, Science, Art and Conservation in South Asia and Australasia, 1800–1920*. Basingstoke and New York: Palgrave Macmillan.

Beattie, James (2011), 'Making home, making identity: Asian garden making in New Zealand, 1850s–1930s'. *Studies in the History of Gardens and Designed Landscapes*, 31(2): 139–159.

Beattie, James (2012), 'Imperial landscapes of health: Place, plants and people between India and Australia, 1800s–1900s', *Health and History*, 14(1): 100–120.

Beattie, James (2012), 'Recent themes in the environmental history of the British Empire'. *History Compass*, 10(2): 129–139.

Beattie, James, Heinzen, Jasper M., Adam, John P. (2008), 'Japanese gardens and plants in New Zealand, 1850–1950: Transculturation and transmission'. *Studies in the History of Gardens and Designed Landscapes*, 28(2): 219–236.

Beers, Susan J. (2001), *Jamu: The Ancient Indonesian Art of Herbal Healing*. Singapore and North Claredon, VT: Periplus; Tuttle Pub. [distributor].

Bhabha, Homi K. (1990), *Nation and Narration*. London and New York: Routledge.

Binney, Keith R. (2005), *Horsemen of the First Frontier (1788–1900) and the Serpent's Legacy*. Neutral Bay, NSW: Volcanic Productions.

Boomgaard, P. (2006), 'The making and unmaking of tropical science: Dutch research on Indonesia, 1600–2000'. *Bijdragen Tot De Taal-, Land- En Volkenkunde*, 162(2–3): 191–217.

Bradley, Raymond S., Jones, Philip D. (1992), *Climate since A.D. 1500*. London and New York: Routledge.

Brázdil, Rudolf, Pfister, Christian, Wanner, Heinz, Storch, Hans, Luterbacher, Jürg (2005), 'Historical climatology in Europe – the state of the art'. *Climatic Change*, 70(3): 363–430.
Breen, Benjamin (2013), 'No man is an island: Early modern globalization, knowledge networks, and George Psalmanazar's Formosa'. *Journal of Early Modern History*, 17(4): 391–417.
Britten, J., Dandy, J. E. (1958), *The Sloane Herbarium: An Annotated List of the Horti Sicci Composing it, with Biographical Accounts of the Principal Contributors*. London: British Museum.
Broadbent, James, Rickard, Suzanne, Steven, Margaret, Museum of Sydney (2003), *India, China, Australia: Trade and Society, 1788–1850*. [Glebe, NSW]: Historic Houses Trust of New South Wales.
Brookes, John (1987), *Gardens of Paradise: The History and Design of the Great Islamic Gardens*. New York: New Amsterdam.
Bruijn, Iris, Diane, Rosemary (2009), *Ship's Surgeons of the Dutch East India Company: Commerce and the Progress of Medicine in the Eighteenth Century*. Leiden: Leiden University Press.
Bruun, Ole, Kalland, Arne, Nordic Institute of Asian Studies (1995), *Asian Perceptions of Nature: A Critical Approach*. Richmond: Curzon Press.
Buller, James (1878), *Forty Years in New Zealand*. London: Hodder and Stoughton.
Bulley, Anne, Pope, John Adolphus, British Association for Cemeteries in South Asia (1992), *Free Mariner: John Adolphus Pope in the East Indies 1786–1821*. London: BACSA.
Burkill, I. H., Birtwistle, William (1966), *A Dictionary of the Economic Products of the Malay Peninsula*. Kuala Lumpur: Published on behalf of the Governments of Malaysia and Singapore by the Ministry of Agriculture and Co-operatives.
Burkill, I. H., Bombay Natural History Society (1965), *Chapters on the History of Botany in India*. Calcutta: Botanical Survey of India.
Burkill, I. H., Haniff, Mohamed (1930), *Malay Village Medicine, Gardens' Bulletin, Straits Settlements*, 6(2): 165–321.
Burton, Antoinette M. (1994), *Burdens of History: British Feminists, Indian Women, and Imperial Culture, 1865–1915*. Chapel Hill: University of North Carolina Press.
Burton, Antoinette M. (2011), *Empire in Question: Reading, Writing, and Teaching British Imperialism*. Durham, NC: Duke University Press.
Cameron, John (1965), *Our Tropical Possessions in Malayan India*. Kuala Lumpur: Oxford University Press.
Carey, Jane, Lydon, Jane (2014), *Indigenous Networks: Mobility, Connections, and Exchange*. London: Routledge.
Chakrabarti, Pratik (2006), '"Neither of meate nor drinke, but what the doctor alloweth": Medicine amidst war and commerce in eighteenth century Madras', *Bulletin of the History of Medicine*, 80(1): 1–38.
Chakrabarti, Pratik (2010), *Materials and Medicine: Trade, Conquest, and Therapeutics in the Eighteenth Century*. Manchester: Manchester University Press.
Chaudhuri, Nani Gopal, Indian History Congress (1970), *Cartier, Governor of Bengal, 1769–1772*. Calcutta: Firma K. L. Mukhopadhyay.
Chester, L. P. (2009), *Borders and Conflict in South Asia: The Radcliffe Boundary Commission and the Partition of Punjab*. Manchester: Manchester University Press.
Clark, Andrew Hill (1949), *The Invasion of New Zealand by People, Plants, and Animals: The South Island*. New Brunswick: Rutgers University Press.

Cook, Harold J. (2007), *Matters of Exchange: Commerce, Medicine, and Science in the Dutch Golden Age*. New Haven: Yale University Press.

Crawford, Dirom Grey (1914), *A History of the Indian Medical Service, 1600–1913*. London: Thacker.

Cronk, Q. C. B. (1988), 'W. J. Burchell and the botany of St Helena'. *Archives of Natural History*, 15(1): 45–60.

Crosby, A. W. (1986), *Ecological Imperialism: The Biological Expansion of Europe, 900–1900*. Cambridge and New York: Cambridge University Press.

Damodaran, V. (1992), *Broken Promises: Popular Protest, Indian Nationalism, and the Congress Party in Bihar, 1935–1946*. Delhi and New York: Oxford University Press.

Darwin, J. (1997), 'Imperialism and the Victorians: The dynamics of territorial expansion'. *English Historical Review*, 112(447): 614–642.

Dasgupta, Surendranath, Santapau, Hermenegild (1958), *History of Botanical Researches in India, Burma and Ceylon pts i–ii* ... Banglore City: Indian Botanical Society.

Dawson, Warren R., British Museum (Natural History) (1958), *The Banks Letters: A Calendar of the Manuscript Correspondence of Sir Joseph Banks, Preserved in the British Museum, the British Museum (Natural History) and other Collections in Great Britain*. London: Printed by order of the trustees of the British Museum.

Deloche, Jean, Walker, Taï (1993), *Transport and Communications in India prior to Steam Locomotion*. Delhi and New York: Oxford University Press.

Digby, Anne, Ernst, Waltraud, Muhkarji, Projit B. (2010), *Crossing Colonial Historiographies: Histories of Colonial and Indigenous Medicines in Transnational Perspective*. Newcastle: Cambridge Scholars.

Dirks, Nicholas B. (2006), *The Scandal of Empire: India and the Creation of Imperial Britain*. Cambridge, MA: Belknap Press of Harvard University Press.

Drakestein, H. v. R. T., Manilal, K. S. (2003), *Van Rheede's Hortus Malabaricus*. Thiruvanathapuram: University of Kerala.

Drayton, R. H. (2000), *Nature's Government: Science, Imperial Britain, and the 'Improvement' of the World*. New Haven: Yale University Press.

Driver, Felix, Samuel, Raphael (1995), 'Rethinking the idea of place', *History Workshop Journal*, 39(1): v–vii.

D'Souza, Rohan (2006), *Drowned and Dammed: Colonial Capitalism, and Flood Control in Eastern India*. Delhi: Oxford University Press.

Dubow, Saul (2006), *A Commonwealth of Knowledge: Science, Sensibility, and White South Africa, 1820–2000*. Oxford and New York: Oxford University Press, 2006.

Dunlap, Thomas R. (1999), *Nature and the English Diaspora: Environment and History in the United States, Canada, Australia, and New Zealand*. Cambridge and New York: Cambridge University Press.

Elvin, Mark (2004), *The Retreat of the Elephants: An Environmental History of China*. New Haven: Yale University Press.

Endfield, Georgina H., Nash, David J. (2002), 'Missionaries and morals: Climatic discourse in nineteenth-century central southern Africa'. *Annals of the Association of American Geographers*, 92(4): 727–742.

Endicott, Kirk M. (1970), *An Analysis of Malay Magic*. Oxford: Clarendon Press.

Enticott, T. O., Canterbury Area Health Board (1993), *Up the Hill: Cashmere Sanatorium and Coronation Hospital, 1910 to 1991*. Christchurch, NZ: Canterbury Area Health Board.

Ernst, Waltraud (2002), *Plural Medicine, Tradition and Modernity, 1800–2000*. London and New York: Routledge.

Escobar, Arturo (1995), *Encountering Development: The Making and Unmaking of the Third World*. Princeton: Princeton University Press.

Fan, Fa-ti (2004), *British Naturalists in Qing China: Science, Empire, and Cultural Encounter*. Cambridge, MA: Harvard University Press.

Figueiredo, J. M. D. (1984), 'Ayurvedic medicine in Goa according to European sources in the sixteenth and seventeenth centuries'. *Bulletin of the History of Medicine*, 58: 225–235.

Forster, Georg, Thomas, Nicholas, Berghof, Oliver (2000), *A Voyage Round the World*. Honolulu: University of Hawai'i Press.

Franklin, M. J. (1995), *Sir William Jones*. Cardiff: University of Wales Press.

Fry, H. T. (1970), *Alexander Dalrymple (1737–1808) and the Expansion of British Trade*. Toronto: University of Toronto Press for the Royal Commonwealth Society.

Gascoigne, John (1998), *Science in the Service of Empire: Joseph Banks, the British State and the uses of Science in the Age of Revolution*. Cambridge and New York: Cambridge University Press.

Gergis, J. I., Fowler, A. M. (2009), 'A history of ENSO events since A.D. 1525: Implications for future climate change'. *Climatic Change*, 92(3–4): 343–387.

Ghosh, Amitav (2008), *Sea of Poppies*. New York: Farrar, Straus and Giroux.

Gilmartin, D. (2003), 'Water and waste: Nature, productivity, and colonialism in the Indus basin'. *Economic and Political Weekly*, 38(48): 5057.

Gimlette, John D. G. (ed.), Inche, Ismail (tr.) (1930), *The Medical Book of Malayan Medicine, Gardens' Bulletin, Straits Settlements*, 6(3): 323–474.

Gimlette, John D. G., Thomson, H. W. (1971), *A Dictionary of Malayan Medicine*. Kuala Lumpur and New York: Oxford University Press.

Golinski, Jan (2005), *Making Natural Knowledge: Constructivism and the History of Science*. Chicago: University of Chicago Press.

Golinski, Jan (2007), *British Weather and the Climate of Enlightenment*. Chicago: University of Chicago Press.

Goss, Andrew (2009), 'Decent colonialism? Pure science and colonial ideology in the Netherlands East Indies, 1910–1929'. *Journal of Southeast Asian Studies*, 40(1): 187–214.

Goss, Andrew (2011), *The Floracrats: State-Sponsored Science and the Failure of the Enlightenment in Indonesia*. Madison: University of Wisconsin Press.

Gosse, Philip (1938), *St. Helena, 1502–1938*. London: Cassell.

Gowing, R. (1995), 'Halley, Cotes, and the nautical meridian'. *Historia Mathematica: International Journal of History of Mathematics*, 22(1): 19–32.

Grab, Stefan W., Nash, David J. (2010), 'Documentary evidence of climate variability during cold seasons in Lesotho, southern Africa, 1833–1900'. *Climate Dynamics*, 34(4): 473–499.

Grove, Richard (1993), 'Conserving Eden: The (European) East India Companies and their environmental policies on St. Helena, Mauritius and in western India, 1660 to 1854'. *Comparative Studies in Society and History: An International Quarterly*, 35: 318–351.

Grove, Richard (1995), *Green Imperialism: Colonial Expansion, Tropical Island Edens, and the Origins of Environmentalism, 1600–1860*. Cambridge and New York: Cambridge University Press.

Grove, Richard (1997), *Ecology, Climate, and Empire: Colonialism and Global Environmental History, 1400–1940*. Cambridge: White Horse Press.

Grove, Richard (2007), 'The great El Nino of 1789 93 and its global consequences: Reconstructing an extreme climate event in world environmental history'. *Medieval History Journal*, 10(1–2): 75–98.

Grove, Richard, Damodaran, Vinita, Sangwan, Satpal (1998), *Nature and the Orient: The Environmental History of South and Southeast Asia*. Delhi and New York: Oxford University Press.

Guest, H. (2007), *Empire, Barbarism, and Civilisation: James Cook, William Hodges, and the Return to the Pacific*. Cambridge and New York: Cambridge University Press.

Hall, Catherine (1992), *White, Male, and Middle-Class: Explorations in Feminism and History*. New York: Routledge.

Hall, Catherine (2002), *Civilising Subjects: Colony and Metropole in the English Imagination, 1830–1867*. Chicago: University of Chicago Press.

Hannigan, T. (2012), *Raffles and the British Invasion of Java*. Singapore: Monsoon Books.

Harris Steven J. (2005), 'Jesuit scientific activity in the overseas missions, 1540–1773'. *Isis*, 96(1): 71–79.

Harrison, Mark (1999), *Climates & Constitutions: Health, Race, Environment and British Imperialism in India, 1600–1850*. Delhi and New York: Oxford University Press.

Headrick, D. R. (1981), *The Tools of Empire: Technology and European Imperialism in the Nineteenth Century*. New York: Oxford University Press.

Heidhues, Mary Somers (1995), 'Dissecting the Indies: The 19th century German doctor Franz Epp'. *Archipel*, 49:25–43.

Herbert, E. W. (2011), *Flora's Empire: British Gardens in India*. Philadelphia: University of Pennsylvania Press.

Hesselink, Elisabeth Quirine, Koninklijk Instituut voor Taal-, Land- en Volkenkunde (Netherlands) (2011), *Healers on the Colonial Market: Native Doctors and Midwives in the Dutch East Indies*. Leiden: KITLV Press.

Hill, Christopher V. (1997), *River of Sorrow: Environment and Social Control in Riparian North India, 1770–1994*. Ann Arbor, MI: Association for Asian Studies.

Hopkins, A. G. (2002), *Globalization in World History*. New York: Norton.

Howe, Stephen (2010), *The New Imperial Histories Reader*. London and New York: Routledge.

Inglis, William Arbuthnot, Bengal (India), Public Works Department, Irrigation Branch (1909), *The Canals and Flood Banks of Bengal*. Calcutta: Bengal Secretariat Press.

Inkster, I. (1985), 'Scientific enterprise and the colonial "model": Observations on Australian experience in historical context'. *Social Studies of Science*, 15(4): 677–704.

Jansen, P. P., van Bendegom, L., van den Berg, J., de Vries, M., Zanen, A. (1979), *Principles of River Engineering: The Non-Tidal Alluvial River*. London and San Francisco: Pitman.

Jasanoff, Maya (2005), *Edge of Empire: Lives, Culture, and Conquest in the East, 1750–1850*. New York: Knopf.

Johns, A. (1999), *Dreadful Visitations: Confronting Natural Catastrophe in the Age of Enlightenment*. New York: Routledge.

Johnson, Henry Mabley, Moloughney, Brian (2006), *Asia in the Making of New Zealand*. Auckland, NZ: Auckland University Press.

278 Select Bibliography

Kamarudin Mat Salleh, Hoashi, Shoko, Chang, Kiaw Lan (1991), *Rafflesia: Magnificent Flower of Sabah*. Kota Kinabalu: Borneo Pub. Co.

Kathirithamby-Wells, J. (2005), *Nature and Nation: Forests and Development in Peninsular Malaysia*. Honolulu: University of Hawai'i Press.

Jeyamalar Kathirithamby-Wells (2009), 'Peninsular Malaysia in the context of natural history and colonial science', in Ooi Keat Jin (ed.), *Themes for Thoughts on Southeast Asia, New Zealand Journal of Asian Studies*, Special number, 11(2): 293–4.

Kelley, Theresa M. (2012), *Clandestine Marriage: Botany and Romantic Culture*. Baltimore: Johns Hopkins University Press.

Keshavamurthy, R. N., Joshi, P. C. (1993), *Advances in Tropical Meteorology: Monsoon Variability, Satellite Applications, and Modelling*. Berlin and New York: Springer.

Khan, Iqtidar A. (1976), 'The middle classes in the Mughal Empire'. *Social Scientist*, 5(1): 28–49.

Kilpatrick, Jane, Crawley, Jane (2007), *Gifts from the Gardens of China: The Introduction of Traditional Chinese Garden Plants to Britain 1698–1862*. London: Frances Lincoln.

Knapen, Han (2001), *Forests of Fortune? The Environmental History of Southeast Borneo, 1600–1880*. Leiden: KITLV Press.

Knox, G. A., Philosophical Institute of Canterbury (Christchurch, NZ) (1969), *The Natural History of Canterbury*. Wellington and Auckland: Reed.

Koerner, Lisbet (1999), *Linnaeus: Nature and Nation*. Cambridge, MA: Harvard University Press.

Kothawale, D. R., Rupa Kumar, K. (2005), 'On the recent changes in surface temperature trends over India'. *Geophysical Research Letters*, 32(18): 1–4.

Krishnamurthy, V., Goswami, B.N. (2000), 'Indian monsoon–ENSO relationship on interdecadal timescale'. *Journal of Climate*, 13(3): 579–595.

Kumar, Deepak (2006), *Science and the Raj: A Study of British India*. Delhi and New York: Oxford University Press.

Kumar, Deepak, Damodaran, Vinita, D'Souza, Rohan (2011), *The British Empire and the Natural World: Environmental Encounters in South Asia*. Delhi: Oxford University Press.

Kumar, Deepak, National Institute of Science, Technology, and Development Studies (India) (1991), *Science and Empire: Essays in Indian Context, 1700–1947*. Delhi: Anamika Prakashan.

Kumar, Dharma (1983), *The Cambridge Economic History of India vol. 2 1757–1970*. Cambridge: Cambridge University Press.

Kumar, K. Rupa, Hingane, L. S. (1988), 'Long-term variations of surface air temperature at major industrial cities of India'. *Climatic Change*, 13(3): 287–307.

Lach, Donald F., Van Kley, Edwin J. (1965), *Asia in the Making of Europe*. Chicago: University of Chicago Press.

Lamb, R. C. (1964), *Birds, Beasts & Fishes: The First Hundred Years of the North Canterbury Acclimatisation Society*. Christchurch, NZ: North Canterbury Acclimatisation Society.

Lambert, David, Lester, Alan (2011), *Colonial Lives across the British Empire: Imperial Careering in the Long Nineteenth Century*. Cambridge: Cambridge University Press.

Latour, Bruno (1987), *Science in Action*, Cambridge, MA: Harvard University Press.

Latour, Bruno (1988), *The Pasteurization of France*. Cambridge, MA: Harvard University Press.

Latour, Bruno (2005), *Reassembling the Social: An Introduction to Actor-Network-Theory*. Oxford: Oxford University Press.
Lee, Jack, Northland Historical Publications Society (1997), *An Unholy Trinity: Three Hokianga Characters*. Russell, NZ: The Society.
Legg, Stephen (2009), 'Of scales, networks and assemblages: The league of nations apparatus and the scalar sovereignty of the government of India'. *Transactions of the Institute of British Geographers*, 34(2): 234–253.
Lester, Alan (2002), 'British settler discourse and the circuits of empire'. *History Workshop Journal*, 54(1): 24–48.
Lester, Alan (2006), 'Imperial circuits and networks: Geographies of the British empire'. *History Compass*, 4(1): 124–141.
Lindberg, David C., Numbers, Ronald L., Porter, Roy (2003), *The Cambridge History of Science*. Cambridge and New York: Cambridge University Press.
Livingstone, D. N. (2002), 'Race, space and moral climatology: Notes toward a genealogy'. *Journal of Historical Geography*, 28(2): 159–180.
Love, Henry Davison (1913), *Vestiges of Old Madras, 1640–1800: Traced from the East India Company's Records Preserved at Fort St. George and the India Office, and from Other Sources*. London: J. Murray.
Ludden, David E. (1985), *Peasant History in South India*. Princeton: Princeton University Press.
Macaulay, Thomas Babington, Tucker, S. Marion (1913), *Macaulay's Essay on Warren Hastings*. London: Longmans, Green, and Co.
MacKenzie, John M. (1988), *The Empire of Nature: Hunting, Conservation, and British Imperialism*. Manchester and New York: Manchester University Press.
MacLeod, Roy (1980), 'On visiting the "moving metropolis": Reflections on the architecture of imperial science'. *Historical Records of Australian Science*, 5(3): 1–16.
MacLeod, Roy (2000), 'Introduction'. *Osiris*, 15: 1–13.
MacLeod, Roy M. (2000), *Nature and Empire: Science and the Colonial Enterprise*. Chicago: University of Chicago Press.
Majumdar, Girija Prasanna (1927), *Vanaspati. Plants and Plant-life as in Indian Treatises and Traditions*. Calcutta: University of Calcutta.
Marks, Shula (1990), 'History, the nation and empire: sniping from the periphery'. *History Workshop Journal*, 29(1): 111–119.
Marsden, William (1986), *The History of Sumatra*. Singapore and New York: Oxford University Press.
Marshall, P. J. (2003), *The Eighteenth Century in Indian History: Evolution or Revolution?* Delhi: Oxford University Press.
Massey, Doreen B. (1995), 'Places and their pasts'. *History Workshop Journal*, 39: 182–192.
Massey, Doreen B. (2005), *For Space*. London and Thousand Oaks, CA: Sage.
McAlpin, Michelle Burge (1983), *Subject to Famine: Food Crises and Economic Change in Western India, 1860–1920*. Princeton: Princeton University Press.
McLane, John R. (1993), *Land and Local Kingship in Eighteenth-Century Bengal*. Cambridge and New York: Cambridge University Press.
McLeod, Murdo J., Rawski, Evelyn Sakakida (eds.) (1998), *European Intruders and Changes in Behaviour and Customs in Africa, America, and Asia before 1800*. Aldershot: Ashgate.
McNab, Robert (1909), *Murihiku: A History of the South Island of New Zealand and the Islands Adjacent and Lying to the South, from 1642 to 1835*. Wellington, NZ: Whitcomb & Tombs.

McPherson, Kenneth (1993), *The Indian Ocean: A History of People and the Sea*. Delhi and New York: Oxford University Press.

Meehl, G. A. (1994), 'Coupled land-ocean-atmosphere processes and South Asian monsoon variability'. *Science* (New York), 266(5183): 263–267.

Mein Smith, Philippa (2005), *A Concise History of New Zealand*. Cambridge and New York: Cambridge University Press.

Metcalf, Thomas R. (2007), *Imperial Connections India in the Indian Ocean Arena, 1860–1920*. Berkeley: University of California Press.

Miller, David Philip, Reill, Peter Hanns (1996), *Visions of Empire: Voyages, Botany, and Representations of Nature*. Cambridge and New York: Cambridge University Press.

Moodie, D. W., Catchpole, A. J. W. (1976), 'Valid climatological data from historical sources by content analysis.' *Science*, 193(4247): 51–3.

Nair, Savithri Preetha (2005) 'Native collecting and natural knowledge (1798–1832): Raja Serfoji of Tanjore as a "Centre of Calculation"'. *Journal of the Royal Asiatic Society*, 15(3): 279–302.

Nash David J., Grab, Stephen W. (2010), '"A sky of brass and burning winds": Documentary evidence of rainfall variability in the kingdom of Lesotho, Southern Africa, 1824–1900'. *Climatic Change*, 101(3): 617–653.

Nash, David J., Endfield, Georgina H. (2002), 'A 19th century climate chronology for the Kalahari region of central southern Africa derived from missionary correspondence'. *International Journal of Climatology*, 22(7): 821–841.

Nash, David, Endfield, Georgina H. (2008), '"Splendid rains have fallen": Links between El Niño and rainfall variability in the Kalahari, 1840–1900'. *Climatic Change*, 86(3–4): 3–4.

Needham, Joseph (1986), *Science and Civilisation in China*, vol.6, with the collaboration of Lu Gwei-Djen and a special contribution by Huang Hsing-Tsung, *Biology and Biological Technology, Pt. 1: Botany*, Cambridge: Cambridge University Press.

Neild-Basu, Susan (1984), 'The Dubashes of Madras'. *Modern Asian Studies*, 18(1): 1–31.

Noltie, Henry J. (2005), *The Botany of Robert Wight*. Ruggell, Liechtenstein and Koenigstein: A.R.G. Gantner.

Noltie, Henry J. (2007), *Robert Wight and the Botanical Drawings of Rungiah & Govindoo*. Edinburgh: Royal Botanic Garden.

Noltie, Henry J., Royal Botanic Garden (Edinburgh, Scotland) (2002), *The Dapuri Drawings: Alexander Gibson and the Bombay Botanic Gardens*. Edinburgh: Antique Collectors' Club in association with the Royal Botanic Garden Edinburgh.

Nourse, J. W. (2013), 'The meaning of Dukun and allure of Sufi healers: How Persian cosmopolitans transformed Malay-Indonesian history'. *Journal of Southeast Asian Studies*, 44(3): 400–422.

Oyen, L. P. A., Nguyen, Xuan Dung (1999), *Plant Resources of South-East Asia, No. 19*. Leiden: Backhuys a Bogor: Prosea Foundation.

Parthasarathi, P. (2011), *Why Europe Grew Rich and Asia Did Not: Global Economic Divergence, 1600–1850*. Cambridge and New York: Cambridge University Press.

Paterson, Lachy (2006), *Colonial Discourses: Niupepa Māori, 1855–1863*. Dunedin, NZ: Otago University Press, 2006.

Pavord, A. (2005), *The Naming of Names: The Search for Order in the World of Plants*. New York: Bloomsbury.

Pawson, Eric (2008), 'Plants, mobilities and landscapes: Environmental histories of botanical exchange'. *Geography Compass*, 2(5): 1464–1477.

Peacock, Daniel J. (1987), *Lee Boo of Belau: A Prince in London*. Honolulu: Pacific Islands Studies Program, Center for Asian and Pacific Studies, University of Hawaii: University of Hawaii Press.

Pearson, Michael N. (2005), *The World of the Indian Ocean, 1500–1800: Studies in Economic, Social, and Cultural History*. Burlington, VT: Ashgate.

Pfister, Christian (1992), 'Monthly temperature and precipitation in central Europe 1525–1979: Quantifying documentary evidence on weather', in Bradley, Raymond S. and Jones, Philip D. (eds.), *Climate Since A.D. 1500*. London: Routledge, pp. 118–152.

Phillips, Richard (2006), *Sex, Politics, and Empire: A Postcolonial Geography*. Manchester: Manchester University Press.

Pieroni, Andrea, Vandebroek, Ina (2007), *Traveling Cultures and Plants: The Ethnobiology and Ethnopharmacy of Migrations*. New York: Berghahn Books.

Pires, Tomé, Cortesão, Armando, Rodrigues, Francisco (1967), *The Suma Oriental of Tomé Pires. Vol. I/II*. Nendeln, Liechtenstein: Kraus Reprint.

Pols, Hans (2009), 'European physicians and botanists, indigenous herbal medicine in the Dutch East Indies, and colonial networks of mediation'. *East Asian Science, Technology and Society*, 3:173–208.

Prakash, Gyan (1999), *Another Reason: Science and the Imagination of Modern India*. Princeton: Princeton University Press.

Pratt, Mary L. (1993), 'Imperial eyes: Travel writing and transculturation'. *Research in African Literatures*, 24(2): 155.

Preston, Diana, Preston, Michael (2004), *A Pirate of Exquisite Mind: Explorer, Naturalist, and Buccaneer: The Life of William Dampier*. New York: Walker & Company.

Pyenson, Lewis (1989), *Empire of Reason: Exact Sciences in Indonesia, 1840–1940*. Leiden and New York: E.J. Brill.

Pyrard, François, Bergeron, Pierre, Bignon, Jérôme (1887), *The Voyage of François Pyrard of Laval to the East Indies, the Maldives, the Moluccas and Brazil*. London: Printed for the Hakluyt Society.

Raby, Peter (1997), *Bright Paradise: Victorian Scientific Travellers*. Princeton: Princeton University Press.

Raj, Kapil (2007), *Relocating Modern Science: Circulation and the Construction of Knowledge in South Asia and Europe, 1650–1900*. Basingstoke and New York: Palgrave Macmillan.

Rangarajan, Mahesh, Sivaramakrishnan, K. (2012), *India's Environmental History*. Delhi: Permanent Black.

Reid, Anthony, *Southeast Asia in the Age of Commerce, 1450–1680*. New Haven: Yale University Press, 1988.

Reyes, Raquel A. (2009), 'Botany and zoology in the late seventeenth-century Philippines: The work of Georg Josef Camel SJ (1661–1706)'. *Archives of Natural History*, 36(2): 262–276.

Richards, John F. (1993), *The Mughal Empire*. Cambridge and New York: Cambridge University Press.

Robinson, Tim (2008), *William Roxburgh: The Founding Father of Indian Botany*. Chichester: Phillimore in association with Royal Botanic Garden Edinburgh.

Ross, Robert (1999), *Status and Respectability in the Cape Colony, 1750–1870: A Tragedy of Manners*. Cambridge: Cambridge University Press.

Royle, Stephen A. (2007), *The Company's Island: St Helena, Company Colonies and the Colonial Endeavour*. London and New York: I. B. Tauris.

Rumpf, Georg Eberhard, Beekman, E. M. (1981), *The Poison Tree: Selected Writings of Rumphius on the Natural History of the Indies*. Amherst: University of Massachusetts Press.

Rumpf, Georgius Everhardus, Beekman, E.M. (2011), *The Ambonese Herbal*. New Haven: Yale University Press.

Saji, N. H., Goswami, B. N., Vinayachandran, P. N.,Yamagata, T. (1999), 'A dipole mode in the tropical Indian Ocean'. *Nature* - London, 6751: 360–362.

Śārṅgadhara, Majumdar, Girija Prasanna, Indian Research Institute (1935), *Upavana-Vinoda: A Sanskrit Treatise on Arbori-Horticulture*. Calcutta: Indian Research Institute.

Schafer, Edward H. (1963), *The Golden Peaches of Samarkand: A Study of T'ang Exotics*. Berkeley: University of California Press.

Schaffer, Simon, Roberts, Lissa, Raj, Kapil, Delbourgo, James (2009), *The Brokered World: Go-Betweens and Global Intelligence, 1770–1820*. Sagamore Beach, MA: Science History Publications.

Schiebinger, Londa L., Swan, Claudia (2005), *Colonial Botany: Science, Commerce, and Politics in the Early Modern World*. Philadelphia: University of Pennsylvania Press.

Schiebinger, Londa L. (2004), *Plants and Empire: Colonial Bioprospecting in the Atlantic World*. Cambridge, MA: Harvard University Press.

Sen, Ranjit (1988), *Social Banditry in Bengal: A Study in Primary Resistance, 1757–1793*. Calcutta: Ratna Prakashan.

Sivasundaram, Sujit (2013), *Islanded: Britain, Sri Lanka, and the Bounds of an Indian Ocean Colony*. Chicago: University of Chicago Press.

Skeat, Walter William, Blagden, Charles Otto (1967), *Malay Magic: Being an Introduction to the Folklore and Popular Religion of the Malay Peninsula*. New York: Dover.

Smith, Bernard (1985), *European Vision and the South Pacific*. New Haven: Yale University Press.

Steenis, Cornelis G. G. J. van (Cornelis Gijsbert Gerrit Jan van), Steenis-Kruseman, M.J. van (1950), *Malaysian Plant Collectors and Collections*. Djakarta: Noordhoff-Kolff.

Steenis, Cornelis G. G. J. van, Backer, Cornelis A., Steenis-Kruseman, Maria J. van (1954), *Louis Auguste Deschamps: A Prominent but Ill-Fated Early Explorer of the Flora of Java, 1793–1798*. London: Natural History Museum.

Steenis-Kruseman, Maria J. van, Steenis, Cornelis G. G. J. van (Cornelis Gijsbert Gerrit Jan) (1985), *Flora Malesiana: Being an Illustrated Systematic Account of the Malaysian Flora…, series I, volume 1*. Koenigstein: Koeltz Scientific Books.

Stern, Philip J. (2007), 'Politics and ideology in the early East India Company-State: The case of St Helena, 1673–1709'. *Journal of Imperial and Commonwealth History*, 35(1): 1–23.

Stern, Philip J. (2009), 'History and historiography of the English East India Company: Past, present, and future'. *History Compass*, 7: 1146–1180.

Stern, Philip J. (2011), *The Company-State: Corporate Sovereignty and the Early Modern Foundations of the British Empire in India*. New York: Oxford University Press.

Tagliacozzo, Eric, Chang, Wen-Chin (2011), *Chinese Circulations: Capital, Commodities, and Networks in Southeast Asia*. Durham, NC: Duke University Press.

Thomas, Adrian P. (2006), 'The establishment of Calcutta botanic garden: Plant transfer, science and the East India Company, 1786–1806'. *Journal of the Royal Asiatic Society*, 16(2): 165–177.

Thompson, Andrew S. (ed.) (2013), *Writing Imperial Histories*. Manchester: Manchester University Press.

Thomson, John T. (1865), *Sequel to Some Glimpses into Life in the Far East*. London: Richardson & Company.

Thorns, David C., Sedgwick, Charles P. (1997), *Understanding Aotearoa/ New Zealand: Historical Statistics*. Palmerston North, NZ: Dunmore Press.

Travers, Robert (2007), 'The eighteenth century in Indian history: A review essay'. *Eighteenth-Century Studies*, 40(3): 492–508.

Trimen, Henry (1887), 'Hermann's Ceylon herbarium and Linnaeus's "Flora Zeylanica"'. *Linnean Journal of Botany*, 24(160): 129–155.

Turnbull, Colin M. (1972), *The Straits Settlements, 1826–67: Indian Presidency to Crown Colony*. London: Athlone Press.

Van Onselen, Charles (1996), *The Seed is Mine: The Life of Kas Maine, a South African Sharecropper, 1894–1985*. New York: Hill and Wang.

Varma, C. V. J., Saxena, K. R., Rao, M. K., India, Central Board of Irrigation and Power (1989), *River Behaviour, Management and Training*. Delhi: Central Board of Irrigation and Power.

Veldkamp, J. F. (2002), '15 June 2002, 300th anniversary of Rumphius' death'. *Flora Malesiana Bulletin*, 13(2): 7–21.

Villiers, J. (1994), 'The vanishing sandalwood of Portuguese Timor'. *Itinerario: Bulletin of the Leyden Centre for the History of European Expansion*, 18(2): 86–96.

Wadley, Reed L. (2005), *Histories of the Borneo Environment: Economic, Political and Social Dimensions of Change and Continuity*. Leiden: KITLV Press.

Walker, Gilbert Thomas, India, Meteorological Office, Poona (1924), *Correlation in Seasonal Variations of Weather, IX: Further Study of World-Weather*. Poona: Meteorological Office.

Walker, David (1999), *Anxious Nation: Australia and the Rise of Asia, 1850–1939*. St. Lucia, Queensland: University of Queensland Press.

Walker, N. D. (1990), 'Links between South African summer rainfall and temperature variability of the Agulhas and Benguela current systems'. *Journal of Geophysical Research: Oceans*, 95(C3): 3297–3319.

Walsh, R. P. D., Glaser, R., Militzer, S. (1999), 'The climate of Madras during the eighteenth century'. *International Journal of Climatology*, 19(9): 1025–1047.

Ward, Kerry (2009), *Networks of Empire: Forced Migration in the Dutch East India Company*. New York: Cambridge University Press.

Wescoat, James L., Wolschke-Bulmahn, Joachim, Dumbarton Oaks, Arthur M. Sackler Gallery (Smithsonian Institution),Dumbarton Oaks Colloquium on the History of Landscape Architecture (1996), *Mughal Gardens: Sources, Places, Representations, and Prospects*. Washington, DC: Dumbarton Oaks Research Library and Collection.

Wheatley, Paul (1964), *Impressions of the Malay Peninsula in Ancient Times*. Singapore: D. Moore for Eastern Universities Press.

Wilson, Kathleen (2004), *A New Imperial History: Culture, Identity, and Modernity in Britain and the Empire, 1660–1840*. Cambridge and New York: Cambridge University Press.

Wolters, O. W. (1967), *Early Indonesian Commerce: A Study of the Origins of Śrīvijaya*. Ithaca, NY: Cornell University Press.

Wolters, O. W. (1970), *The Fall of Śrīvijaya in Malay History*. Ithaca, NY: Cornell University Press.

Wong, Lin K. (1960), 'The Trade of Singapore, 1819–69', *Journal of the Malayan Branch of the Royal Asiatic Society*, 33(4): 1–315.

Wurtzburg, Charles E. (1954), *Raffles of the Eastern Isles*. London: Hodder and Stoughton.

Zimmermann, Francis (1989), *Le discours des remèdes au pays des épices: Enquête sur la médecine hindoue*. Paris: Payot.

Index

Bold entries refer to illustrations or tables.

Academia Leopoldina, 60
acclimatisation, 235
   acclimatisation gardens, 23, 44
   of cinchona, 207
   of Indian plants in New Zealand, 222, 235–6, 237, 238
Aceh, 38
Acosta, Christoval, 37
actor-network theory, 5, 46
Adam, Frederick, 70
Adams, T. W., 239
Addams-Williams, C, 142
Agrawal, Arun, 28
agriculture
   Bengal, 85
   decline in productivity, 82
   revenue extraction, 82
Agriculture and Horticulture Society of India, 27, 70
Agri-Horticultural Society of Madras, 70
Alam, Muzaffar, 81
Alexander, William, 190
Ali, Ahmed, 22
Ali, Murdan, 28
Alpinus, Prosper, 37
Alvares, Simāi, 200
Ambiona, 203
Andaya, Barbara, 148
Anderson, Clare, 8
Anderson, James, 23
Andhra Pradesh, 63
Antelope (ship), 167, 169
   Keate's *An Account of the Pelew Islands*, 168–9, 170, 171–3
   visual records of voyage, 173–**4**, 175–**6**, 177
Arcot, 36, 41, 49
Aristotle, 194
Arnold, David, 32n43
Arnold, Joseph, 159
   on *Rafflesia*, 157–8

artists, Indian, 28–9, 60, 66
Ashmole, Philip and Myrtle, 250, 266
Asiatic Society, 59
Auckland Acclimatisation Society, 238–9
Aurangzeb, Emperor, 40, 42, 49, 83
Australasia
   East India Company trade networks, 222–4
   as sub-imperial hub of India, 221
Australia, 222
   introduction of Indian animals, 223
   trade with India, 222–3

Bacon, Francis, 151
Balambangan, 177, 178, 179, 180, 185
Balasore, 202
Balfour, Isaac Bayley, 50n9
Ballantyne, James Robert, 19
Ballantyne, Tony, 5, 30, 221
bandal, 133
Bangalore, 239
Banks, Joseph, 24, 65, 151–3, 155, 158–60, 173, 182–3, 265
   'Memorial on Tea', 24–5
   scientific network, 152
   sponsorship of plant prospecting, 203–4
Banks Library and Herbarium, 160
Bankura, 23
Banten (Bantam), 202
Barkman, Todd, 162
Barlow, Robert, 253
Baron, Samuel, 40
Barus, 198
Bastin, John, 160–1, 163
Batavia, 43, 47, 155, 207, 209
Batavian Society of Arts and Sciences, 155
Bates, Henry Walter, 163
Bauba, Cojee, 43

Bayly, Christopher, 81
Beaman, John, 162
Beatson, Alexander, 266
Beattie, James, 5, 6
Becher, Richard, 86, 87
Benares, 83
Bengal, 23, 27, 86
  agricultural economy, 85
  climate change, 82
  East India Company rule, 84:
    administrative reform following famine, 93–4; despotic nature of, 85–6;
    dual system, 86–7; economic crisis under, 86; inadequate response to famine, 89–90; interference in grain market, 90–1; revenue extraction, 82, 83–4, 85, 87, 93
  famine (1770), 87–94, 97: administrative reform, 93–4; deaths, 87, 88–9, 92; depopulation, 87–8, 89, 93, 94–5; disease, 88; erosion of traditional systems, 91–2; impact of interference in grain market, 90–1; impact of modernisation, 91; inadequate government response to, 89–90; local responses to, 94; peasant resistance, 97; profiteering from, 90; social banditry, 95–6
  famine in medieval and early modern period, 83
  geographical and settlement characteristics, 84–5
  impact of Maratha raids, 82
  Mughal rule: famine prevention, 83; revenue extraction, 82
  social structure, 85
  see also water management in Bengal
Bengal Sanitary Drainage Act (1895), 140–1
Bengkulu (Bencoulen, Benkulen), 45, 46, 152, 156, 159, 204, 206
Bentham, George, 68, 69, 76
benzoin, 195–6
betel palm, 148

betel quid, 196
Bhutan (Boutan), 24, 73
Bidie, G., 239
Bihar (Behar), 24, 84, 92
  famine, 83, 87, 88
Bijapur, 40
biota barons, 231
  New Zealand, 231–8
Birbhum, 93, 95, 96, 97
Bishunpur, 95, 97
Blackmore, John, 255, 256
Blackwall, Richard, 41
Bombay, 27, 29
  see also meteorological observations
Bombay Courier, weather records, 104, 118–19, 121
Bombay Literary Society, 108, 109, 110
Bontius, Jacob, 19, 37, 202
Boorsma, W G, 208–9
Boot, Francis, 69
Borneo, 177
  Rafflesia, 149
botanical gardens
  Calcutta Botanical Gardens, 25, 68, 204, 205, 227, 239
  classification of plants, 150
  India, 23
  institutionalisation of science, 150
  interconnections between, 6
botany
  as component of imperial state, 152
  East India Company, 22–7, 147–8
  establishment of university chairs in, 201
  European trading companies, 147–8
  on eve of colonisation, 21–2
  in pre-colonial India, 22
  see also Madras, medicine and botany in; plant classification; *Rafflesia*; Wight, Robert
Botany Bay, 222
Brennan, Lance, 98n2
Brett, James De Renzie, 240–1
British Museum, 69, 151, 160
Browne, Samuel, 36–8, 40–1, 43, 44, 47
Brown, Robert, 64, 69, 76, 160, 161
Buchanan, Francis, 26, 30, 63, 68, 91, 205–6

Buckeridge, Nicholas, 252
Buitenzorg Botanic Gardens, 207, 208
    see also botanical gardens
Bulkley, Edward, 36, 38, 42–9
Bullart, Isaac, 188
Bunwoot Island, 179, 180
Burchell, William, 250, 266
Burdwan, 96
Burke, Edmund, 84, 172
Burkill, Isaac Henry, 163n4, 206, 207–8
Burma (Myanmar), 27
Burman, Johannes, 65
Byfield, Edward, 262

cabinets of curiosities, 201
Calcutta, 23, 25, 49, 66, 70, 73, 90, 94, 102, 132, 142, 222, 235
Calcutta Botanical Gardens, 25, 68, 204, 227, 239
    see also botanical gardens
Caldwell, James, 181, 182
Camelli (Kamel), George, 47
camphor, 45, 195, 196, 198, 199
Candolle, Alphonse de, 26–7, 77n8
Candolle, Augustin Pyramus de, 60, 64, 68, 76
Canterbury, 229–32, 234–6, 239–41
Canterbury Acclimatisation Society, 235
    see also acclimatisation
Canton, 25, 227
Cape of Good Hope, 257, 258
Cartier, John, 88
Casey, R. G., 128–9, 143
Cashmere, 232
caste, 21
Cavenagh, Orfeur, 205, 207
Ceylon (Sri Lanka), 27, 45, 200
    Chakrabarti, Pratik, 30, 40
China, 19, 40, 45, 178, 190, 222, 227
    imports of *materia medica*, 197–9
Chittagong, 90
Chotanagpur, 84–5, 97
Christchurch, 232, 234, 236
Chuars, 96–7
cinchona, 207
cinnamon, 44, 147, 179, 180, 194
classification systems

importance of, 149–50
    see also plant classification
Cleghorn, Hugh F. C., 63, 239
climate change, 7, 9, 121, 221, 271
    famine, 82
climatology, historical, 110–11
    see also meteorological observations
Clingingsmith, D., 82
Clive, Robert, 87, 240
clove, 196
Clusius, Carolus, 37, 152, 201
Cochin, 202
coffee, 23, 27, 239, 262, 263, 270
Coimbatore, 71
Colaba Observatory, 104, 111
colonialism
    attitudes toward local knowledge, 19–20
    centrality of natural knowledge, 35
    cooperation, 20–1
    core–periphery approach to, 17–18
    post-colonial scholarship, 17, 18
commerce, as ideological paradigm, 170–1
conservation, 28
content analysis, and historical climatology, 110–11
Cook, James, 151, 169, 170, 173–4, 177, 179, 187, 190
Coply, John Singleton, 167
Coromandel Coast, 27, 35, 40, 66, 123
Cornwallis, Lord, 86, 94–5
Cortés, Hernán, 188–9
cotton, 23, 27, 71,93, 254, 270
Crawfurd, John, 161
Cronk, Quentin, 250, 266
Crosby, Alfred, 237, 238
cross-cultural encounters, 168
    Antelope's voyage, 171–3: visual records of, 173–4, 175–6, 177
    Forrest's *A Voyage to New Guinea*, 179–89: 'A Magindano Marriage', **181**; description of Dory, 183–4; philosophical commentary, 186; portrait of Forrest, 186–7, 188–9; 'View of Dory Harbour', 181–2, 184–5; as work of natural history and imperial strategy, 185

cross-cultural encounters – *continued*
   Keate's *An Account of the Pelew Islands*, 168–9, 170
   Lee Boo, 169
Cuddalore, 41
Cunningham, James, 47
Cuttack, 137

Dacca, 83, 93
Dalrymple, Alexander, 169, 173, 177–8, 189
   General Collection of Nautical Publications, 178
   on importance of visual imagery, 178–9
Dalzell, Nicholas A., 71
Dampier, William, 201
Dance, Nathaniel, 187
Darwin, Charles, 266–7
Darwin, Erasmus, 155
Darwin, John, 21
Davis, M., 82
Day, Tony, 210
decolonisation, seeds of, 17
Deschamps, Louis Auguste, 149
Desfontaine, John, 264–5
development, impact on famines, 80–1, 91
Devis, Arthur William, 173–4, 177
   drawing of Ara Kooker, **174**–6
   drawing of Lee Boo, **176**–7
De Waal, A., 91
Dioscorides, 150
Dirks, Nick, 83–4
Djundishapur (Jundishapur), 194
Domett, Alfred, 240
Don, David, 69
drainage, 138–42
Drake, Francis, 201
Drake, Thomas and Selina, 238
Drayton, Richard, 6, 21
Du Bois, Charles, 36, 47, 48
Dubow, Saul, 29
Dunlap, Thomas, 235, 237
Dutch East India Company (VOC), 43, 149, 152, 201–3,211
Dutton, John, 250, 252
Dutt, R P, 81

East India Company, *see* English East India Company
East India Company Museum, 155, 159, 160, 163
Edessa, 194
Edgeworth, M. P., 27, 71, 75
elites, privileged in networked analyses, 7–8
El Niño, 82, 99n32, 102, 104, 105, 122, 256–**7**, 258
Elphinstone, Mountstuart, 103, 108–9, 111–13, 114, 118–19
L'Empereur, Nicolas, 29, 202, 203
endemics (plants), 193, 196, 197, 199, 206, 249, 266
English East India Company
   Australasian trade networks, 222–4
   Bengal famine (1770), 89–90
   botanical explorations, 22–7
   conservationism, 270
   criticisms of, 84
   despotic nature of rule by, 85–6
   dual system of rule, 86–7
   encouragement of botanical investigations, 22–3
   expansion in Southeast Asia, 153
   importance of botanical knowledge, 42, 147–8
   lack of studies of surgeon-naturalists, 63
   meteorological observatories, 102
   plant prospecting, 201
   recording of natural phenomena, 121
   relations with Mughals over Madras, 40–2
   reliance on local drugs, 43
   revenue and agricultural regimes, 80
   revenue extraction, 82, 83–4, 85, 93: economic impact of, 86; harshness of, 87
   as rogue state, 84
   as self-sustaining global system, 131
   transformative effect of, 270
environmental history, 270
   and imperial history, 3
   informal imperial networks, 221
   institutional analyses, 6

mobilities, 6
networked approaches to, 4–9:
  place, 9–10; scale, 10–13
spatial conceptions in, 1, 3–4
environmentalism, 28
environmental modification
  informal imperial networks, 221
  New Zealand, 236, 237
  role of settlers, 221
Epidemic Commission (1864), 139
Epp, Franz, 209
Equiano, Olaudah, 168
Escobar, Arturo, 129

Falconer, Hugh, 234
Famine Commission, 80
famines
  Bengal (1770), 87–94, 97: administrative reform, 93–4; deaths, 87, 88–9, 92; depopulation, 87–8, 89, 93, 94–5; disease, 88; erosion of traditional systems, 91–2; impact of interference in grain market, 90–1; impact of modernisation, 91; inadequate government response to, 89–90; local responses to, 94; peasant resistance, 97; profiteering from, 90; rebellion, 96; social banditry, 95–6
  in British India, 80
  debates over causes of, 81
  East India Company rule, 84
  environmental changes, 80
  erosion of traditional systems, 91–2
  impact of modernisation, 80–1, 91
  in medieval and early modern India, 83
  under Mughal rule, 83
  resulting from climate change, 82, *see also* climate change
  vulnerability to, 80
Fatehpur Sikri, 83
Fernandez, Emanuel, 205
Floud commission (1793), 85
Forbes, Henry O, 162
Forrest, Thomas, and *A Voyage to New Guinea*, 178, 179–89

'A Magindano Marriage', **181**
description of Dory, 183–4
philosophical commentary, 186
portrait of Forrest, 186–7, 188–9
'View of Dory Harbour', 181–2, 184–5
as work of natural history and imperial strategy, 185
Forster, George, 172
Forster, Johann Reinhold, 179
Fort St. David, 41
Fort St. George, 23, 36, 40, 41, 45
Franklin, Michael, 59–60
free market economics, enshrined in colonial policy, 82
Fryer, John, 43
Funan, 196

Gardner, George, 62, 71, 76
Ghatsheela, 97
Ghosh, L., 140
Gibson, Alexander, 29
Gilmartin, David, 129, 144n5
Given, David, 226
globalisation, 270
Glorious Revolution, 49
Goa, 21, 200, 202
Golconda, 36, 40
Golinski, Jan, 103
Goodwin, John, 264
Gosh, Nur Mohamed, 208
Gosse, Philip, 253
Govindoo (Indian artist), 29, 66
Graham, J, 27
Graham, Robert, 65, 67
Greece, 194
Greville, Robert Kaye, 64, 67, 73, 75
Griffith, William, 27, 63, 69, 73, 75, 205
Grimm, Hermanus Nicholas, 203
Grove, Richard, 3, 21, 28, 63, 82, 102, 130, 250, 256, 265, 270

Hall Catherine, 2
Halley, Edmond, 254–5
Hamilton, William, 181
Haniff, Mohamed, 208
Hasan, Abul, 40

Hasskarl, Justus Charles, 207
Hastings, Warren, 89, 93–4, 95, 96, 172, 173
Hawaii, 237, 238–9
Hawkesworth, John, 169–70
Hearne, Thomas, 181
Hector, James, 239
Heraclitus, 9
herbaria, 36, 59, 67–8, 69, 73, 74, 150
Heynes, Benjamin, 66
Hickey, Thomas, 190
historiography
 networked approaches, 4–9: place, 9–10; scale, 10–13
 new imperial history, 2, 3, 130, 143
 spatial turn in, 1–2
Hodges, William, 173, 174, **175**
Home, Henry (Lord Kames), 170
Hoogly, 97
Hooker, Joseph Dalton, 27, 33n51, 67, 73, 74, 204–5, 207, 241
Hooke, Robert, 37
Hooker, William Jackson, 64, 66–7, 74, 75, 207
Hopkins, A. G., 129
Horeke, 224, 227
Horsfield, Thomas, 154–5, 159–60, 163, 204
Hume, David, 170, 171
Hunter, W. W., 87, 88, 90
hunting, 233
Husain, Amanullah, 22
hybrid cultures, 20, 30, 46, 49, 210, 222
hybridisation (botanical), 238

immobility, 9
imperial careering, 5, 231
imperial history
 core–periphery approach to, 2
 environmental history, 3
 mobilities, 6
 networked approaches to, 4–9: place, 9–10; scale, 10–13
 new imperial history, 2, 3, 130, 143
 spatial conceptions in, 1, 3
 spatial turn in, 1–2
India
 Australasian trade networks, 222–4
 botany in pre–colonial, 22
 British attitudes towards Indians, 222
 colonists' fear of climate, 221, 228, 230
 introduction of New Zealand plants, 239
 partition of, 12
 role in Pacific region, 221
 stagnation theory of scientific knowledge, 22
 see also Bengal; Madras, medicine and botany in; meteorological observations; water management in Bengal
Indian Ocean Dipole (IOD), 104
indigenous knowledge, 20, 28
 Malay-Indonesian *materia medica*, 202–3, 205–6, 209–11: *Medical Book of Malayan Medicines*, 210–11
international trade
 East India Company-Australasian trade networks, 222–4
 Malay-Indonesian *materia medica*, 194–7: Arab trade, 198; China, 197–9; transplantations and introductions, 196–7, 199

Jacquemont, Victor, 27
James, William, 180
Jamestown, 252, 256
Japan, 40
Java, 147, 149, 154, 155, 157, 159, 196, 202, 204, 207
Jesuit missionaries, 19, 47
Johnson, Edmund, 71
Jones, William, 25–6, 59–60
Junghuhn, Franz Wilhelm, 207, 208
Jurin, James, 117
Jussieu, A. L. de, 68

Kamel (Camelli), George, 47
Karnataka, 40
Kashmir, 27, 232
Kathirithamby-Wells, Jeyamalar, 8–9
Keate, George, *An Account of the Pelew Islands*, 168–9, 170, 171–3
Kelly, Theresa, 60
Kerala, 63, 71

Kew Gardens, 66–7, 151, 152, 227, 265
Khan, Daud, 40, 41, 42, 45
Khan, Ghulam Husein, 89
Khan, Mohammed Reza, 88
Khan, Qasim, 40, 41
Khan, Selim, 41
Khan, Zu'lfiqar, 40, 41
Kingston, Beverley, 223
Kloppenburg-Versteegh, Johanna, 209
Koenig, Johann Gerhard, 21, 66, 204
Koorders, S. H., 162
Kyd, Robert, 23, 32n25

Lambert, Aylmer Bourke, 69
land reclamation, 141–2
Lang, J., 134–5
La Niña, 256–7
Larmessin, Nicholas de, 188
Latour, Bruno, 5, 11, 35, 46
Lee Boo, 167–8, 169, **176**
Legg, Stephen, 11
lemon grass, 196
Leslie, John, 24
Lester, Alan, 130
letter-writing, 219
Lindley, John, 61, 69, 76
linguistic skills, 203
Lin I., 197
Linnaean Society, 69, 151, 152, 157, 160
Linnaeus, Carolus, 60, 64, 78n18, 150–1
Lockyer, Charles, 42
Logan, J. R., 206
Long, J., 27
Lushington, Stephen, 66

McAlpin, Michelle, 81, 91
Macao, 190
Macartney, Lord, 190
Macaulay, Thomas Babington, 19, 84
McDonnell, Thomas, 224–7, 242
  garden layout, **226**
McGrigor, James, 103, 105–6, 113, 114, 117, 118
Machardo, Alfred Dent, 207
McKay, David, 152
MacKenzie, John, 2

McLane, John, 83, 86, 94
McLelland, John, 27, 70, 73
MacLeod, R., 30
McLuer, John, 189–90
Maconochie, Allan, 63
Madagascar, 258
Madras Literary Society, 70
Madras, medicine and botany in, 35–6
  drugs available from bazaars, 43–4
  experimentation, 44–5, 46
  gardens, 44–5
  hospital, 42–3, 46
  importance of settlement, 40
  international networks, 46–8
  Madras Naturalist, 65–6
  precarious position of settlement, 42
  preparation and marketing of drugs, 43
  spaces for exchange of natural and medical knowledge, 36
  surgeons and their plant collections, 36–8
  surgeons' collaboration with local practitioners, 37–8, 49–50
  surgeons' deployment of plant collections, 48–9
  surgeons' observations of Indian counterparts, 44
  surgeons' role in diplomatic relations with Mughals, 40–2, 49
  transmission of *materia medica*, 36
Mahomet, Dean, 168
Mai, 167, 168
Maingay, A. C., 205
Majapahit, 196
Majumdar, G. P., 22
Malabar, 21
malaria, 139, 207
Malay-Indonesian *materia medica*
  benzoin, 195–6
  clove, 196
  colonial science, 204–6
  European plant prospecting, 211: colonial science, 204–6; colonial scientific services, 207–9; difficult relations with locals, 205–6; Dutch East India Company,

Malay-Indonesian *materia medica*
 – *continued*
 201–3; East India Company, 201; Joseph Banks' role, 203–4; Portuguese, 199–201
 indigenous knowledge, 202–3, 209–11: difficult relations with locals, 205–6; *Medical Book of Malayan Medicine*, 210–11; resistance to European influences, 210; survival of, 210
 international trade, 193, 195–7: Arab trade, 198; China, 197–9; transplantations and introductions, 196–7, 199
 lemon grass, 196
 medical practitioners, 194–5
 oral transmission of plant knowledge, 195
 in post-colonial era, 211–12
 sandalwood, 196
 shamans, 195
Malcolmson, John Grant, 70
Maluka (Moluccas), 149, 204
Manilla, 45
Manna, 157, 158
Manucci, Niccolao, 42, 43
Maratha raids, impact of, 82
Marsden, William, 152–3, 204
 The History of Sumatra, 153
Marshall, John, 83
Marshall, P., 81
Martin, William, 238
Maskelynne, Nevil, 255
Mason, F., 27
Massey, Doreen, 3, 9, 12
materia medica, as feature of culture and civilisation, 194
 see also Malay-Indonesian *materia medica*
Mauritius, 257, 266
May, Mr (Superintendent for the Nadia rivers), 132–3, 134
medicine, *see* Madras, medicine and botany in; Malay-Indonesian *materia medica*
Megaw, W. D., 28
Meijer, Willem, 162
Melaka, 47, 199, 200, 204, 205, 210

Menzies, Archibald, 69
Merrill, E. D., 208
Metcalf, Thomas R., 221
meteorological observations by British colonists in India, 102
 analysis in weather diaries: comparison with recent records, 119, 121; extreme events, 111–13, 114, **115–16**; precipitation, 110–11, **112**; temperature, 114–**18**, 119, **120**
 Bombay Courier, 104, 118–19, 121
 climatology of South Asia, 104–5
 continuing importance of, 121
 contribution to climate science, 122
 early nineteenth century India, 104
 historical climatology, content analysis, 110–11
 motivations for, 102–3
 tradition of recording, 102
 weather diaries, 103–4: James McGrigor, 105–6, 113, 114, 117, 118; Jasper Nicolls, 106–8, 110, 113–14, 116–17, 118; Lucretia West, 109–10, 111–13, 114, 118–19; Mountstuart Elphinstone, 108–9, 111–13, 114, 118–19; value of, 122–3
Midnapore, 82, 85, 96, 135
Mindanao, 181
Mitter, Raja Digamber, 139, 140
mobilities, 6, 9–10
modernisation, impact on famines, 80–1, 91
Mooltan, Neil, 238
Moon, A., 27
Morland, George, 172
Mughals/Mughal Empire
 botanical knowledge, 22
 famine prevention, 83
 impact of collapse of, 81, 82
 Madras' relations with, 40–2, 49
 revenue extraction, 82, 83
Munor, W., 27
Munro, Thomas, 65
Munro, William, 71, 75
Murshidabad, 90, 97
Muter, Dunbar Douglas, 219, **220**, 233
 move to New Zealand, 219–20

Muter, Elizabeth, 220, 241
  move to New Zealand, 219–20
  Travels and Adventures, 219
Mysore, 226

Naidu, Kumaru Yachama, 41
Napier, 240
Nash, David, 111
Nees von Esenbeck, Christian, 68, 76
Negapatam, 66
Nepal, 27, 87–8
networked approaches to imperial and environmental history, 4–9
  place, 9–10
  scale, 10–13
New Guinea, 178, 179–89
New Zealand, 225, 241–2
  acclimatisation of plants, 222, 235–6, 237, 238
  attractiveness for migrants, 228
  East India Company 'biota barons', 231–8
  emigration to, 228: appeals to India-based Europeans, 229, 231–2; East India Company migrants, 229, 230–1
  environmental impact of Empire, 220–1
  environmental modification, 236, 237
  as healthy migrant destination, 221–2, 228–9, 230
  Indian-based place names, 232, 240
  introduction of Indian animals, 232–4, 235, 237, 239–40
  introduction of Indian plants, 234–5, 236–7: rhododendrons and azaleas, 238; sources, 237, 238–9;
  Thomas McDonnell, 224–7
  introduction of plants to India, 239
  landscape connections with India, 240–1
  trade with India, 223–4
  Treaty of Waitangi (1840), 227
New Zealand Company (NZC), 228
Nicolls, Colonel (Chief Engineer of Bengal), 139

Nicolls, Jasper, 103, 106–8, 110, 113–14, 116–17, 118
Noltie, Henry, 29

opium, 92, 224, 227
opium poppy, 45
Orang Asli, 208
Orissa, 84, 85, 88
da Orta, Garcia, 21, 37, 200–1
Oxley, Thomas, 206

Padang, 158
Padtbrugge, Robert, 203
Pahud, C. F., 207
Palamau, 98
Palau, 168, 169, 171–2, 177, 189
Parkinson, John, 37
Patna, 83
Pawson, Eric, 5
Pegu, 38, 48
Pekalongan, 209
Penang, 153, 204, 205
pepper, 147, 152, 156–7, 179, 194, 196, 199, 263
Peradeniya, 71
Persia, 21
Persoon, Christiaan Hendrik, 64
Petiver, James, 36, 37, 38, 44, 45, 46, 47
Pettipoli, 36
photography, 27
physic gardens, 44
  see also botanical gardens
Pires, Tomé, 199–200
Pitt, Thomas, 45
places, in networked analyses, 9–10
plantations, 17
plant classification
  as aid to efficient exploitation, 152
  aim of, 62
  basic rules of, 60–1
  De materia medica, 150
  herbaria, 150
  importance of, 149–50
  Linnaean system, 150–1
  natural classification system, 64
  problems facing Indian botanists, 61–2
Rafflesia, 160–1, 162
  see also Rumphius

Platearius, Matthaeus, 194
Plukenet, Leonard, 65
Poona (Pune), 108
Pope, John Adolphus, 148
Portugal, commercial expansion, 199–200
postcolonialism, 20, 59
print culture, 219
Pulau Lebar, 156
Pulo Condore, 47
Pyenson, Lewis, 20
Pyke, Isaac, 257, 259, 260, 262, 264

Qutb Shah dynasty, 40

Rafflesia
  characteristics of, 147
  discourse of imperial control and classification, 148
  discovery of, 156–8
  fascination with, 161–2
  first recording of, 149
  iconic nature of, 162
  as metaphor for East India Company, 161
  naming of, 160–1
  Rafflesia arnoldii, 160
  Rafflesia padma, 149
  re-classification of, 162
  scientific research on, 162
  as symbol of tropic region, 148
  in travel accounts, 162
Raffles, Thomas Stanford, 153–4, 155–6, 204
  discovery of *Rafflesia*, 156
  naming of *Rafflesia*, 160–1
  support for Horsfield, 155
  on wonders of Southeast Asian natural world, 156–7
Raj, Kapil, 59, 60
Rajmahal, 83
Rajshahi, 97
Rangarajan, M., 91, 98
Raychaudhuri, T., 82
Ray, John, 37, 47
Rennefort, S. de, 252–3
Rennell, James, 87
Rhijne, Wilhelm ten, 47
Richardson, John L. C., 229

Ridley, H. N., 207, 210
river control, and East India Company, 143
  drainage, 138–42
  embankments and flood control, 135–8
  land reclamation, 141–2
  navigation, 132–5
Robinson, C. K., 132
Roxburgh, William, 23, 25, 26, 27, 60, 63, 65, 66, 123, 250, 266
Royal Society, 37, 44, 48, 151, 152, 153
Royle, John Forbes, 27, 63, 69, 76
Royle, Stephen, 250
Rumphius (Georg Everard Rumpf), 21, 47, 149, 155, 202, 203
  The Ambonese Herbal, 149, 203
  Thesarus Amboiniensis, 149
Rungiah (Indian artist), 29, 66
Russell, Patrick, 66
Rutherford, Daniel, 64

Saharunpur Botanic Garden, 28, 69
St. Helena, 249–50
  astronomical observations from, 254–5
  botanical garden established, 265
  Burchell's scientific observations, 266
  climate, 251–2, 256–8
  coffee growing, 262, 263
  deterioration of resources, 255–6
  droughts and floods, 256–7, 258, 259, 262, 264, 265–6: effects of, 259; soil erosion, 260–1
  early years of East India Company rule, 252–4
  East India Company takes possession of, 250
  environmental degradation, 250–1
  environmental impact of colonialism, 250
  final years of East India Company rule, 265–7
  Halley's scientific observations, 254–5
  Napoleon's exile on, 266–7
  plant introductions, 259–60

problems with wild swine, 255–6
reforestation, 261, 262–3
wood shortages, 256, 263, 264–5
yam cultivation, 261
Salerno, 194
Salleh, Kiah bin Haji Mohamed, 208
Samalcotta, 25
sandalwood, 44, 196, 198, 199, 201
Sassetti, Filoppo, 202
scale, 270
  in networked analyses, 10–13
Science and Empire (Delhi seminar, 1985), 18
scientific knowledge, and colonialism, 16–17
  attitudes toward local knowledge, 19–20
  on eve of colonisation, 21–2
  primary sources, 18–19
  relationship between, 19
Sen, Amartya, 91, 97
Serampore, 26
Shakespeare, William, 17
Sharp, William, 187
Sherwin, John Keyse, 186–7, 188
Shore, John, 89
Shuter, James, 65
Sinclair, John, 63
Singapore, 102, 204
Singapore Agricultural and Horticultural Association, 205
Singapore Botanical Gardens, 207–8
Singh, Luchman, 29
Sivaramakrishnan, K., 91, 98
Smith, Adam, 90–1, 170, 171
Smith, Bernard, 169
Smith, Henry, 47
Smith, James Edward, 69
Society of Apothecaries, 48
Southeast Asia
  East India Company's expansion into, 153
  fascination for European scientists, 149
  see also visualisation of Southeast Asia
spatiality
  in environmental history, 3–4
  in imperial history, 1–2, 3

Spoilum, 190
Srivijaya, 196, 198
Star, Paul, 231
Stern, Philip, 131
Stevens, Michael, 8
Stewart, John, 64
Stocks, John Ellerton, 71, 76
Stratchey, Henry, 85–6
subaltern groups, 8
sugar/sugar cane, 23, 98, 235, 254, 270
Sumatra, 147, 149, 152, 158, 159
Sunda Islands, 196
Surat, 21, 43, 116, 190
  cloth, 184
Sydney Botanic Garden, 227
Sylhet, 23

Tahiti, 169–70
Tamil Nadu, 63
Tannock, David, 239
taxonomy, *see* plant classification
tea, 24–5, 147, 227, 270
Tegal, 209
Tennessee Valley Authority (TVA), 129
Theophrastus, 194
Thomas, Nicholas, 168, 173
Thomson, A. S., 229
Thomson, John Turnbull, 228
Thomson, T., 33n49, 74
Timor, 196
Tirupati, 41
tobacco, 45
Tranquebar, 21
transplantation (botanical), 180, 185, 193, 197, 199, 210
Treub, Melchior, 207, 208
Tropospheric Biennial Oscillation, 105
Truman Doctrine, 129
Turner, Dawson, 157, 158

Upas tree, 155, 164n22

Van der Burg, Cornelis Leendert, 206
Van Rheede, Heinrich, 21, 29, 37, 65, 77n4, 202, 203
  Indicus Malarabaricus, 203
Verelst, Harry, 86, 87, 88
Vesalius, Andreas, 199

visualisation of Southeast Asia, 168
  Dalrymple on importance of visual imagery, 178–9
  East India Company exploratory voyages, 169, 179, 190
  Forrest's *A Voyage to New Guinea*, 179–82: 'A Magindano Marriage', **181**; philosophical commentary, 186; portrait of Forrest, 186–**7**, 188–9; 'View of Dory Harbour', 181–2, 184–**5**; as work of natural history and imperial strategy, 185
  portrayal of native Africans, 172
  records of *Antelope's* voyage, 173–**4**, 175–**6**, 177
Vizagapatam, 46
Vorderman, A. G., 208

Waddington, Robert, 255
Waitangi, Treaty of (1840), 227
Waitz, F. A. C., 209
Walker-Arnott, George, 64, 67, 68, 69, 75
Walker, George Warren, 71, 76
Walker, Gilbert, 102
Wallace, Alfred Russel, 163
Wallerstein, Immanuel, 11
Wallich, Nathaniel, 26–7, 32n43, 63, 66, 68, 71, 75
Walpole, Horace, 84
Ward, Kerry, 8
Ward, Nathaniel, 206
Wassink, T. Geerlof, 209–10
water management in Bengal
  East India Company, 131–2, 143: conception of rivers, 131; drainage, 138–42; embankments and flood control, 135–8; land reclamation, 141–2; language of control, 131; revenue collection, 135; river improvement and navigation, 132–5
  governor Casey's ambitions, 128–9
  post-Second World War development paradigm, 129
  problem of Bengal's rivers, 128
Watson, Brook, 167
weather diaries, *see* meteorological observations

Weaver, Barry, 250
Webber, John, 173, 174, 177
Wedgebrough, John, 173
Wellesley, Arthur, 108
West, Edward, 104, 109
West, Lucretia, 103–4, 109–10, 111–13, 114, 118–19
White, Robert, 173
Wight, Robert, 5–6, 21, 29, 75
  appointed Madras Naturalist (1826–28), 65–7
  botanical networks, 58, 64, **72**
  in Britain (1831–34), 67–9
  Catalogue, 69
  collaborators in India, 66, 71–3
  collections of, 59
  commissioning of Indian artists, 66
  Contributions, 68, 69
  correspondence with W. J. Hooker, 66–7
  difficulties in classifying Indian plants, 65
  economic botany work, 70–1
  education in Edinburgh, 64
  elected to fellowship of Linnean Society, 69
  English collaborators, 69
  European collaborators, 68
  field trip in India (1826–27), 66
  geographical field of activity, 63
  hopes for Indian botany, 62
  Icones Plantarum Indiae Orientalis, 70
  Illustrations of Indian Botany, 64, 70
  in India (1819–26), 64–5
  in India (1834–53), 70–3
  lack of botanical literature, 64–5
  in London, 68–9
  natural classification system, 64
  number of new species described by, 63–4
  problems facing Indian botanists, 61–2
  Prodromus, 69
  publications in India, 70
  retirement in Britain (1853–72), 74
  Scottish contacts and collaborators, 67–8
  Scottish Enlightenment tradition, 63

Spicilegium Neilgherrense, 64, 70
Willdenow, Karl Ludwig, 64
Williamson, J., 82
Wilson, Henry, 167, 173
Wilson, John Cracroft, and New Zealand, 231–7, 242
 environmental modification, 236
 introduction of Indian animals, 232–4, 235
 introduction of Indian plants, 234–5, 236–7
Wilson, William, 234

Xie Lingyun, 197

Zheng He, 198, 199
Zoological Club of the Linnaean Society of London, 159

CPI Antony Rowe
Eastbourne, UK
December 03, 2019